Mineral-Filled Polymer Composites

Mineral-Filled Polymer Composites

Selection, Processing, and Applications

Edited by

Hanafi Ismail, S.M. Sapuan, and R.A. Ilyas

CRC Press is an imprint of the
Taylor & Francis Group, an **informa** business

First edition published 2022
by CRC Press
6000 Broken Sound Parkway NW, Suite 300, Boca Raton, FL 33487-2742

and by CRC Press
2 Park Square, Milton Park, Abingdon, Oxon, OX14 4RN

© 2022 Taylor & Francis Group, LLC

CRC Press is an imprint of Taylor & Francis Group, LLC

Reasonable efforts have been made to publish reliable data and information, but the author and publisher cannot assume responsibility for the validity of all materials or the consequences of their use. The authors and publishers have attempted to trace the copyright holders of all material reproduced in this publication and apologize to copyright holders if permission to publish in this form has not been obtained. If any copyright material has not been acknowledged please write and let us know so we may rectify in any future reprint.

Except as permitted under U.S. Copyright Law, no part of this book may be reprinted, reproduced, transmitted, or utilized in any form by any electronic, mechanical, or other means, now known or hereafter invented, including photocopying, microfilming, and recording, or in any information storage or retrieval system, without written permission from the publishers.

For permission to photocopy or use material electronically from this work, access www.copyright.com or contact the Copyright Clearance Center, Inc. (CCC), 222 Rosewood Drive, Danvers, MA 01923, 978-750-8400. For works that are not available on CCC please contact mpkbookspermissions@tandf.co.uk

Trademark notice: Product or corporate names may be trademarks or registered trademarks and are used only for identification and explanation without intent to infringe.

ISBN: 978-1-032-11661-7 (hbk)
ISBN: 978-1-032-11677-8 (pbk)
ISBN: 978-1-003-22101-2 (ebk)

DOI: 10.1201/9781003221012

Typeset in Times
by KnowledgeWorks Global Ltd.

Contents

Preface vii
Authors Biography ix
Contributors xiii

Chapter 1 Application of Mineral Fillers in Polymer Composites for Industrial Applications 1

    A.K. Nurdina, Y.Z.N. Htwe, and M. Mariatti

Chapter 2 Mineral-Filled Composite: A Review on Characteristics, Applications, and Potential Materials Selection Process 25

    M.T. Mastura and M. Noryani

Chapter 3 Epoxy Resins for Interphase Strengthening of Textile-Reinforced Composites for Structural Applications 45

    C. Signorini and A. Nobili

Chapter 4 Recent Advances in Nanofillers for Multidisciplinary Applications of Polymer Nanocomposites 67

    Dang Mao Nguyen, Patrick Perré, Thi Phuong Thao Nguyen, Quoc Bao Bui, and DongQuy Hoang

Chapter 5 Utilization of Natural Zeolite as Filler in Improving the Mechanical Properties of Unsaturated Polyester Composite 101

    H. Nasution, H. Harahap, and D.M. Putra, Winny

Chapter 6 Effect of Glut Palmitate Coupling Agent on Vulcanized Silica-Filled Natural Rubber 121

    Dalina Samsudin, Faiezah Hashim, Noor Aishatun Majid, and Hanafi Ismail

Chapter 7 Effect of Gamma Irradiation on the Properties of Sepiolite-Filled Ethylene Propylene Diene Monomer Composites 137

    N.A. Mohd Zaini, Hanafi Ismail, A. Rusli, and Sofian Ibrahim

Contents

Chapter 8 Properties of Sepiolite-Reinforced Irradiated Linear
Low-Density Polyethylene Nanocomposites 153

Siti Nadia Aini Ghazali and Zurina Mohamad

Chapter 9 Effects of Multiwalled Carbon Nanotubes, Compatibilizers and
Silane Coupling Agent on the Mechanical and Morphological
Properties of Feldspar/Polypropylene Hybrid Composites 169

M.N.M. Ansari, A. Atiqah, and H. Ismail

Chapter 10 Ultrasonicated Dolomite as Potential Reinforcing Mineral
Filler in Polymer and Copolymer-Based Composites 199

*Asfa Amalia Ahmad Fauzi, Azlin Fazlina Osman,
Khairul Anwar Abdul Halim, and Hanafi Ismail*

Chapter 11 Modified Carboxymethyl Cellulose/Halloysite Nanotube
(CMC/HNT) Using Sodium Dodecyl Sulfate (SDS) 211

*Kathiravan Suppiah, Rozyanty Abdul Rahman, Pei Leng Teh,
and Cheow Keat Yeoh*

Index 231

Preface

Mineral-Filled Polymer Composites: Selection, Processing, and Applications provides an exhaustive overview of the latest research, trends, applications, and future directions of advanced mineral fiber-reinforced polymer composites. Recently, unavoidable increases in industrial activity have triggered a rising demand for more efficient materials. These materials are subjected to increasingly tight requirements, including higher strength and modulus, desirable electrical and thermal conductivity, cheap cost, low coefficients of thermal expansion, and appropriate heat distortion temperature. Such specifications require the combination of several materials to achieve desirable characteristics. Therefore, a combination of mineral filler materials has been widely used in polymers, and these are gaining acceptance in various types of engineering applications. Currently, mineral-filled polymer composites have been utilized for several applications, i.e., automotive, buildings, biomedical, boat hulls, sports, and ballistic applications, because of the advantages of being low cost and light weight as well as having excellent rigidity and high mechanical strength. Therefore, in this book, research regarding material selection, processing, and applications of macro-nano-sized mineral-reinforced polymer composites was presented. In concurrent engineering, all the activities that are conducted must work in parallel to ensure the participation of all elements to reduce lead time while improving quality and cost. The best practice of the design process is to employ the principle of concurrent engineering where all the important elements are associated and deliberate in a concurrent manner. Thus, this book also covers the systematic material selection tools of mineral-filled polymer composites including the analytical hierarchy process (AHP), analytical network process (ANP), and technique of ranking preferences by similarity of the ideal solution (TOPSIS). Covering novel methods for the selection and synthesis of mineral-filled polymer composites and their properties, the book starts by reviewing the application of mineral fillers in polymer composites for various types of engineering applications. From there, it features chapters covering fabrication techniques and the frictional properties of specific mineral-filled polymer composite materials such as organic, inorganic, basalt, calcium carbonate, nanotube, clay, feldspar, zinc oxide, silica, zeolite, sepiolite, alumina, magnetite, montmorillonite, rubber, dolomite, halloysite, and biomineral fiber-reinforced polymer composites. Also covered is research on polymer nanocomposites and particulate polymer composites. This book is a research book for the student, academician, and industry professional. Throughout this book the principles governing the behavior of mineral-filled composite materials in the field of engineering and their applications are emphasized.

Authors Biography

Hanafi Ismail is currently the Director of Innovation Centre and Consultation, Universiti Sains Malaysia, Fellow Academy of Science Malaysia (FASc) and ex-Dean School of Materials and Mineral Resources Engineering. Professor Hanafi has won many awards including the Khwarizmi International Award 2000, APCTT (Asia Pacific) 2000 International Award, ISESCO Prize in Science & Technology 2001 and the silver medal at the International Exhibition of Invention in 2002, 2004 and 2009. In 2005, he won the gold medal at the International Trade Fair IENA, and in 2007, he won the gold medal with special mention by jury at the 56th World Exhibition of Innovation, Research and New Technologies. He also won the gold medal at the International Invention, Innovation, Industrial Design and Technology Exhibition (I-TEX 2003, 2004, 2007, 2008 and 2010) and the silver medal at the Science & Technology Expo 2003, 2006 and 2010. In 2010, he won the gold medal, double gold and Special Award from Russia at the British Invention Show (BIS 2010) and the gold medal at the Seoul International Invention Fair. In 2011, the professor won the gold medal and Best Invention Award at the 22th International Invention, Innovation, Industrial Design and Technology Exhibition (I-TEX 2011) and the gold medal and Grand Eco Award Prize at the International Trade Fair, Ideas, Inventions and New Products. In 2012, Professor Hanafi won the KIWIE Prize and Thailand Special Award at the Korea International Women's Invention Exposition (KIWIE 2012). In 2013, he won the gold medal at the 24th International Invention, Innovation & Technology Exhibition (ITEX 2013) and the gold medal at the 6th International Invention Fair in the Middle East (IIFME). In 2014, the professor won the gold medal and Special Award from Asia Invention Association (AIA) at the 25th International Invention, Innovation & Technology Exhibition (ITEX 2014). In 2016, he won the gold medal and three Special Awards from Highly Innovative Unique Foundation Saudi Arabia and Universitatea Technics Din Cluj-Napoca Romania at the 8th European Exhibition of Creativity and Innovation (EUROINVENT 2016). At the International Conference on Innovation in Polymer Science and Technology (IPST 2019) in 2019, Professor Hanafi was awarded the "Innovation in Polymer Science & Technology Award" by the Indonesian Polymer Association. He also was awarded "Excellent Research Award" for his outstanding international scholastic achievement in Polymer Science and Technology by the Croatian Inventors Network. He has published more than 722 research papers in various polymer ISI international journals and is currently on the Editorial Board for Polymer *Plastic Technology & Engineering* (ISI, Marcel Dekker, USA); *Research Journal of Environmental and Earth Sciences* (Maxwell Science), *ASEAN Engineering Journal, Iranica Journal of Energy and Environment, Iranian Polymer Journal* (ISI, Springer); *Central European Journal of Engineering* (Springer); *Journal of Composites and Biodegradable Polymers* (Savy Publishers); and *Journal of Vinyl and Additive Technology* (ISI, Wiley). He is on the Editorial Board for *Polymer Testing* (ISI, Elsevier) and *Journal of Rubber Research* (ISI, Springer) and Chief Editor for Progress in *Rubber Plastic and Recycling Technology* (SAGE), an ISI journal. At the national level, he is also on the Editorial Board for *Journal of Physical Science* (Scopus), *International Journal of Automotive and Mechanical Engineering* (Scopus) and *Journal of Electron Microscopy Malaysia*. Professor Hanafi is a Fellow at the Science Academy of Malaysia and was the Top Malaysian Scientist 2012 and 2014.

S.M. Sapuan is a professor of composite materials at Universiti Putra Malaysia (UPM). He earned his B.Eng. degree in Mechanical Engineering from the University of Newcastle, Australia, in 1990, his MSc from Loughborough University, UK, in 1994 and his PhD from De Montfort University, UK, in 1998. His research interests include natural fiber composites, materials selection and concurrent engineering. To date, he has authored or coauthored more than 1521 publications (730 papers published/accepted in national and international journals; 16 authored books; 25 edited books; 153 chapters in books and 597 conference proceedings/seminar papers/presentation, 26 of which are plenary and keynote lectures and 66 of which are invited lectures). S.M. Sapuan was the recipient of the Rotary Research Gold Medal Award 2012; The Alumni Medal for Professional Excellence Finalist, 2012 Alumni Awards, University of Newcastle, NSW, Australia and the Khwarizmi International Award (KIA). In 2013, he was awarded the 5 Star Role Model Supervisor award by UPM. He has been awarded "Outstanding Reviewer" by Elsevier for his contribution to reviewing journal papers. He received the Best Technical Paper Award in UNIMAS STEM International Engineering Conference in Kuching, Sarawak, Malaysia. S. M. Sapuan was recognized as the first Malaysian to be conferred Fellowship by the US-based Society of Automotive Engineers International (FSAE) in 2015. He was the 2015/2016 recipient of the SEARCA Regional Professorial Chair. In the 2016 ranking of UPM researchers based on the number of citations and h-index by SCOPUS, he was ranked the 6 of 100 researchers. In 2017, he was awarded IOP Outstanding Reviewer Award by the Institute of Physics, UK; the National Book Award; The Best Journal Paper Award, UPM; Outstanding Technical Paper Award, Society of Automotive Engineers International, Malaysia and Outstanding Researcher Award, UPM. He also received in the 2017 Citation of Excellence Award from Emerald, UK; from SAE Malaysia the Best Journal Paper Award; IEEE/TMU Endeavour Research Promotion Award; Best Paper Award by Chinese Defence Ordnance and Malaysia's Research Star Award (MRSA) from Elsevier. In 2019, he was awarded Top Research Scientist Malaysia (TRSM 2019) and Professor of Eminence Award from AMU, India.

R.A. Ilyas is an assistant professor in the School of Chemical and Energy Engineering, Universiti Teknologi Malaysia, Malaysia. He received his Diploma in Forestry at Universiti Putra Malaysia, Bintulu Campus (UPMKB), Sarawak, Malaysia, from May 2009 to April 2012. In 2012, he was awarded the Public Service Department (JPA) Scholarship to pursue his Bachelor's Degree (BSc) in Chemical Engineering at Universiti Putra Malaysia (UPM). Upon completing his BSc. program in 2016, he was again awarded the Graduate Research Fellowship (GRF) by UPM to undertake a PhD degree in the field of Biocomposite Technology & Design at the Institute of Tropical Forestry and Forest Products (INTROP) UPM. R.A. Ilyas's research interests include polymer engineering, material engineering, natural fibers, biocomposites and nanocomposites. He was the recipient of the MVP Doctor of Philosophy Gold Medal Award UPM 2019 for Best PhD Thesis and Top Student Award, INTROP, UPM. In 2018, he was awarded recognized as the Outstanding Reviewer by *Carbohydrate Polymers*, Elsevier, UK; Best Paper Award (11th AUN/SEED-Net Regional Conference on Energy Engineering); Best Paper Award (Seminar Enau Kebangsaan 2019, Persatuan Pembangunan dan Industri Enau Malaysia) and National Book Award 2018. R.A. Ilyas also was listed among the world's Top 2% Scientist (Subject-Wise) Citation Impact during the Single Calendar Year 2019. His main research interests are polymer engineering (biodegradable polymers, biopolymers, polymer composites and polymer-gels) and material engineering (natural fiber-reinforced polymer composites, biocomposites, cellulose materials and nano-composites). He has authored or coauthored more than 221 publications (68 papers published/accepted/submitted in national and international journals, 1 authored book, 10 edited books, 68 chapters in books, 2 research bulletins, 5 Journal Special Issues as Guest Editor and 6 editor/coeditor for conference/seminar proceedings and 61 conference proceedings/seminar papers/presentations).

Contributors

M.N.M. Ansari
Institute of Power Engineering
Universiti Tenaga Nasional
Kajang, Malaysia

A. Atiqah
Institute of Microengineering
  and Nanoelectronics
Universiti Kebangsaan Malaysia
Bangi, Malaysia

Quoc Bao Bui
Sustainable Developments in Civil
  Engineering Research Group
Faculty of Civil Engineering
Ton Duc Thang University
Ho Chi Minh City, Vietnam

Asfa Amalia Ahmad Fauzi
Faculty of Chemical Engineering
  Technology
Universiti Malaysia Perlis
  (UniMAP)
Arau, Malaysia

Siti Nadia Aini Ghazali
Faculty of Engineering
School of Chemical and Energy
  Engineering
Universiti Teknologi Malaysia
Johor Bahru, Malaysia

Khairul Anwar Abdul Halim
Faculty of Chemical Engineering
  Technology
Center of Excellence Geopolymer
  and Green Technology
  (CEGeoGTech)
Universiti Malaysia Perlis
  (UniMAP)
Arau, Malaysia

H. Harahap
Department of Chemical Engineering
Faculty of Engineering
Universitas Sumatera Utara
Medan, Indonesia

Faiezah Hashim
Faculty of Applied Sciences
Universiti Teknologi MARA
Arau, Malaysia

DongQuy Hoang
Department of Polymer and Composite
  Materials
Faculty of Materials Science
  and Technology
University of Science, Vietnam
  National University
Ho Chi Minh City, Vietnam

Y.Z.N. Htwe
School of Materials and Mineral
  Resources Engineering
Universiti Sains Malaysia
Nibong Tebal, Malaysia

Sofian Ibrahim
RAYMINTEX Plant
Malaysian Nuclear Agency
Kajang, Malaysia

Hanafi Ismail
School of Materials and Mineral
  Resources Engineering
Universiti Sains Malaysia
Nibong Tebal, Malaysia

Noor Aishatun Majid
Faculty of Applied Sciences
Universiti Teknologi MARA
Arau, Malaysia

M. Mariatti
School of Materials and Mineral Resources Engineering
Universiti Sains Malaysia
Nibong Tebal, Malaysia

M.T. Mastura
Fakulti Teknologi Kejuuteraan Mekanikal dan Pembuatan
Centre on Advance Research of Energy
Universiti Teknikal Malaysia Melaka
Melaka, Malaysia

Zurina Mohamad
Faculty of Engineering
School of Chemical and Energy Engineering
Universiti Teknologi Malaysia
Johor Bahru, Malaysia

H. Nasution
Department of Chemical Engineering
Faculty of Engineering
Universitas Sumatera Utara
Medan, Indonesia

Dang Mao Nguyen
Laboratoire Innovation Matériau Bois Habitat Apprentissage (LIMBHA)
Ecole Supérieure du Bois
Nantes, France

Thi Phuong Thao Nguyen
Department of Biomedical Science
VNUK Institute for Research and Executive Education
The University of Danang
Danang City, Vietnam

A. Nobili
Research Centre "CRICT"
Department of Engineering "Enzo Ferrari"
University of Modena and Reggio Emilia
Modena, Italy

M. Noryani
Fakulti Kejuruteraan Mekanikal
Centre on Advance Research of Energy
Universiti Teknikal Malaysia Melaka
Melaka, Malaysia

A.K. Nurdina
School of Materials and Mineral Resources Engineering
Universiti Sains Malaysia
Nibong Tebal, Malaysia

Azlin Fazlina Osman
Faculty of Chemical Engineering Technology
Center of Excellence Geopolymer and Green Technology (CEGeoGTech)
Universiti Malaysia Perlis (UniMAP)
Arau, Malaysia

Patrick Perré
Laboratoire Innovation Matériau Bois Habitat Apprentissage (LIMBHA)
Ecole Supérieure du Bois
Nantes, France

D.M. Putra
Department of Chemical Engineering
Faculty of Engineering
Universitas Sumatera Utara
Medan, Indonesia

Rozyanty Abdul Rahman
Faculty of Chemical Engineering Technology
Polymer Engineering
Universiti Malaysia Perlis
Arau, Malaysia

A. Rusli
School of Materials and Mineral Resources Engineering
Universiti Sains Malaysia
Nibong Tebal, Malaysia

Contributors

Dalina Samsudin
Faculty of Applied Sciences
Universiti Teknologi MARA
Arau, Malaysia

C. Signorini
Research Centre "CRICT"
University of Modena and Reggio Emilia
Modena, Italy

Kathiravan Suppiah
Faculty of Chemical Engineering
    Technology
Polymer Engineering
Universiti Malaysia Perlis
Arau, Malaysia
and
Department of Chemical Engineering
Faculty of Engineering
Universitas Sumatera Utara
Medan, Indonesia

Pei Leng Teh
Faculty of Chemical Engineering
    Technology
Polymer Engineering
Universiti Malaysia Perlis
Arau, Malaysia

Winny
Universitas Sumatera Utara
Medan, Indonesia

Cheow Keat Yeoh
Centre of Excellence for
    Frontier Materials Research
    (CFMR)
Polymer Engineering
Universiti Malaysia Perlis
Arau, Malaysia

N.A Mohd Zaini
Faculty of Applied Sciences
Universiti Teknologi MARA,
    Perlis Branch, Arau
    Campus
Arau, Malaysia

1 Application of Mineral Fillers in Polymer Composites for Industrial Applications

A.K. Nurdina, Y.Z.N. Htwe, and M. Mariatti
Universiti Sains Malaysia
Nibong Tebal, Malaysia

CONTENTS

1.1 Introduction ...1
1.2 Hybridization of Mineral Fillers in Polymer Composites ...3
1.3 Mineral Fillers ...3
    1.3.1 Mica ...4
    1.3.2 Silica ...5
    1.3.3 Calcium Carbonate ($CaCO_3$) ...6
    1.3.4 Talc ...8
    1.3.5 Kaolin ...10
1.4 Filler Characteristics and Their Effect on Composite Properties ...11
    1.4.1 Particle Shape ...12
    1.4.2 Particle Size and Distribution ...13
    1.4.3 Particle Surface Area and Surface Energy ...15
    1.4.4 Particle-Matrix Compatibility ...15
1.5 Applications ...16
    1.5.1 Automotive Applications ...16
    1.5.2 Electrical Applications ...18
    1.5.3 Housing Material ...19
1.6 Conclusions ...19
Acknowledgment ...19
References ...19

1.1 INTRODUCTION

Recently, unavoidable increases in industrial activities have triggered a rising demand for more efficient materials. These materials are subjected to increasingly tighter requirements, including higher strength and modulus, desirable electrical and thermal conductivity, cheap cost, low coefficients of thermal expansion and

DOI: 10.1201/9781003221012-1

appropriate heat distortion temperature. Such specifications require the combination of several materials to achieve desirable characteristics. This is possible with composite materials in which the components can synergistically function to address the application's needs (Friedrich et al., 2005). Therefore, a combination of filler materials has been widely used in polymers, and these are gaining acceptance in various types of engineering applications. Generally, in terms of thermal and mechanical properties of the polymers, the combination potentially boosts the polymer's properties at reduced cost.

Fillers are solid-form additives, and they are basically different from the plastic matrix in terms of composition and structure. They are commonly added for cost reduction, but the addition of mineral fillers into a polymer can improve the various properties including thermal and mechanical properties, creep resistance stiffness, shrinkage and heat deflection temperature. However, the presence of the mineral filler generally deteriorates toughness and strength (Vincent et al., 2014). The physical and chemical properties of the filler is very crucial because they determine the plastic's performance (Nurdina et al., 2009a). Notably, the effect of these inorganic fillers on the composite's mechanical properties can be influenced by various factors, such as the composite's shape, particle size, aggregate size, surface morphology and general matrix properties (Molnar et al., 2000).

Malaysia is well endowed with mineral resources such as limestone, silica, clay, barite, feldspar, mica and granite. Malaysia exports low-grade or semi-value-added industrial minerals to developed countries like America, Japan and Taiwan. Specifically, Singapore plays a major role in trading Malaysian minerals for consumption in the manufacturing industries (Osman & Mariatti, 2006). Mineral fillers are used in many applications, including in the painting, paper and plastic industries. However, the most commonly used filler in the plastic industry is talc. Particularly, it has a broad-based application in the automotive industry. For example, it is largely used in bumper covers, and it is being used in more interior applications such as instrument panels (Phipps, 2014). The use of talc by manufacturers as a filler in polypropylene (PP) composites (de Oliveira et al., 2019) has been growing since 1980. As the most used filler in PP composites and as the main filler, talc has a dominant position today. Manufacturers did not shift their paradigm because they have confidence in the good stability, processability (Wu et al., 2015) and tensile properties of talc-filled PP. Nevertheless, the use of talc is becoming more expensive, especially for an importing country like Malaysia, which mainly lacks talc sources.

Several other mineral fillers including limestone, silica, clay, mica and wollastonite are becoming increasingly important as fillers in the polymer industry because they can replace talc in PP. Furthermore, these mineral fillers are abundantly available at several locations throughout Malaysia. Limestone ($CaCO_3$) is regarded as an inexpensive mineral filler that can be utilized at high filler loadings and improve the flexural modulus of PP. It also exhibits an excellent surface finish, as well as viscosity control (Moreno et al., 2015). On the other hand, sheet-like platy fillers like talc, mica and kaolin have been reported to enhance rigidity (Jang, 2016). Mica is regarded as a plentiful mineral and by using regular grinding methods, mica can be easily cleaved into thin flakes. When utilized as a filler in specific thermoplastic material, the ultra-thin flakes reveal high aspect ratios, thereby conveying a high reinforcement level

(Lapčík et al., 2018). Moreover, mica has excellent thermal insulating properties that reduce the plastic flammability when incorporated (Nurdina et al., 2009b). Silica is notable for its extremely low thermal expansion coefficient, which is caused by the great Si-O bond energy in silica-filled composite materials. This attracted attention from several researchers who utilized it to optimize the mechanical properties and decrease the polymer composite's coefficient of thermal expansion (CTE) (Habib et al., 2017). The plastics industry demands fine filler particle size, preferably below 10 μm, with narrow particle-size distribution and particle shapes according to the function of the filler in the plastic matrix. Specifically, an elongated and flaky particle shape is essential for tensile strength, whereas a spherical and cubical particle shape improves impact strength. Soft minerals such as limestone exhibit excellent surface finishing of plastics. Hence, individual minerals have their peculiar advantages as fillers, and they enhance certain properties. Better still, various types of hybrid fillers in polymer composites have been acknowledged by many sources. These hybrid mineral fillers, which comprise more than one type of mineral particle, generally enhance various plastic properties, including mechanical and thermal properties.

1.2 HYBRIDIZATION OF MINERAL FILLERS IN POLYMER COMPOSITES

Hybrid composites have been used in multiple applications such as sports equipment, aircraft and so on. These composites are still attracting a great deal of attention because through the fabrication of hybrid composites it is much easier to tailor the properties needed for a particular application compared with using only a single material. A material with certain characteristics can be obtained with hybrid composites, which is appropriate for the end use of the application (Desai et al., 2007).

There are various kinds of potential reinforcing materials that may be used in hybrid composites. Therefore, there are several studies on the "hybrid impact" or the synergy impact of every material, when used in hybrid composites. Hence, there is an increasing desire to generate hybrid composites that can satisfy the demands of different industrial applications. However, these applications require composite materials to have abrasion resistance, optical clarity and low volume shrinkage, and to improve electrical, thermal, and mechanical properties of reinforcing materials (Lee et al., 2012).

Leong et al. (2004) reported that the effects of hybrid composites can generally be discussed in three conditions. The most popular impact is the economic effect, whereby a more costly filler is incorporated into a cheap material. The second hybrid fillers' impact involves the capability of fabricating a wider array of properties (i.e., thermal, physical and mechanical) to match the desired characteristics. Last, hybridization can achieve advantages from improvements in the functional and mechanical properties.

1.3 MINERAL FILLERS

Generally, fillers are materials added to a formulation to reduce the cost of the compound. Selecting and optimizing these materials properly can enhance economic properties and other properties like mechanical behavior and processing. Fillers have been classified in many ways ranging from their shapes to their specific

TABLE 1.1
Characteristics of Common Mineral Fillers in Term of Cost, Coefficient of Thermal Expansion (CTE) and Shape

Mineral Fillers	Density (g/cm³)	CTE (ppm/°C)	Shape	Hardness
Mica	2.883	8.0	Flake	2.5–3
Silica	2.65	12.3	Elongate/cubical	7
Calcium carbonate	2.71	10.0	Elongated/cubical	3
Talc	2.76	16.3	Flake	1
Kaolin	2.65	18.6	Flake	2–2.5

characteristics. For simplicity, a filler can be classified into two categories, as extenders and functional fillers (Zaaba & Ismail, 2019). An extender primarily occupies space, and is mainly used to lower the formulation cost. However, a functional filler has a definite and required function in the formulation apart from cost. Today, mineral fillers are used as functional fillers in different polymer applications to optimize toughness, stiffness, electric insulation and dimensional stability or to reduce dielectric loss (Almeshal et al., 2020). Table 1.1 summarizes the characteristics of common mineral fillers in terms of density, CTE, shape, and hardness.

1.3.1 Mica

Mica is a generic name given to the family of hydrous potassium aluminum silicates that have identical physical properties. Some popular micas include muscovite, phlogopite, biotite, lepidolite and vermiculite. Muscovite mica is a common constituent of acid igneous rock (such as granite or alaskite) and vein pragmatic rock. Muscovite is quarried by itself or as a by-product from the production of other commercial minerals. Muscovite mica is often referred to as white or ruby mica, whereas phlogopite is called amber silica. The color is due to stains, which can be categorized into primary stains or secondary stains based on the surface, as well as the bulk impurities. Muscovite mica has a theoretical chemical composition of $K_2A_{14}(Al_2Si_6O_{20})(OH)_4$. The molecular structure is composed of three planes for each layer. The center is made up of a pseudo-octahedral gibbsite plane, which is bonded chemically by the bridging of oxygen and hydroxyl groups to a couple of tetrahedral silica planes. The two-dimensional layer is negatively charged, and it is held to next-door layers by a 12-fold coordination of potassium ions interacting with 6 atoms of oxygen from every layer. It is a weak ionic interaction due to impurities, which replace multiple potassium ions in the natural mica. This allows the mineral to be easily delaminated into thin sheets along these imperfect planes. Once all the imperfect planes have been broken, it is very difficult to further delaminate the remaining mica particles (Xiang et al., 2010). Mica's molecular structure is displayed in Figure 1.1.

Mica has high strength and stiffness, a low CTE, high thermal conductivity, good chemical and temperature resistance, excellent dielectric properties, low solubility in water and low hardness. It is more effective in some polymer types (polyolefin,

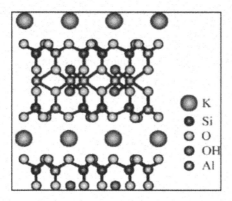

FIGURE 1.1 Molecular structure of mica. (From Keller et al., 2011; image used with permission from AIP Publishing.)

thermoplastic polyesters, polyamides and polar styrene) than in others (polycarbonate, polystyrene and acrylonitrile-butadiene-styrene [ABS]). Hence, mica bas been widely used to reinforce PP composites, which have been found to possess improved mechanical properties when used with coupling agents because of enhanced adhesion and effective reinforcement (Lapčík et al., 2018). Specifically, the commonly used coupling and adhesion promoters include silanes, organosilicon compounds, azidosilanes, chloro-paraffins and PPs, which contain carboxy groups. Yazdani et al. (2006) investigated the effect of silane coupling agents and maleic anhydride grafted PP on PP/mica. On the other hand, Deshmukh et al. (2011) examined the impact of adding mica to the mechanical properties of polybutylene terephthalate (PBT) composites. Reports indicated that the composites exhibited good interfacial interaction without using any surface modifier or coupling agent. Also, the tensile strength of mica-filled composites was found to increase by adding up to 10 wt% mica. After this, the tensile strength decreased until it became stable, although the value was still higher than that of the PBT matrix. A maximum improvement in the mica-filled composites' strength is approximately 9%. However, modified mica reportedly enhanced the mechanical properties, particle dispersion in the matrix and elastic properties of the composites.

1.3.2 Silica

Silica is the name given to a set of minerals made up of a single silicon atom and two oxygen atoms, and the chemical formula of silica is SiO_2. Mineral silica can be found in nine varying crystalline forms or polymorphs, whereby the three key forms are referred to as tridymite, quartz and cristobalite (Fauziyah et al., 2019). Silica is normally seen in the crystalline form of quartz. A crystalline structure is one in which atoms are in a repeating or periodic range over a great atomic distance (Callister, 2000). Generally, there are some grades of silica with good reinforcing properties, which are available either in crystalline (quartz) or amorphous forms. According to Wypych (2000), crystalline silica fillers include ground silica (or silica flour), sand

and a form of quartz-tripoli; the amorphous types include diatomaceous earth. In addition to naturally occurring silica known as mineral silica, silica is also produced by precipitation or by fumed and fused methods.

Silica has been used as a filler in many applications such as rubber products, refractory concrete, electronic applications, plastics etc. (Habib et al., 2017). Mineral silica is directly extracted from deposits after which it is physically processed. After a thorough washing, kiln drying, grinding and air floatation, deposits of high-quality mineral silica may be utilized as fillers in plastic either in a particulate form or after further pulverizing to silica flour (Dijkstra et al., 2013). Mineral silica is abundant and widely available in nature. It has excellent whiteness and brightness, and it is an inexpensive mineral powder that is inert to acids, alkalis and chemicals (Wu et al., 2015). Mineral silica has a remarkably high melting point of about 1610°C, which is higher than copper, aluminum and iron. In addition, mineral silica has a CTE of about 12.3 ppm/°C. Silicas possess high thermal conductivity, good electrical insulation properties and good transparency. The hardness is about 7.0 Mohr, and it also has good abrasion resistance. These characteristics make mineral silica in the form of silica flour the most popular filler for plastic composites. The exceptionally low CTE of silica, which produces high Si-O bond energy in silica-filled composite materials, has attracted a great deal of attention because it enhances mechanical properties and reduces the CTE of polymer composites (Yang et al., 2005). Ahmad et al. (2008) examined the impact of structural changes in silica filler on the CTE of underfilled encapsulants. They reported that the CTE value of the produced composite was significantly influenced by the degree of crystallinity of the silica filler. The results also revealed that the composite's CTE was not influenced by particle size, or particle distribution of the filler. According to Ahmad et al. (2008), different particle shapes of silica filler affected the flexural and tensile properties of epoxy polymer composites.

Mineral silica can be modified by using a variety of surface treatments. The most common modification is with organic silicones or silanes, but titanate, waxes and inorganic fluorides can also be used (Zoukrami et al., 2007). Mineral silica is typically treated with 0.5–1.0 wt% of amino-, epoxy-, vinyl-, or mercapto-trialkoxysilanes. There are several studies on the modification of silica, especially for nano-silica fillers (Wen et al., 2004; Riku et al., 2005). Riku et al. (2005) examined the impact of compatibilization on PP/elastomer/micro-silica composites. It was found that the microstructure of the composites was determined by the type of compatibilizer used. For instance, adding maleic anhydride grafted polypropylene (PP-g-MAH) as a compatibilizer was found to enhance the stiffness, as well as the toughness of the PP/elastomer/micro-silica.

1.3.3 Calcium Carbonate ($CaCO_3$)

Ground calcium carbonates represent the most popular fillers as they are widely utilized in various plastic applications. Calcium carbonate is known by many names including marble, limestone, calcite, chalk, aragonite, dolomite, coral, shell and whiting. Carbonate is probably one of the most extensively utilized mineral additives due to its low abrasion, whiteness, widespread availability in broad particle-size arrays and low cost (Nurdina et al., 2009b). Limestone and dolomite are the primary carbonaceous rocks. Limestone consists of the mineral calcite, which is the thermodynamically stable form of calcium carbonate. Aragonite, a metastable polymorph, can be irreversibly converted to calcite by heating to 400°C in dry air. The presence of water accelerates this transformation. The solid-state structures of the two forms are composed of alternating calcium cations and a trigonal planer carbonate anion. The packing differences of these ionic strands determine the physical differences between calcite and aragonite. Such an ionic structure is quite different from most of the lamellar mineral structures.

Although calcium carbonate is compatible with most resin systems, one must take care that it does not encounter strong acidic reagents because if it is attacked by acids then carbon-dioxide gas is given off. The low acid resistance limits the usable oxygen carbon calcium loading level of calcium carbonate in some polymer matrix applications. Heating calcium carbonate to temperatures between 800°C and 900°C will also liberate carbon dioxide gas. Interestingly, these conditions are not encountered in the processing of most resins (Hoque et al., 2013). Surface-treated grades of calcium carbonate are commercially available. Because standard silanes are not effective with carbonates, stearates or metallic stearates are usually the surface treatment of choice. Stearate allows for improved dispersion and reduction of agglomeration, especially for fine particle-size grades. The stearate treatment renders the mineral surface more hydrophobic, thereby aiding the wet-out. However, the stearate does not strongly interact with the resin; therefore, an increased physical strength is often obtained with a coupling agent (Lv et al., 2020). Stearate treatment is best carried out during the grinding phase of manufacturing. The freshly exposed new surfaces are immediately contacted with the reagent before agglomeration can occur. Different levels of treatment between 0.5% and 1.2% have been reported, but the high surface area of the precipitated grades may have treatments up to 10% by weight.

Incorporating rigid particulate fillers in a polymer matrix generally exerts an embrittling impact, which decreases the system's impact strength. Most of the studies on the modification of semi-crystalline polymers with rigid particles reported a considerable toughness loss compared with a neat polymer. Using calcium carbonate as a toughening agent is a novel concept; however, it mainly improves the good properties, at the expense of the PP strength. Thus, rigid particles should be deboned for creating enough free volume or cavities in the blend at a sub-micron-size level to achieve the necessary toughening mechanism. This also appears like cavitations that form in a rubber-toughened system (Zuiderduin et al., 2003). Figure 1.2 displays the micro-mechanistic model of the toughening impact.

In a previous study, Liang (2012) examined the impact of nanometer calcium carbonate on the crystallization properties of glass fiber-reinforced poly (p-phenylene sulfide) (PPS) nanocomposites. The results revealed that the nanometer particles can promote the heterogeneous nucleation in the PPS matrix. Toughening of PP with $CaCO_3$ particles can overcome the drawbacks in low-temperature brittleness and notch sensitivity. Gaymans et al. (2003) enhanced the durability of isotactic PP with $CaCO_3$ particles and suggested an ideal particle-size window, which contributes to improving the PP durability. Zhang et al. (2006) also reported that the same particle size influences the toughening performance of $CaCO_3$, while also noting the

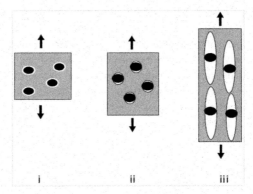

FIGURE 1.2 Toughening mechanism with rigid particles. (From Zuiderduin et al., 2003; image used with permission from Elsevier.)

significance of optimizing the filler loading and molecular weight of the polymer matrix. In addition to their toughening effect, $CaCO_3$ particles can also influence the crystallization activity of semicrystalline PP.

1.3.4 Talc

Talc has the chemical formula $Mg_6Si_8O_{20}(OH)_4$ and the molecular structure is shown in Figure 1.3. The mineral is made up of neutral layers consisting of a central 28 brucite plane bonded chemically by the bridging of the oxygen atoms to 2 tetrahedral silica planes. Individual layers are interned by weak van der Waals forces. This differs from other minerals such as mica, in which the layers are interned by ionic forces or in kaolin, whereby hydrogen bonding forces hold together the aluminosilicates layers. Because of this weak interaction, talc is easily delaminated, and it is usually processed to particles retaining a relatively high aspect ratio of up to 20:1. This weak interaction is also the major reason talc is such a soft mineral. The outer layers easily peel off, providing the lubricity characteristics associated with talc (Haddar et al., 2017).

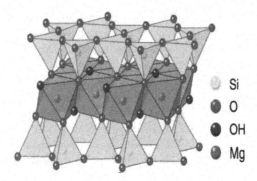

FIGURE 1.3 The molecular structure of talc. (From Barua et al., 2019; image used with permission from Elsevier.)

Talc has a very white color and a large degree of smoothness and softness, thereby providing exceptional coverage, high sheen to finished parts and good luster. Talc particles are a series of particles with a small plate-shaped structure and when aligned, they offer improved physical properties to finished parts. Hence the particle size and the shape determine the slip or lubricity tendency. It is generally difficult to disband talc in traditional plastic equipment because of the total tendency for further bulking. The sensitivity of the material is less susceptible to pH changes; therefore, it is utilized in applications in which little acidity constitutes a problem. Other talc forms are available, such as foliated or acicular, depending on the crystalline form of the ore, but generally, these types of talc products are not used in plastic applications. Compared with most natural minerals, talc has a very hydrophobic surface because of the high ionic character of the central magnesium plane, the neutrality of layers, the uniform polarity of the structure and the symmetry. These characteristics contribute to making the outer silica surfaces of the mineral much less hydrophilic than other silicate minerals. This greater hydrophobicity is often an advantage and makes talc generally more compatible in polymeric resins (Shakoor & Thomas, 2014).

As a plastic filler, talc is used in special applications because it cannot be used as a sole filler in molding formulas; therefore, it is generally utilized in combination with other filler materials. Hence, it can facilitate removal from the molds and assist in achieving better sheen or a gloss on parts. It also helps to lower the wear of extrusion die through its lubricating effect. Moreover, talc can promote better fire retardancy and assist in the processing of final products in different plastic sealants, as well as mastics. As an aid, talc can be useful in specific color applications, which makes it suitable for use as a filler for producing parts that contact acids. It can also be used as a viscosity modifier to enhance the physical properties of a finished product.

PP is regarded as the widest volume plastic utilization of talc. The structural strength (i.e., stiffness) and high temperature creep resistance is provided by talc, which is required for automotive and appliance applications. However, the major drawbacks of talc in PP are its low impact and scratch resistance (Wu et al., 2015). In their study, Leong et al. (2004) proved that adding talc as a specific filler in PP can modify the polymer properties to a large extent. They reported that the tensile modulus was increased with the filler loading, whereas tensile strength, as well as Izod impact strength, were reduced. Lapcik et al. (2008) also investigated the effects of talc filler on the mechanical properties of PP composites. Based on the results, the mechanical strength of the PP composite was reportedly increased with increasing filler content. This was attributed to the excellent dispersion, high order (i.e., crystal-like lattice) of the microparticles in a three-dimensional PP matrix and mutual synergistic impact, which created a specified bond between the individual particles and the polymer matrix (Lapcik et al., 2008). The surface modification of talc can be achieved with coupling agents like silane, titanate etc. (Shelesh-Nezhad and Taghizadeh, 2007; Anuar, 2008). These agents are used to modify the interfacial area amid the inorganic filler and the organic polymer for bonding improvement.

Several studies have investigated the impact of divergent talc concentrations on the mechanical performance of the PP/talc composites. Nevertheless, the findings indicate certain inconsistencies. Haddar et al. (2017) reported that 5–10 wt% talc concentration enhanced the mechanical properties and hardness values of talc/PP composites.

Lapcik et al. (2008) observed a steady improvement in microhardness from 34.94 for pure PP to 38.118 N/mm² for 30 wt% talc concentration. The reported trend has been verified by the authors in an equivalent rise in the bending intensity from the initial 21.18 to 39.20 MPa for a 30 wt% concentration of talc. The study showed that adjustments to the calculated mechanical parameters were identified when the talc content increased. A positive effect on hardness and crystallinity was found by Haddar et al. (2017) with 30 wt% talc additive, whereas a reduction in impact strength was reported at the same time. However, the increase of talc concentration has led to an increase in hardness to some point (6 wt% or 9 wt%) after which a decreasing trend was noticed. The reported variations in the trends of talc-filled polymer composites are attributed to the uneven distribution of the filler because the type and distribution of the filler could significantly affect the performance of the PP/talc compound. On the other hand, surface modification of the filler particles by silanes has reportedly affected rheology of the melt-filled polymers through enhanced particle dispersion and decreased melt viscosity when acting in a lubricant form or surfactant.

1.3.5 KAOLIN

Kaolinite is a white, non-porous, non-swelling, natural aluminosilicate mineral. It is often referred to as clay, even though its physical properties greatly differ from other commercial clay silicates such as bentonites or fire clays. Kaolin is one of the 31 most finely divided and highly refined naturally occurring minerals. Its chemical formula is $Al_4Si_4O_{10}(OH)_8$ (Mustafa, 2012), and the molecular structure is shown in Figure 1.4. Kaolin is a platy silicate, meaning it is an inorganic polymer with two basic monomer structures, such as silica tetrahedron and alumina octahedron. Also, kaolin holds an unceasing octahedral layer together with a joined octahedral layer, slanted on a triangular side. It is bound on one side by an incessant silica layer, which comprises a tetrahedron with three shared oxygens, and every fourth (apical) oxygen is pointed in a similar direction, forming a layer of connected ring with the hexagonal openings (Sheikh et al., 2017).

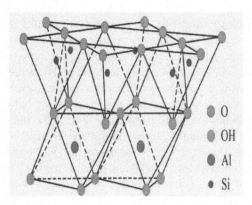

FIGURE 1.4 Molecular structure of kaolin. (Bhattacharyya & Gupta, 2008; image used with permission from Elsevier.)

Hydrous and fully calcined kaolin are relatively inert to dilute acids and bases; therefore, they are often used in corrosive-environment applications. The metakaolin form, however, is particularly susceptible to acids. A further advantage of the high purity of kaolin is its surface inertness. Because the surface is so inert, low levels of surfactants are highly effective in dispersing the mineral. The slightly acidic surface, however, can hinder curing in some systems employing free radical curing catalysts (Xanthos, 2005). The use of kaolin as a filler in thermoplastics is a field of considerable interest because it offers a combination of unique properties. The platy natural shape and the exceptionally fine particles of kaolin provide reinforcement and great impact resistance (Guessoum et al., 2012). Notably, clays represent natural products, therefore, they are cost-effective compared with synthetic competitive materials that may experience potential development (Srinivasan, 2011).

Compounding composites, whereby particles of kaolin are dispersed in the polymeric matrix, encounter substantial processing challenges because of great surface energy and the existence of polar groups. The non-dispersive phenomena of kaolin fillers will result in non-uniform properties. Few studies in the literature have reported the development of kaolin-filled polymer composites (Carvalho et al., 2001; Ansari & Price, 2004; Buggy et al., 2005; Ainur, 2006). Carvalho et al. (2001) studied the behavior of the PP/kaolin composites, especially with respect to tensile and morphological properties. Based on the results, the discontinuity points have been introduced to the matrix because of the existing bare non-adherent kaolin particles, and the agglomerates with sharp edges in the composites. To solve the problem of dispersion of kaolin, Ainur (2006) examined the impact of stearic acid, as well as quaternary ammonium cationic treatments on the mechanical performance of PP/kaolin composites. Better particle dispersion was obtained with quaternary ammonium treatment, which produced a high impact strength composite. Also reported was the presence of a soft interface around the surface of every kaolin, which acted as a shock absorber during the impact test.

Dispersing the layers of clay silicate into a thermoplastic (i.e., PP) at a nanometer level is difficult. In several studies, the melt intercalation, which includes the mixing of the layered silicates into a polymer matrix directly, was to prepare PP-clay nanocomposites (Yen et al., 2004; Thabo et al., 2009; Yang et al., 2009). This process was improved by modifying the given montmorillonite or the smectite clays to be more hydrophobic. The modified filler was then utilized with a maleic anhydride compatibilizer, or with hydroxyl-modified PP. The organo-modification of the clay has been carried out generally by the ion exchange with double-tailed ammonium cations, thereby increasing the static and dynamic elastic moduli, barrier properties, flame retardance, and solvent resistance.

1.4 FILLER CHARACTERISTICS AND THEIR EFFECT ON COMPOSITE PROPERTIES

The impact of inorganic fillers on the mechanical property of composites largely depends on the shape and size of the particle, particle-matrix compatibility and surface area. The matrix-particle compatibility is related to the ability of polymers to coat and adhere to the given filler (Kundie et al., 2018).

1.4.1 PARTICLE SHAPE

The particle shape of most mineral filler is approximated as a cube, sphere, block, needle, plate or fiber even though some have a mixture of shapes. The shape of the particles exerts a huge influence on the flexural modulus of composites. Usually, the shape is discussed in terms of aspect ratio, which describes the length to thickness ratio of the particle (DeArmitt & Rothon, 2016). However, for fibers and the acicular particles, it represents the ratio of the mean length to the mean diameter. For the platy particles, it is the mean diameter of a circle, with similar area as the face to mean thickness of the plate (Wahyuni & Soeswanto, 2019). Some examples of general ranges of aspect ratios for various particle shapes are provided in Table 1.2.

Generally, the reinforcing capacity of fillers increases with increasing particle anisotropy (i.e., aspect ratio); hence, fillers and reinforcements are commonly differentiated by the degree of anisotropy. The fillers with a plate-like geometry such

TABLE 1.2
Filler Characterization

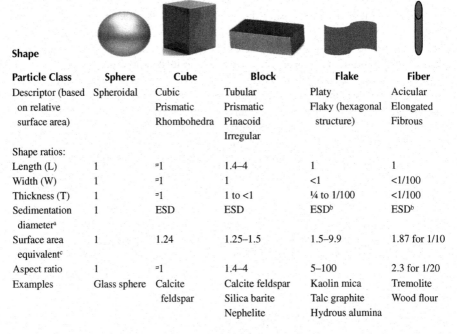

Shape					
Particle Class	Sphere	Cube	Block	Flake	Fiber
Descriptor (based on relative surface area)	Spheroidal	Cubic Prismatic Rhombohedra	Tubular Prismatic Pinacoid Irregular	Platy Flaky (hexagonal structure)	Acicular Elongated Fibrous
Shape ratios:					
Length (L)	1	≃1	1.4–4	1	1
Width (W)	1	≃1	1	<1	<1/100
Thickness (T)	1	≃1	1 to <1	¼ to 1/100	<1/100
Sedimentation diameter[a]	1	ESD	ESD	ESD[b]	ESD[b]
Surface area equivalent[c]	1	1.24	1.25–1.5	1.5–9.9	1.87 for 1/10
Aspect ratio	1	≃1	1.4–4	5–100	2.3 for 1/20
Examples	Glass sphere	Calcite feldspar	Calcite feldspar Silica barite Nephelite	Kaolin mica Talc graphite Hydrous alumina	Tremolite Wood flour

[a] According to Stoke's law, ESD = equivalent spherical diameter or the diameter of the sphere having the same volume as that of the particle.
[b] Must be modified for greater than 4-1 maximum to minimum particle dimension.
[c] Equivalent to a spherical diameter of 1; an approximation of the area when the particle has a volume equivalent to an ESD of 1.

as mica, talc or layered silicates reinforce polymers better than spherical fillers, whereas the effects of glass fibers can be stronger (Vallittu et al., 2022). The modulus is expected to increase with the aspect ratio. However, Janos and Bela (2008) found that the stiffness of short glass fiber-filled PP is independent of the fiber length and diameter. According to Cho et al. (2006), the large aspect ratio could increase stress concentration, whereas impact resistance is reportedly increased with a decrease in the particle size.

Notably, melt viscosity is heavily reliant on the aspect ratio of fillers such that viscosity increases with increasing aspect ratio at equal loading levels. Therefore, glass spheres give good processing rheology but poor stiffness; glass fiber, with its high aspect ratio, provides the opposite (Ishak, 2013). In theory, a critical aspect ratio is necessary for a composite to allow a functional filler to receive applied stress; otherwise, the stress will pass around the filler and remain in the plastic matrix. The shape or aspect ratio of a mineral also varies with particle size. Finer materials (less than 1 micron) usually have a lower aspect ratio (Gallagher & McDonald, 2013).

Ahmad et al. (2008) examined the impact of varying percentages of the filler loadings, as well as shapes on the mechanical and thermal properties of silica mineral composites. Figure 1.5 shows the scanning electron microscope (SEM) images of different silica particles. The angular structure of mineral particles of silica demonstrates the shape with one or more sharp angles on the surface; however, the cubical shape shows smooth angles compared with the angular shape. The length of elongated mineral silica particles is longer compared with the width of particulates. Fused silica comprises different types, including spherical, hexagonal and cubical shapes, among other irregular shapes.

The micrographs of elongated, angular silica-filled epoxy composites are shown in Figure 1.6. The elongated filler shapes with a higher particle surface area leads to greater contact space between the matrix and the filler. Thus, the interphase of the composites from the micrograph is strong perhaps due to good adhesion with the matrix, or the silica contacts.

1.4.2 Particle Size and Distribution

Conventionally, particle size reflects the diameter of the particle, but the values are a corresponding spherical diameter (equivalent spherical diameter [ESD]). The particle-size distribution data are useful for comparing the relative fineness of a sample against parallel particle shapes. Generally, particle-size distribution is deduced as the median ESD. The median demonstrates that half of the particles possess a greater ESD and half of them possess a smaller ESD regardless of the size of the smallest and largest particles that considerably influences the performance of the filler (Marghalani, 2010). In composites, applied stress can be moved from a polymer matrix to a stiff and strong filler. Such a transfer of stress can be more effective when a filler is smaller due the presence of a larger surface area. When the particles possess a higher aspect ratio (i.e., needle-like, platy or fibrous in shape), the intercept of stress propagation is better via the matrix. According to Bouwman et al. (2004), the particle-size distribution, width and median size significantly affect the packing density of composite materials. Specifically, the

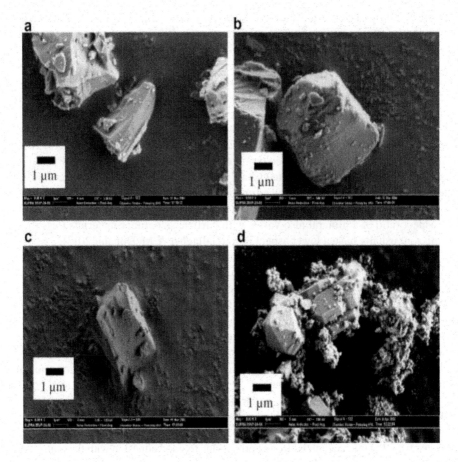

FIGURE 1.5 SEM micrographs of different shapes of silica fillers. (a) Silica mineral, angular shape. (b) Silica mineral, cubical. (c) Silica mineral, elongated. (d) Fused silica, irregular shape. (From Ahmad et al., 2008; image used with permission from Elsevier.)

density increases with increasing particle distribution width and median size. Hence, the addition of a powder with a larger median and similar size distribution width increases the packing density. Bouwman et al. (2004) also reported that the median size of particles has a pronounced impact on the composite's behavior. Janos and Bela (2008) stated that particle size greatly influences the composite properties as strength and modulus increased sometimes, whereas impact strength and deformability decreased when particle size was decreased. Large particles can considerably alter and often deteriorate the deformation, as well as the composites' failure characteristics. It is also easy to debond them from the matrix, thereby resulting in premature failure. Notably, there is a higher tendency for filler aggregation when the particle size is decreased. Then, the extensive aggregation could lead to deficient homogeneity, low-impact strength and rigidity and the aggregated filler particles could act as crack initiation sites during impact.

Application of Mineral Fillers in Polymer Composites

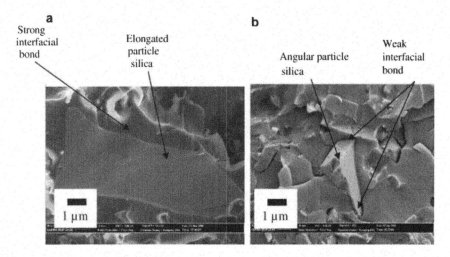

FIGURE 1.6 SEM images of epoxy filled with elongated silica and angular silica. (From Ahmad et al., 2008; image used with permission from Elsevier.)

1.4.3 PARTICLE SURFACE AREA AND SURFACE ENERGY

The specific surface area of a filler is closely related to its particle-size distribution, which directly influences the composite properties. The adsorption of small molecular weight additives and the polymer adsorption are proportional to the matrix/filler interface area. Thus, the adsorption of additives can alter the stability, whereas the matrix/filler interaction would significantly influence the mechanical properties such as tensile strength, yield stress and impact resistance (Móczó & Pukánszky, 2016). The surface free energy of fillers can determine the matrix/filler interaction, as well as particle/particle relationship. Whereas the former exerts a noticeable effect on the composites' mechanical properties, the latter can determine the aggregation of particles. However, these two interactions can be modified through surface treatment. This non-reactive treatment often results in improved dispersion and increased filler/matrix interaction. In addition, chemical or physical coupling can lead to improved strength. Generally, most of the fillers and reinforcements can be surface coated, but the amount and characteristic of the coating substance should be carefully decided to ensure successful filler application (Janos & Bela, 2008).

1.4.4 PARTICLE-MATRIX COMPATIBILITY

An intimate contact between the matrix and the filler particles is essential regardless of the shape and size of the filler because air gaps are zero strength points. Compound strength can be enhanced through good wetting of the filler by the matrix. In fact, the strength can be further improved if the matrix adheres to the surface of the filler via chemical bonding, as illustrated in Figure 1.7. Hence, surface coatings are usually utilized for optimizing the compatibility of the filler-matrix, as well as adhesion. The mineral, to which any type of organic chemical has been

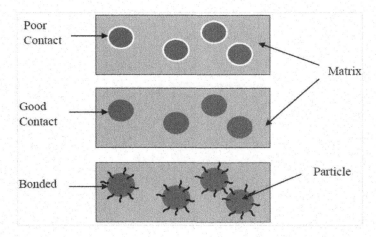

FIGURE 1.7 The differential contact between matrices and particles.

imparted, is considered as surface treated. The surface treatment is differentiated from the surface modification based on functionality (DeArmitt & Rothon, 2016). The surface-treated filler can be coated using a processing aid, which might bond to the filler and cannot bond to the matrix. Thus, it can act as a specific wetting agent, thereby making the filler surface more intimately coated and hydrophobic by the polymer matrix. In contrast, surface treatment is used for particle deagglomeration and dispersion, thereby facilitating higher filler loading. Usually, the surface-modified filler carries a coupling agent, which is attached to the surface via covalent bond. The coupling agent can be bound to the matrix via chain entanglement or chemical reaction. These coupling agents can be used as the surface modifiers, which offer similar functions as the surface treatments to enhance matrix adhesion, improving physical properties and environmental stability.

1.5 APPLICATIONS

1.5.1 Automotive Applications

The automotive industry is one of the largest consumers of raw materials in manufacturing because about 50 million vehicles are produced annually (Fentahun & Savaş, 2018), which consumes approximately 9 million tons of polymer-based material. Generally, the standard specification of materials in the automotive industry mainly depends on the functional areas of the vehicle, such as exterior components, interior parts or under-hood systems. These areas have diverse requirements regarding service temperature range, weather and chemical resistance, mechanical properties and aesthetics (Wells, 2013).

Therefore, new materials, such as mineral-filled PP, are being developed to produce parts of the exterior body to satisfy heat stability requirements (140°C to 160°C), high impact strength, toughness (no splintering), petrol resistance and stiffness (Hahladakis et al., 2018). Also, when PP was utilized for car bumpers it was observed to provide high-impact resilience and absorption; hence, it is often utilized for the front and the back-bumper core. PP creates a substantially cost savings and reduces weight by about 50% when substituted in the steel bumper system. Automotive seat-back substrates are huge blow-molded parts of incredibly low melt flow to high melt strength PP. The automotive market is regarded as a major market of PP-based on the easy recycling of PP, which is crucial in automotive applications (Grigore, 2017). Mineral-filled thermoplastic composite materials have been progressively utilized in the automotive industry. Minerals are used for reducing cost and enhancing the properties of thermoplastic composites. There are many types of mineral fillers used in these applications such as talc, calcium carbonate, mica and clay.

PP is regarded as the largest volume plastic use for talc, which provides structural strength (i.e., stiffness) and high-temperature creep resistance required for the automotive applications. A typical formulation of talc-filled PP contains 10–40 wt% talc. In addition to its thermal and structural property improvement, talc contributes to achieve better dimensional stability and enhances the thermoforming opacity. The purity of talc is mainly important for thermal properties. Talc-filled masterbatches exist at levels of loading of up to 75 wt%. The dark talc is mostly utilized for the exterior parts, and for interior automotive engineering applications where the color is of little concern. The compounds for the applications often contain talc and calcium carbonate. Talc loading levels higher than 40 wt% are often difficult to achieve by extrusion processing due to feeding problems. The slippery nature of the mineral surface makes the continuous feeding operation difficult at high rates unless premixing is undertaken.

In addition to talc and calcium carbonate, mica is also used in automotive applications. Mica is less expensive than fiberglass, so it is often used as a partial replacement. Mica helps to improve the anisotropic properties obtained with glass fiber. The large aspect ratio of mica increases melt viscosity in resins compared with other functional fillers. Therefore, higher processing temperatures are usually required. This would greatly alter the flow characteristics. Under isothermal flow, flakes tend to orient their faces tangent to the velocity profile. Thus, when filling a mold cavity, the flakes ideally would be aligned parallel to the walls near the mold surface but perpendicular to the surface in the center of the part. Some typical automotive parts of mica-filled thermoplastic composites are blow-molded, e.g., seat backs and fender liners (Friedrich & Almajid, 2013).

PP reinforcement by microfillers and nanofillers can yield composites of high toughness and rigidity. PP-clay nanocomposites were prepared at Toyota Central R&D through 45 melt intercalations of montmorillonite organo-clays with PP modified with either maleic anhydride or hydroxyl groups (Nilagiri Balasubramanian & Ramesh, 2018). Toyota Motor Company pioneered this approach to create a nylon 6/clay hybrid, which can be utilized for making timing belt covers. It is the first practical utilization of polymeric nanocomposites in automotive applications (Usuki, 2016). The tensile modulus of the nanocomposite was twice that of the nylon 6. In fact, the coefficient of linear thermal expansion was condensed by half for nanocomposites that contain approximately 1.6 vol% of the clay mineral. This coefficient of linear thermal expansion represents the main factor in dimensional stability and is

TABLE 1.3
The Properties of PP with Talc and CaCO$_3$ Used in Automotive Applications

Product	Melt Flow Index (g/10 min)	Tensile Strength (MPa)	Young's Modulus (MPa)	Impact Strength (kJ/m^2)
Copolymer PP/20% CaCO$_3$	10.0	24.0	1890	5.1
Copolymer PP/20% talc	7.0	25.0	2200	4.0
Copolymer PP/30% talc	1.2	27.6	3199	14.7
Homopolymer PP/40% talc	1.2	27.6	3199	14.7

a significant factor in manufacturing large parts of vehicles. However, utilizing the thermoplastic nanocomposites in automotive applications depends on satisfying rigorous demands of performance and cost. Every application might require variation in the production process while making specific parts for specific uses (Chandra & Roy, 2009). Table 1.3 summarizes the properties of talc and CaCO$_3$-filled PP composites, which are exploited in automotive applications.

1.5.2 Electrical Applications

The notable application of thermoplastic composites in the electrical field is in cable and wire, which is mainly dominated by polyvinyl chloride (PVC) due to its formulation flexibility, easy processing and low cost. Halogen, which is present in polymer systems, is more corrosive to copper compared with the non-halogen-based systems. Also, chlorinated compounds can lead to unacceptable emissions from traditional incinerators. Because of growing concerns in the industry and several regulatory concerns about combustion, toxicity, corrosives and environmental influences at the manufacture and disposal point, there seems to be an unsustainability in the widespread utilization of PVC in the foreseeable future (Islam et al., 2018).

PVC cables for electrical applications often use calcium carbonate as a filler. The outer sheathing of flexible PVC cable uses between 30 and 40 wt% ground calcium carbonates. However, carbonates for electrical-insulator PVC are required to be very pure. All ingredients must have low ionic impurities and low water content to meet the minimum volume resistivity test (American Society for Testing and Material [ASTM] D495). Although calcium carbonate is the major filler used in PVC applications, metakaolin is also an important mineral. Calcined kaolin is used primarily to improve the electrical properties of PVC wire and cable insulation compounds. Other advantages that are obtained with kaolin are improved stiffness and heat and creep resistance. Surface treated kaolins are usually used in these applications, especially if long-term electrical properties are of concern. Metakaolin products can double the volume resistivity of PVC composites. However, fully calcined kaolin provides slightly less improvement in volume resistivity, as it mainly imparts better color.

1.5.3 Housing Material

Mica-filled thermoplastics are used widely in household materials. Some typical commercial products of mica-filled polyolefin are air conditioners, heater housings, instrument panels, battery trays and fan shrouds. Mica in PP-polyethylene copolymer foam is used for loudspeakers and musical instruments. Uniformity and improved vibrational properties are found with mica due to the high velocity of sound in the mineral; hence, the higher speed allows for more compact speaker cones. Calcium carbonate could improve rigidity and density and act as a processing aid in PVC, but most of the mechanical properties of the plastic will be reduced. The primary uses of carbonate in rigid PVC applications are in pipes (conduit), extruded goods and flooring tiles. The PVC material used in pipe and conduit applications is widely regulated by the Plastic Pipe Institute, ASTM requirements and the National Sanitary Foundation. Because low aspect ratio mineral additives are deleterious to mechanical properties such as tensile strength, only 0 and 5 phr filler can be used in potable water or pressure pipes. Conduit and general piping usually contain 2- to 3-micron sizes of carbonate at loading levels of up to 40 phr. In corrosive or acidic environments, calcium carbonates are not effective in PVC piping because of their alkaline nature.

1.6 CONCLUSIONS

Considering the distinct mineral fillers that are available worldwide, there could be questions over the existence of an ideal filler and to what extent such an ideal filler can be developed. Addressing such questions can be simple because it depends on the needs of the end applications and whether it requires specific characteristics in terms of chemical, electrical, physical and other properties. Therefore, users and researchers should be fully aware of the merits and demerits of the mineral employed for the development of polymer composites. Mineral fillers like limestone, silica, clay and mica have the potential to replace talc as fillers in polymer composites.

ACKNOWLEDGMENT

The authors thank Universiti Sains Malaysia (USM) for the USM fellowship scheme granted to the second author. We are grateful to the Malaysian Ministry of Education for awarding us a Fundamental Research Grant (MRSA Grant 6071284) and School of Materials and Mineral Resources Engineering, USM for the use of their facilities.

REFERENCES

Ahmad F. N., Mariatti, J., Samayamutthrian, P., & Khairun Azizi, M. A. Effect of particle shape of mica mineral on the properties of epoxy composites. *Composites Science and Technology*, 68 (2008) 346–353.

Ainur, S. Polypropylene hybrid composites filled with talc and kaolin: characterization of mechanical, morphology and thermal properties, Master's Thesis, Universiti Sains Malaysia (2006).

Almeshal, I., Tayeh, B. A., Alyousef, R., Alabduljabbar, H., & Mohamed, A. M. Eco-friendly concrete containing recycled plastic as partial replacement for sand. *Journal of Materials Research and Technology*, 9(3) (2020) 4631–4643.

Ansari, D. M, & Price G. J. Correlation of mechanical properties of clay filled polyamide moulding with chromatographically measured surface energies. *Polymer*, 45 (2004) 3663–3670.

Anuar, H., Ahmad, S. H., Rasid, R., Ahmad, A., & Busu, W. W. Mechanical properties and dynamic mechanical analysis of thermoplastic-natural-rubber-reinforced short carbon fiber and kenaf fiber hybrid composites. *Journal of Applied Polymer Science*, 107(6) (2008) 4043–4052.

Barua, S., Gogoi, S., Khan, R., & Karak, N. Silicon-based nanomaterials and their polymer nanocomposites. In *Nanomaterials and polymer nanocomposites*, pp. 261–305. Niranjan Karak, Elsevier (2019).

Bhattacharyya, K. G., & Gupta, S. S. Adsorption of a few heavy metals on natural and modified kaolinite and montmorillonite: a review. *Advances in Colloid and Interface Science*, 140(2) (2008) 114–131.

Bouwman, A. M, Bosma, J. C., Vonk, P., Weeselingh, J. H. A, & Frijlink, H. W. Which shape factor(s) best describe granules. *Powder Technology*, 146 (2004) 66–72.

Buggy M., Bradley G., & Sullivan A., Polymer-filler interaction in kaolin/nylon 6,6 composites containing a silane coupling agent. *Composites: Part A*, 36 (2005) 437–442.

Callister, W. D. *Fundamentals of materials science and engineering* (Vol. 471660817). London: Wiley (2000).

Carvalho, A. J. F., Curvelo, A. A. F, & Agnelli, J. A. M. A first insight on composites of thermoplastic starch and kaolin. *Carbohydrate Polymer*, 45 (2001) 189–194.

Chandra, M., & Roy, S. K. *Plastic technology handbook*, p. 896. Fourth Edition. Boca Raton, FL: CRC Press, Taylor & Francis Group (2009).

Cho, J., Joshi, M. S., & Sun, C. T. Effect of inclusion size on mechanical properties of polymeric composites with micro and nano particles. *Composites Science and Technology*, 66 (2006) 1941–1952.

DeArmitt, C., & Rothon, R. Particulate fillers, selection and use in polymer composites. In *Encyclopedia of polymers and composites*, pp. 1–19. Berlin, Heidelberg: Springer-Verlag (2016).

de Oliveira, C. I. R., Rocha, M. C. G., de Assis, J. T., & da Silva, A. L. N. Morphological, mechanical, and thermal properties of PP/SEBS/talc composites. *Journal of Thermoplastic Composite Materials*, (2019). https://doi.org/10.1177/0892705719876678.

Desai, A., Auad, M. L., Shen, H., & Nutt, S. R. Hybrid composite phenolic foams. *Composites and polycon 2007*. Tampa, FL: American Composites Manufacturing Association (2007).

Deshmukh, G. S., Peshwe, D. R., Pathak, S. U., & Ekhe, J. D. A study on effect of mineral additions on the mechanical, thermal, and structural properties of poly(butylene terephthalate) (PBT) composites. *Journal of Polymer Research*, 18(5) (2011) 1081–1090.

Dijkstra, J., Gaudin, C., & White, D. J. Comparison of failure modes below footings on carbonate and silica sands. *International Journal of Physical Modelling in Geotechnics*, 13(1) (2013) 1–12.

Fauziyah, N. A., Hilmi, A. R., Fadly, T. A., Asrori, M. Z., Mashuri, M., & Pratapa, S. Dynamic tensile and shear storage moduli of PEG/silica-polymorph composites. *Journal of Applied Polymer Science*, 136(17) (2019) 47372.

Fentahun, M. A., & Savaş, M. A. Materials used in automotive manufacture and material selection using Ashby charts. *International Journal of Materials Engineering*, 8 (2018) 40–54.

Friedrich, K., & Almajid, A. A. Manufacturing aspects of advanced polymer composites for automotive applications. *Applied Composite Materials*, 20(2) (2013) 107–128.

Friedrich, K., Fakirov, S., & Zhang, Z. *Polymer composites: from nano to macro scale*, p. 367. New York: Springer (2005).

Gallagher, L. W., & McDonald, A. G. The effect of micron sized wood fibers in wood plastic composites. *Maderas. Ciencia y tecnología, 15*(3) (2013) 357–374.

Gaymans, R. J., Zuiderduin, W. C. J., Westzaan, C., & Hue, J. Toughening of polypropylene with calcium carbonate particles. *Polymer, 44*(1) (2003) 261–275.

Grigore, M. E. Methods of recycling, properties and applications of recycled thermoplastic polymers. *Recycling, 2*(4) (2017) 24.

Guessoum, M., Nekkaa, S., Fenouillot-Rimlinger, F., & Haddaoui, N. Effects of kaolin surface treatments on the thermomechanical properties and on the degradation of polypropylene. *International Journal of Polymer Science, 2012* (2012) 549154.

Habib, E., Wang, R., & Zhu, X. X. Monodisperse silica-filled composite restoratives mechanical and light transmission properties. *Dental Materials, 33*(3) (2017) 280–287.

Haddar, N., Ammar, O., Bouaziz, Y., & Mnif, N. Talc as reinforcing filler in polypropylene compounds : effect on morphology and mechanical properties. *Polymer Sciences, 3*(1) (2017) 8.

Hahladakis, J. N., Velis, C. A., Weber, R., Iacovidou, E., & Purnell, P. An overview of chemical additives present in plastics: migration, release, fate and environmental impact during their use, disposal and recycling. *Journal of Hazardous Materials, 344* (2018) 179–199.

Hoque, M. E., Shehryar, M., & Islam, K. N. Processing and characterization of cockle shell calcium carbonate ($CaCO_3$) bioceramic for potential application in bone tissue engineering. *Wood Material Science and Engineering, 2*(4) (2013) 132.

Ishak, Z. A. M. Effect of clay addition on mechanical properties of unsaturated polyester/glass fiber composites. *International Journal of Polymer Science*, (2013) 2013. Volume 2013.

Islam, I., Sultana, S., Kumer Ray, S., Parvin Nur, H., & Hossain, M. Electrical and tensile properties of carbon black reinforced polyvinyl chloride conductive composites. *C—Journal of Carbon Research, 4*(1) (2018) 15.

Jang, K. S. Mineral filler effect on the mechanics and flame retardancy of polycarbonate composites: Talc and kaolin. *e-Polymers, 16*(5) (2016) 379–386.

Janos, M., & Bela, P. Polymer micro and nanocomposites: structure, interactions, properties. *Journal of Industrial and Engineering Chemistry, 14* (2008) 535–563.

Keller, A., Fritzsche, M., Ogaki, R., Bald, I., Facsko, S., Dong, M., ... & Besenbacher, F. Tuning the hydrophobicity of mica surfaces by hyperthermal Ar ion irradiation. *The Journal of Chemical Physics, 134*(10) (2011) 104705.

Kundie, F., Azhari, C. H., Muchtar, A., & Ahmad, Z. A. Effects of filler size on the mechanical properties of polymer-filled dental composites: a review of recent developments. *Journal of Physical Science, 29*(1) (2018) 14.

Lapcik, L., Jindrova, P., Lapcikova, B., & Tamblyn, R. Effect of the talc filler content on the mechanical properties of polypropylene composites. *Journal of Applied Polymer Science, 110*(5) (2008) 2742–2747.

Lapčík, L., Maňas, D., Lapčíková, B., Vašina, M., Staněk, M., Čépe, K., ... & Rowson, N. A. Effect of filler particle shape on plastic-elastic mechanical behavior of high density poly (ethylene)/mica and poly (ethylene)/wollastonite composites. *Composites Part B: Engineering, 141* (2018) 92–99.

Lee, D. J., Oh, H., Song, Y. S., & Youn, J. R. Analysis of effective elastic modulus for multiphased hybrid composites. *Composites Science and Technology, 72*(2) (2012) 278–283.

Leong, Y. W., Bakar, M. B. A., Ishake, Z. A. M., Ariffn, A., & Pukanszky, B. Comparison of the mechanical properties and interfacial interactions between talc, kaoline, and calcium carbonate filled polypropylene composites. *Journal of Applied Polymer Science, 91*(5) (2004) 3315–3326.

Liang, Ji-Zhao. Crystallization of glass fiber-reinforced poly (p-phenylene sulfide) nanocomposites. *Polymer International*, *61*(4) (2012) 511–515.

Lv, X., Kang, M., Chen, K., Yuan, L., Shen, S., Sun, R., & Song, L. Preparation of fluorescent calcium carbonate and visualization of its dispersion states in polypropylene. *Journal of Composite Materials*, *54*(7) (2020) 913–921.

Marghalani, H. Y. Effect of filler particles on surface roughness of experimental composite series. *Journal of Applied Oral Science*, *18*(1) (2010) 59–67.

Móczó, J., & Pukánszky, B. "Particulate fillers in thermoplastics." In *Fillers for polymer applications*, pp. 51–93. Cham, Switzerland: Springer (2016).

Molnar, Sz., Pukanszky, B., Hammer, C. O., & Maurer, F. H. J. Impact fracture study of multicomponent polypropylene composites. *Polymer*, *41* (2000) 1529–1539.

Moreno, J. F., da Silva, A. L. N., da Silva, A. H. M. D. F. T., & de Sousa, A. M. F. Preparation and characterization of composites based on poly (lactic acid) and $CaCO_3$ nanofiller. In *AIP conference proceedings*, Vol. 1664, No. 1, p. 020008. Melville, NY: AIP Publishing LLC (2015).

Nilagiri Balasubramanian, K. B., & Ramesh, T. Role, effect, and influences of micro and nano-fillers on various properties of polymer matrix composites for microelectronics: a review. *Polymers for Advanced Technologies*, *29*(6) (2018) 1568–1585.

Mustafa, S. N. Effect of kaolin on the mechanical properties of polypropylene/polyethylene composite material. *Polymer*, *6* (2012) 8.

Nurdina, A. K., Mariatti, M., & Samayamutthirian, P. Effect of single-mineral filler and hybrid-mineral filler additives on the properties of polypropylene composites. *Journal of Vinyl and Additive Technology*, *15*(1) (2009a) 20–28.

Nurdina, A. K., Mariatti, M., & Samayamutthirian, P. Mechanical properties and morphology of calcium carbonate and mica filled polypropylene composites. *Malaysian Journal of Microscopy*, *5*(1) (2009b) 113–118.

Osman, A. F., & Mariatti, M. Properties of aluminum filled polypropylene composites. *Polymers and Polymer Composites*, *14*(6) (2006) 623–633.

Phipps, J. S. Engineering minerals for performance applications: an industrial perspective. *Clay Minerals*, *49*(1) (2014) 1–16.

Riku, U., Ulla, H., Santeri, P., & Jukka, S. Compatibilazation of PP/elastomer/microsilica composites with functionalized polyolefin: effect on microstructure and mechanical properties. *Polymer*, *46* (2005) 7923–7930.

Shakoor, A., & Thomas, N. L. "Talc as a nucleating agent and reinforcing filler in poly (lactic acid) composites. *Polymer Engineering and Science*, *54*(1) (2014) 64–70.

Sheikh, S. H., Yin, X., Ansarifar, A., & Yendall, K. The potential of kaolin as a reinforcing filler for rubber composites with new sulfur cure systems. *Journal of Reinforced Plastics and Composites*, *36*(16) (2017) 1132–1145.

Shelesh-Nezhad, K., & Taghizadeh, A. Shrinkage behavior and mechanical performances of injection molded polypropylene/talc composites. *Polymer Engineering and Science*, *47*(12) (2007) 2124–2128.

Srinivasan, R. Advances in application of natural clay and its composites in removal of biological, organic, and inorganic contaminants from drinking water. *Advances in Materials Science and Engineering*, (2011) 2011. Volume 2011.

Thabo, G., Suprakas, S. R., Walfer, W.F., & Arjun, M. Morphology and properties of nanostructured materials based on polypropylene/poly (butylenes succinate) blend and organo clay. *European Polymer Journal*, *45* (2009) 353–367.

Usuki, A. Nylon 6-clay hybrid: from invention to practical use. *R&D Review of Toyoda CRDL*, *47*(1) (2016) 45–55.

Vallittu, P. K., & Sevelius, C. Resin-bonded, glass fiber-reinforced composite fixed partial dentures: a clinical study. *The Journal of Prosthetic Dentistry*, *84*(4) (2000) 413–418.

Vincent, S. R., Jaafar, M., & Palaniandy, S. Properties of calcium carbonate/MICA and calcium farbonate/talc filled polypropylene composites. *Journal of Engineering Science*, *10* (2014) 41.

Wahyuni, N. L. E., & Soeswanto, B. The effects of particle size and content on morphology and mechanical properties of rice straw and coal fly ash filled-polypropylene composites. *Journal of Physics: (2019) Conference Series*, *1175*(1) (2019) 012282.

Wells, P. Sustainable business models and the automotive industry: a commentary. *IIMB Management Review*, *25*(4) (2013) 228–239.

Wen, H. R., Ming, Q. Z, Min, Z. R., & Friedrich, K. polypropylene composites filled with in-situ grafting polymerization modified nano-silica particles. *Journal of Materials Science*, *39* (2004) 3475–3478.

Wu, J. H., Chen, C. W., Wu, Y. T., Wu, G. T., Kuo, M. C., & Tsai, Y. Mechanical properties, morphology, and crystallization behavior of polypropylene/elastomer/talc composites. *Polymer Composites*, *36*(1) (2015) 69–77.

Wypych, G. *Handbook of filler*, Second Edition. Toronto, Canada: ChemTec Publishing (2000).

Xanthos, M. *Functional fillers for plastics*, p. 432. Weinheim, Germany: Wiley (2005).

Xiang, Y., Hou, Z., Su, R., Wang, K., & Fu, Q. The effect of shear on mechanical properties and orientation of HDPE/mica composites obtained via dynamic packing injection molding (DPIM). *Polymers for Advanced Technologies*, *21*(1) (2010) 48–54.

Yang C. C., Ling C., & Xuehong, L. Oriented clay-induced anisotropic crystalline morphology in poly (ethylene naphthalate)/clay nanocomposites and its impact on mechanical properties. *Composites Part A: Applied Science and Manufacturing*, *40*(4) (2009) 423–430.

Yang, Y., Sato, R., & Kawai, K. Autogenous shrinkage of high-strength concrete containing silica fume under drying at early ages. *Cement and Concrete Research*, *35*(3) (2005) 449–456.

Yazdani, H., Morshedian, J., & Khonakdar, H. A. Effect of maleated polypropylene and impact modifiers on the morphology and mechanical properties of PP/mica composites. *Polymer Composites*, *27*(6) (2006) 614–620.

Yen, T. V., Guru, S. R., James, E. M., & Charles L. M. Reinforcement of elastomeric polypropylene by nano-clay fillers. *Polymer International*, *53* (2004) 1071–1077.

Zaaba, N. F., & Ismail, H. Thermoplastic/natural filler composites: a short review. *Journal of Physical Science*, *30*(Supp.1) (2019) 81–99.

Zhang, Q.-X., Yu, Z.-Z., Xie, X.-L., & Mai, Y.-W. Crystallization and impact energy of polypropylene/CaCO3 nanocomposites with nonionic modifier. *Polymer*, *45* (2006) 5985–5994.

Zoukrami, F., Haddaoui, N., Vanzeveren, C., Sclavons, M., & Devaux, J. Effect of compatibilizer on the dispersion of untreated silica in a polypropylene matrix. *Polymer International*, *57*(5) (2007) 756–763.

Zuiderduin, W. C. J., Westzaan, C., Huetink, J., & Gaymans, R. J. Toughening of polypropylene with calcium carbonate particles. *Polymer*, *44* (2003) 261–275.

2 Mineral-Filled Composite

A Review on Characteristics, Applications, and Potential Materials Selection Process

M.T. Mastura and M. Noryani
Universiti Teknikal Malaysia Melaka
Melaka, Malaysia

CONTENTS

2.1	Introduction	26
2.2	Mineral-Filled Polymer Composites	27
	2.2.1 Type of Minerals	27
	2.2.2 Properties of Mineral-Filled Polymer Composites	28
	2.2.3 Applications of Mineral-Filled Polymer Composites	29
2.3	Methods of Material Selection on Polymer-Based Composites	30
	2.3.1 Analytical Hierarchy Process (AHP)	32
	2.3.2 Analytical Network Process (ANP)	32
	2.3.3 Technique of Ranking Preferences by Similarity of the Ideal Solutions (TOPSIS)	32
	2.3.4 Another Potential Material Selection Tools	33
	2.3.4.1 Multi-Attribute Utility Theory (MAUT)	33
	2.3.4.2 Preference Selection Index (PSI)	33
	2.3.4.3 Elimination and Choice Expressing the Reality (ELECTRE)	33
	2.3.4.4 Simple Additive Weighting (SAW)	33
	2.3.4.5 Vlse Kriterijumska Optimizacija Kompromisno Resenje (VIKOR)	34
	2.3.4.6 Data Envelopment Analysis (DEA)	34
	2.3.4.7 Preference Ranking Organization Method for Enrichment Evaluations (PROMETHEE)	34
	2.3.4.8 Regression Analysis	35
2.4	Characteristics of Mineral in Material Selection	35
2.5	Conclusions	37
	Acknowledgment	38
	References	38

2.1 INTRODUCTION

In concurrent engineering, all the activities that are conducted must work in parallel to ensure the participation of all elements considered to reduce lead time while improving quality and cost. The best practice of the design process is to employ the principle of concurrent engineering where all the important elements are associated and deliberate in a concurrent manner. Prasad (2014) explained the fundamentals of concurrent engineering and how it is employed as integrated product development. As this approach was first practiced in 1989, the objective of concurrent engineering was to ensure that industrial development met customer satisfaction in a shorter lead time and at a lower cost (Pennell and Winner, 1989). In product development, Sohlenius (1992) showed the process design cycle under concurrent engineering, which included the materials selection process. It was suggested that this process was to be conducted concurrently along with product design and modeling, manufacturing process design, manufacturing system design, prototype testing and detailed process and manufacturing planning. Fast-forward to the 21st century and Sapuan and Abdalla (1998) in their study emphasized the process of material selection conducted under a concurrent engineering approach. Later, the application of concurrent engineering was found widely in composite-based design where selection of the type of material is very crucial. Employment of concurrent engineering could save more time when experimenting with various types of possible composites that have different unique characteristics. Studies on the composite-based design that performed in a concurrent engineering manner have been compiled in a book authored by Sapuan (2017). The book shows various tools and techniques for selecting materials from composite-based materials for various design applications. Hence, the application of concurrent engineering is beneficial for design and materials engineers.

Material selection is a process in which all potential materials are evaluated based on the selection requirements that should be satisfied by material characteristics. The potential materials are listed based on literature reviews or market investigation. Mansor et al. (2013) chosen 10 potential materials for the design of a composite hand-brake lever. The materials were chosen based on the literature review stating that no natural fiber had been used for the hand-brake lever before. There is also another way of listing potential materials based on their availability. Mastura et al. (2017b) had chosen the potential materials from those available locally. It is not only reduced the cost of transportation, but widened the application of local natural fiber and increased the local economy. There are more examples of material selection processes performed by other researchers for various applications. They prove that the material selection process is important in the design process and particularly by design engineers. Shaharuzaman et al. (2019a) performed the material selection in parallel when designing a composite automotive side door.

Until today, many decision-making tools had been employed by engineers in selecting materials based on their applications, including the analytic hierarchical process (AHP), vlse kriterijumska optimizacija kompromisno resenje (VIKOR), preference ranking organization method for enrichment evaluations (PROMTHEE) and quality functional deployment (QFD). No one tool could be assumed as the best tool in the material selection process. Many studies have been conducted by researchers to find out the most common decision-making tools employed in selecting the best materials.

Mineral-Filled Composite

Noryani, Sapuan, and Mastura (2018a) showed in their paper that AHP is the most commonly used decision-making tool in selecting the most suitable natural fiber composites. Moreover, statistical analysis was used as a tool to select the best material in automotive applications as reported by Noryani et al. (2018b). In this chapter, a review on the material selection of mineral-filled polymer composites is conducted by discussing the selection criteria and tools employed by past researchers until 2020.

2.2 MINERAL-FILLED POLYMER COMPOSITES

Natural resources are classified into two general types: renewable and non-renewable (Figure 2.1). Renewable resources are materials that able to be regenerated after harvest and their supply is infinite. Non-renewable resources are materials that could not be regenerated after being used and their supply is finite. Non-renewable materials are mineral and energy resources such as metal and non-metal and fossil fuels. These types of material can be recycled after the useful life is ended and can be disposed of in a landfill. The supply of non-renewable resources depends on the size of reserve and material consumption from industrial technology. Therefore, action must be taken to prepare for material depletion. One way to reduce mineral consumption is by blending the mineral with another type of material to become a composite. Consequently, the amount of mineral in a material would be reduced and the composite materials would have superior material properties due to reinforcement. For example, clay is one of the inorganic fillers commonly found in mineral composites due to its high natural abundance. Other examples of mineral fillers for composites are nano-clay, silver nanoparticles and calcium carbonate. In the following section, mineral-based composite will be introduced together with the applications and any issues with the materials. Studies from the year 2000 to 2020 are cited.

2.2.1 Type of Minerals

A mineral is a solid substance not made by an organism that naturally occurs, has a definite chemical composition and has a systematic and repeating pattern of internal

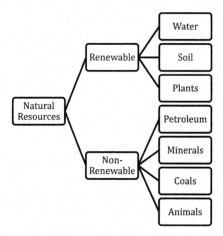

FIGURE 2.1 Classifications of natural resources.

structure. On Earth, plenty of mineral resources are varied based on their mineral formulae. Each mineral material is unique, and a complex method is used to classify the type of mineral materials. A mineral is a type of material that has a wide range of species that are modified based on the weathering process and geologic conditions. Therefore, a systematic and efficient classification method is needed as the discovery of this type of material is quite common. A long process is implied in characterizing the new formation of minerals found by the miners. Bosi, Biagioni, and Oberti (2019) proposed the classification method of minerals based on chemical identification. Aboudi Mana et al. (2017) stated that the Grim classification system is the most useful approach in classifying clay minerals into four main groups, such as kaolinite, illite, smectite and vermiculite. They also discussed the importance of environmental characteristics of all types of clays based on their physical and mechanical properties.

2.2.2 Properties of Mineral-Filled Polymer Composites

Having various types of minerals implies that mineral materials have various properties. The properties of the mineral depend on several factors, including mineral composition, microstructure and phase changes. Generally, the addition of fillers in composites function as a reinforcing element used to improve the mechanical, rheological and thermal properties of the base materials. Excellent properties, such as higher modulus and rigidity of the filler, transfer the loaded stress from the matrix to the filler under good interfacial bonding between the filler and the matrix. The effectiveness of the function of the fillers eventually increases the tensile strength. Well-dispersed fillers with a smaller size that fill in the void spaces in the matrix exhibit good interfacial bonding between the two materials in the composite, as mentioned by Abdul Khalil et al. (2019). Sothornvit et al. (2010) reported improvement of the antimicrobial properties when the clay fillers were added to polysaccharide-based polymers for the food packaging industry. Chen et al. (2017) conducted a study to investigate the mechanical properties of the granite after being exposed to high temperatures. They found that degradation of the mechanical properties of granite occurred when Young's modulus, uniaxial compressive strength and fracture toughness were decreased. Aizan et al. (2017) studied the physical properties of by observing their size, structure and water absorption. In their study, they found that the diameter of the small particles in clays is often less than 2 µm, and the structure of clay is more like a sheet. Another important property of the clay is water absorption in which the clay is classified based on its swelling behavior. Rheological properties of the nano-clay were studied by Nazar et al. (2020). They concluded that the water absorption property of nano-clay could reduce the amount of free water and consequently increase viscosity and yield stress of cementitious materials. Nano-clay significantly influences the rheological properties of cementitious materials. Saw et al. (2020) mentioned in their study that the three mineral fillers used in a polypropylene (PE)-ethylene copolymer composite were silica, kaolin and wollastonite. The fillers were used to accelerate the thermomechanical degradation mechanism and generate oxidized products during extrusion. These materials are compounded using a twin-screw extruder. Furthermore, there is a study that found graphene and its derivatives influenced the rheological behavior of cement composite (Kashif et al., 2020).

Nanoparticles that flocculated structures entrapped the water molecules and affect the flow behavior of the composite materials. It is very important to characterize the mechanical properties of cement-based composites. Therefore, the molecular modeling approach exhibits improvement in mechanical properties caused by good bonding and stability of atoms in the interface region. Cao et al. (2019) studied the mechanical properties of concrete material. They found that the mechanical properties of concrete depend on water absorption, particle size and constitutions of macro-calcium carbonate. For cement materials, the higher content of micro-calcium carbonate particles significantly accelerates the hydration process. The cementitious-based composite also showed excellent material properties with the recycled nanomaterials. From the study conducted by Chinchillas-chinchillas et al. (2020), there is a significant increase in compressive and flexural resistance, reduction in porosity, improvement in the resistance of water penetration and reduction of capillary absorption and drying shrinkage. The study also showed that this type of composite could be an alternative material for product development that requires higher quality, durability and sustainability. Additional basalt powder in composite materials effectively improves thermomechanical stability with an increasing amount of basalt powder. This inorganic filler showed superior mechanical properties in stiffness and hardness of PE-based composites in a study conducted by Klozi et al. (2018). Alghadi, Tirkes, and Tayfun (2020) reported that perlite mineral filler could improve the mechanical properties of the acrylonitrile-butadiene-styrene (ABS) copolymer with respect to the tensile strength, elongation and Youngs' modulus. Moreover, in thermal properties, 5% concentration of perlite mineral filler increased the glass transition temperature of ABS but caused a slight decrease in melt flow index value of unfilled ABS. They also concluded that a 5% concentration of perlite mineral filler in ABS copolymer exhibited the best performance and was the most suitable candidate for ABS composite.

2.2.3 Applications of Mineral-Filled Polymer Composites

Generally, in medical applications, metals like titanium, stainless steel and chromium alloys are traditionally applied in orthopedic implants in fracture surgeries. However, due to the non-biodegradability feature, secondary surgery is needed to remove the implant to avoid more complications caused by corrosion (Bommala, Krishna, and Rao 2019). Extensive research has been conducted to find suitable biodegradable materials in medical applications. Nur et al. (2019) reported a work on magnesium-based composite that resembled the properties of natural bone. This type of bio-composite is mainly used for the application of the biodegradable implants in medical technology. Babilotte et al. (2019) reported a study on a three-dimensional (3D)-printed polymer-mineral composite for application in bone tissue engineering. Study on the fabrication and characterization process of this composite material identified specific properties and the composites improved biological integration of the 3D-printed scaffold. Long et al. (2019) conducted a study on a sustainable cement-based composite facilitated by 3D printing technology for building and construction applications. High-quality and sustainable cement-based composites consist of microcrystalline cellulose, which increases the compressive and flexural strength significantly. Moreover, the employment of cement-based composite effectively reduces CO_2 emissions by 6.22%. Mechtcherine et al. (2020) reported the new type of composite materials that use minerals to impregnate carbon fiber composites. This novel material creates a variety of opportunities because of it has excellent mechanical properties over a wide range of temperatures, is non-corrosive and has excellent bonding with concrete matrices. In another application, Sathish (2020) reported a study on nanocomposites composed of clays, polymer and graphene oxide that were prepared for the application similar to lithium-ion batteries. The composite had been characterized in a controlled laboratory environment. Li et al. (2019) investigated the application of flake graphite-carbon nanofiber-modified bentonite that is used in constructing form-stable phase change material composites. This composite is used as a potential candidate in a thermal energy storage system, especially in smart building energy conservation. Furthermore, Ferrara et al. (2019) reported an application of flax fibers in cementitious material to form a composite. The cement-based composite showed no significant reduction in tensile strength. Antimicrobial properties of the clay nanotube-based composites have widened the application of this mineral composite into microbe-resistant biocidal textiles, paints, filters, wound dressings, drug delivery systems, antiseptic sprays and tissue-engineering scaffolds (Stavitskaya et al., 2019).

2.3 METHODS OF MATERIAL SELECTION ON POLYMER-BASED COMPOSITES

Currently, many tools are used in material selection. In general, there are two main processes in material selection, screening and ranking (Jahan et al., 2010). In the screening process, cost per unit property, Ashby's chart, artificial intelligence, materials in the product selection tool and questionnaires are the screening methods most frequently used. Different approaches are used in artificial intelligent methods, such as computer-aided systems, knowledge-based systems, case-based reasoning and neural network. Optimization and multi-criteria decision making (MCDM) are two categories included in the ranking process in material selection. MCDM is used to help design engineers in the manufacturing process to select the materials based on certain materials characteristics, industry requirements and customer preferences. There are two categories in MCDM: multi-attribute decision making (MADM) and multi-objective decision making (MODM). MADM consists of evaluating and choosing a process in decision making, whereas MODM considers planning and designing (Tzeng & Huang 2011). In this study, several tools in MCDM such as AHP, analytical network process (ANP), preference selection index (PSI), technique of ranking preferences by similarity of the ideal solutions (TOPSIS), VIKOR, multi-attribute utility theory (MAUT), elimination and choice expressing the reality (ELECTRE), simple additive weighting (SAW), data envelopment analysis (DEA), PROMETHEE, quality function deployment (QFD), quality function deployment for the environment (QFDE) and questionnaires are reviewed from the years 2000 to 2020. Based on a report in 2015, Tramarico et al. (2015) mentioned that AHP, TOPSIS and ANP are the top three tools frequently used. Recently, as shown in Figure 2.2, a new approach using statistical analysis (stepwise regression) was introduced by Noryani et al. (2020).

Mineral-Filled Composite

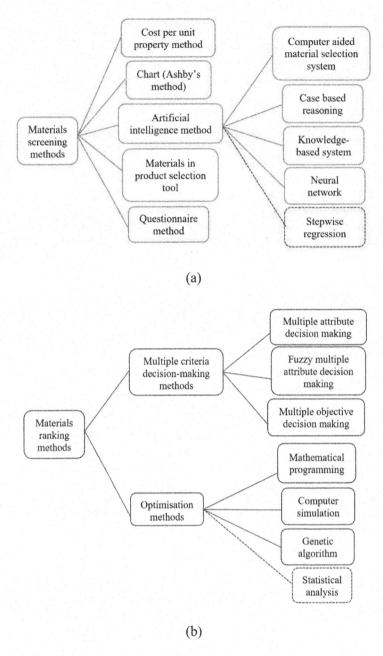

FIGURE 2.2 Classification of (a) screening and (b) ranking methods in material selection. (From Noryani et al., 2019.)

2.3.1 ANALYTICAL HIERARCHY PROCESS (AHP)

AHP is a formative technique that helps solve the mathematical and psychological complex decisions in a worldwide application. This method was developed by Saaty (2008) in the 1970s and has been extensively studied in many fields around the world. To select the materials based on certain criteria, especially in natural fiber composites, this tool has been used to meet the product specification in the manufacturing industry. The flexibility and friendly use of the methodology allows the commercialization of this method in diverse applications such as conceptual design and manufacturing process selections (Al-Oqla et al., 2015; Das, Bhattacharya, and Sarker, 2016; Hambali et al., 2009, 2010, 2011; Mansor et al., 2013; Mastura et al, 2017a; Mayyas et al., 2011; Sapuan, 2005). Bumper beam, parking brake lever, paddle box system, dashboard panel, anti-roll bar, and gearbox are the automotive components involved in their studies. AHP also can give a better result with a combination of other MCDMs such as TOPSIS, ELECTRE and PROMETHEE (Kuo et al., 2017; Peng and Xiao, 2013; Yousefpour and Rahimi, 2014).

2.3.2 ANALYTICAL NETWORK PROCESS (ANP)

ANP is more general compared with AHP, this method does not require independence among elements like AHP, in which the decision criteria is considered to be interrelated of one another in making the final decision. The process involved in this approach is to produce the super matrix by comparing the criteria in the complete system. In the year 2013, a study on non-metallic gears under multifunctional design requirements was done by using this tool to select the materials (Milani et al., 2013). Furthermore, ANP was combined with another tool, such as PROMETHEE, that can overcome the limitation of uncertainty results using ANP tools in materials selection in a hybrid environment (Peng and Xiao, 2013). Moreover, ANP was applied in an electronic firm, supply selection and hazardous substance management (Gencer and Gürpinar, 2007; Hsu and Hu, 2009).

2.3.3 TECHNIQUE OF RANKING PREFERENCES BY SIMILARITY OF THE IDEAL SOLUTIONS (TOPSIS)

Final selection is done by using a concept of compromise solution, which is the process implemented in the TOPSIS tool. This approached was proposed by Tzeng and Huang (2011b). The process in TOPSIS used the shortest and farthest Euclidean distance from the superlative solution and the negative ideal solution, respectively. A study to select the optimal hybrid bio-composite of the thermoset matrix in manufacturing the bumper beam in the automotive application was conducted by using this method (Mansor et al., 2014). Mayyas et al. (2016) also reported about the application of TOPSIS to choose automobiles' body panels. Furthermore, the benefits of TOPSIS, which can deal with dual quantitative and qualitative natures, increase the preference from the user to consider TOPSIS as the tool in material selection.

Mineral-Filled Composite

2.3.4 ANOTHER POTENTIAL MATERIAL SELECTION TOOLS

2.3.4.1 Multi-Attribute Utility Theory (MAUT)

In the 1970s, MAUT was the structural methodology design that balanced all factors in multiple objectives. The first study that applied this method was on the alternative locations for a new airport in Mexico City. Malak et al. (2009) proposed a new conceptual design that reduced the time selected by the engineers. A single alternative in which the information does not tolerate rational support is eliminated from the process selection. In the year 2015, the National Academy of Sciences recommended this tool to investigate safer design alternatives with new technologies (Ogle, Dee, and Cox, 2015). This tool also was applied in machine reconfigurability models (Hasan, Jain, and Kumar, 2013), supplier selection and order allocation (Sanayei et al., 2008).

2.3.4.2 Preference Selection Index (PSI)

Mayyas et al. (2013) used PSI to develop a sustainability model within the context of an automobile structure or body-in-white. A benchmark using principal component analysis (PCA) is used by Mayyas to make a better decision in the selection of the materials. A comparative study of three different types of materials selection problems by Maniya and Bhatt (2010) found that PSI is the most appropriate technique in materials selection. Also, the relative importance between alternative materials selection attributes is finally defined and the best solution was the unique approach by PSI.

2.3.4.3 Elimination and Choice Expressing the Reality (ELECTRE)

ELECTRE I was the initial MCDM tool model. It was first developed by Roy in the year 1968 and the improved version in 1983 was called ELECTRE IV (Tzeng and Huang, 2011a). Shanian et al. (2008) reported a novel application of another version of ELECTRE III that was improved Simons' procedure for group materials selection underweighting the uncertainty of a thermal loaded conductor coversheet. The best alternative material to the poorest alternative was listed reflecting that all criteria in the manufacturing process are provided using this method. The application was done on the bipolar plate using a polymer electrolyte fuel cell (Shanian and Savadogo, 2006).

2.3.4.4 Simple Additive Weighting (SAW)

The simplicity of this method is probably the why SAW become the most preferred decision-making tool by researchers when the method was introduced in 1954 (Shackleton & Spurgeon, 1982). Churchman and Ackoff (1954) were the first to utilize the SAW method to cope with a portfolio selection problem. SAW was applied in materials selection on several alternatives including composites and other materials used for a bipolar plate in proton exchange membrane fuel cells (Taherian & Nasr, 2012). Also, in Taherian (2014) review paper, he discussed the details of materials, fabrication and materials selection using SAW. The advantages of this friendly method were also applied in materials selection for piezoelectric applications, polymers and photovoltaic modules (Chauhan, Vaish, and Bowen, 2013).

2.3.4.5 Vlse Kriterijumska Optimizacija Kompromisno Resenje (VIKOR)

The uniqueness of this method was the optimization of a complex system in determining the list of compromise, a list of the solution and the interval of weight stability between the initial weight. San Cristóbal (2011) used VIKOR in a big project by the Spanish Government to select the Renewable Energy Plan to utilize the energy consumption to the plan such as wind power, hydroelectric, solar thermal, solar thermos-electric, photovoltaic, biomass and biogas. San Cristóbal (2011) also used the weighting process in the AHP method to identify the importance level of the criteria to help the decision-makers assign a value to the preference. A comprehensive version of VIKOR that overcomes the traditional was propose by created by Jahan et al. (2011). The new upgraded system increased the exactness of materials selection found multiple applications. An improved version of VIKOR created by Opricovic (2011) is used to overcome the main error in the original version by using a simpler approach in different applications. A recent study used this approach to select the car-side door impact together with AHP to identify the weighting of product design specifications from the automobile industry (Shaharuzaman et al., 2019b).

2.3.4.6 Data Envelopment Analysis (DEA)

The DEA model is a non-parametric method that does not require a complex function for variables. The advantage of using DEA is the capability of handling a huge variable. To solve a decision model in the manufacturing technology selection problem, Khouja (1995) used DEA in early 1994. Mousavi-Nasab and Sotoudeh-Anvai (2017) classified DEA as a support tool for materials selection problems after performing TOPSIS and complex proportional assessment (COPRAS). Moreover, they mentioned DEA does not require setting the weight for the input and output during the decision-making process. This eliminates the bias problem compared with other MCDMs. DEA was used to identify the best combination of vendor specifications on the performance parameter to select 27 industrial robots. This method is widely used in supplier selection in many industries, such as automotive (Mathiyazhagan, Sudhakar, and Bhalotia, 2018), telecommunications (Narasimhan, Talluri, and Mendez, 2001), and manufacturing (Liu, Ding, and Lall, 2000). Based on an article reviewed by Ho et al. (2010), almost 18% of the article used DEA as a tool for supplier selection. In general, the criteria studied were quality management, overall performance, efficiency, delivery process and distance of the supplier.

2.3.4.7 Preference Ranking Organization Method for Enrichment Evaluations (PROMETHEE)

The methodology using outranking relations is implemented in PROMETHEE. The alternatives for each attribute can be identified by pairwise comparisons. Jiao et al. (2011) mentioned the advantages of PROMETHEE, which does not involve a normalization process, that can minimize errors during decision making. A study by Das and Kumar (2015) was done to choose the most suitable materials with the desired properties of enhanced durability, low operational and manufacturing process and better performance by using PROMETHEE. A better final decision on the selection of the materials can be finalized by combining other MCDMs, such as AHP, ANP, ELECTRE, and VIKOR (Peng and Xiao, 2013; Chothani, Kuchhadiya, and Solanki, 2015; Patra and Dan, 2013).

2.3.4.8 Regression Analysis

Regression analysis in material selection was introduced by Noryani et al. (2018b) as one of the material selection tools using quantitative measurement from the raw data. For example, in their study stepwise regression is used to identify the significant criteria for hand-brake lever parking selection. To overcome the subjective preference in other selection tools in weighting process selection, this regression analysis used the coefficients from the statistical model as the weightage of each criterion.

Sun and Gollnick (2014) mentioned that MCDM tools can simplify the process selection of worldwide applications. Existing tools like AHP, ANP, TOPSIS, VIKOR, PROMTHEE and ELECTRE would be a problem to design engineers when choosing which tools would be appropriate to use based on the given problem design. Misleading design decision making happens when the wrong tool is used. Recent researchers have emphasized the integration of MCDM tools to increase decision making; therefore, the decision is more trustworthy and safer to apply. The most important decision in material selection is to identify the criteria, subcriteria and their relevant weight that satisfy industry requirements. Each of these tools has its limitations and advantages in various applications. Table 2.1 summarizes the advantages and disadvantages of these tools.

2.4 CHARACTERISTICS OF MINERAL IN MATERIAL SELECTION

Minerals or inorganics materials have unique characteristics that make them different from other types of materials. Unlike natural fibers, mineral materials have a wide range of types with different chemical compositions and properties. Selection from these types of materials would be a challenge because various options are available and it is difficult for the design engineer to carefully select the most suitable mineral materials for a certain application. Therefore, there has been no specific study that solely focuses on material selection of mineral-based materials. In this section, studies by past researchers that reported on the experimental selection of mineral materials are presented. The selection characteristics were chosen based on the application requirements.

Previously, Schneider et al. (2019) experimentally selected the suitable mineral materials to be impregnated with carbon fiber for composites. The potential materials were selected with identical chemical and mineralogical properties of micro-cements, but different diameters were used to select which composites would be impregnated with carbon fiber. In their study, it was crucial to attain the optimum mechanical performance with the maximum particle size of micro-cements. Impregnation of carbon fiber with the finer micro-cement showed an excellent bonding condition and lead to better mechanical performance. Thus, physical properties, such as the size of the mineral-based impregnation materials for composites, influenced the mechanical performance of the resultant composites. Kakhramanov, Mustafayeva, and Allakhverdiyeva (2019) studied the effect of various mineral

TABLE 2.1
Command Tools in Materials Selection of Natural Fiber Composites

Tools	Advantages	Disadvantages
AHP	• Easy to use • Adjustable relative score and flexible selection process in pairwise comparison for all criteria	• Significant effect of final decision based on weightage of the criterion • Subjective preference on weigh in selection process
ANP	• Dependent process selection • High accuracy base on priorities	• Unconvincing finding because of the uncertainty
MAUT	• Consider uncertainty in the process selection	• Huge input needed and the preference needs to be precise
TOPSIS	• Compensatory methods that allow trade-offs between criteria; insignificant criterion is eliminated to increase the result	• Ignore correlation of the attributes and criteria, difficult to weight and keep consistency of judgment
PSI	• No weighting and ranking procedure • Direct procedure to calculate the rating score to evaluate the performance of the alternative	• Untrusted finding because bias occurs in the scaling scheme for qualitative factors
ELECTRE	• All pairs of alternatives were considered in outranking steps • Qualitative and quantitative data are allowed	• Additional threshold should be introduced and can influence the decision-making process
DEA	• Increase the efficiency and make it more user friendly • Capable of handling multiple inputs and outputs	• Does not deal with imprecise data; full knowledge of input and output is required
PROMETHEE	• Outranking method; consider all alternatives in a pairwise comparison • Simple, clear and stable	• No weighting assignment
SAW	• Easy, simple calculation and no complex computer programs needed	• The result is not representative as a whole • Some of the result is not reasonable
VIKOR	• Include the difference between the estimation and the ideal alternative	• Subjective weight during the process selection • Huge amounts of data are required
Stepwise regression	• Quantitative measurement from the raw data • No subjective preference and decrease bias	• Comparing the significant criteria from the result with other candidates is a limitation

fillers based on the technological parameters of the process of extrusion of composites. The potential mineral fillers were montmorillonite, bentonite and aluminum hydroxide. Material selections were performed experimentally by considering the effect of the mineral fillers on the processing composites based on low-density and high-density PE (LDPE and HDPE). The application of the composite material is the area of fire resistance. They found in their study that different mineral fillers had different effects on the technological characteristics of the extrusion process of polymer-based composites. Moreover, Sheng et al. (2018) concluded in their study that the selected material for polymer-mineral composites is based on the response surface to fulfill all the requirements for the composites in the engineering application. Khan and Syed (2019) reported in their study that the important criteria related to mineral materials are flexural strength, flexural fatigue, wear, shear bond strength, cell viability, bio-mineralization and bacterial leakage. These important criteria were carefully studied and the mineral materials that could satisfy the criteria that complied with the medical technology would be selected as the most suitable mineral materials. In a construction application, Alghamri et al. (2018) presented a study in their paper on the selection of powder minerals for the cementitious matrix composites. Three different powder minerals were examined: reactive magnesium oxide, silica fume and bentonite. These three powder minerals have different advantages in which the magnesium oxide has a great potential as a self-healing agent and is able to yield irreversible and stable hydration while being compatible with the cement matrix. On the other hand, silica fume reacted with free calcium hydroxide, $Ca(OH)_2$ and water to form stable insoluble and densified calcium silicate hydrate. Unlike magnesium oxide, bentonite is an abundant, inexpensive option and has adequate binding properties and is easy to handle. Hence, they selected reactive magnesium oxide as the core material for the composite. Also, Zhang et al. (2018) reported a study on the expanded graphite/PE glycol composite phase change material, which is mainly used in asphalt pavements. Expanded graphite was selected as the supporting material based on its thermal properties. Characterization of the composite was performed by measuring the X-ray diffraction (XRD) analyses, differential scanning calorimeter and thermogravimetric analyzer for thermal stability. Scanning electron microscope was used to assess the pore structure of the materials. Fourier transform-infrared (FT-IR) spectrum was used to evaluate the interaction between expanded graphite and PE glycol.

2.5 CONCLUSIONS

Mineral-based composite was introduced in the industry to produce a high-quality performance of biomaterials. Material consumption and the size of materials influence the supply of non-renewable resources of the mineral and energy from the material. The behavior of the mineral, such as the peculiar and wide range in their properties and chemical compositions, make this material difficult to classify. The mineral-based composite exhibits diversity in mechanical, physical, thermal and chemical properties for multiple applications. There are many issues of mineral-based composites: oxidization on the composite; water absorption because of swelling and graphene, which affects the rheological behavior of the composites. An efficient and systematic material selection is needed to categorize this material. Integrated tools are used to produce a final decision that meets product specifications and customer satisfaction. Many tools were used to emphasize the process selections, but each of the tools has its advantages and limitations. AHP, ANP, and TOPSIS were the three most commonly used tools for materials selection that can optimize cost and time. Unlike natural fiber composites, no study has been found in selecting the mineral materials for the composites by using any of the decision-making tools. Further studies must be conducted to investigate the proper selection process of mineral-based composites by using systematic decision-making tools.

ACKNOWLEDGMENT

The authors would like to thank Universiti Teknikal Malaysia Melaka for the opportunity to conduct this study.

REFERENCES

Abdul Khalil, H.P.S., E.W.N. Chong, F.A.T. Owolabi, M. Asniza, Y.Y. Tye, M.R. Nurul Fazita, M.K.M. Haa, Z. Nurmiati, and M.T. Paridah. 2019. "Enhancement of Basic Properties of Polysaccharide-Based Composites with Organic and Inorganic Fillers : A Review." *Applied Polymer Science* 136 (2): 47251. https://doi.org/10.1002/app.47251

Aboudi Mana, S.C., M.M. Hanafiah, and A.J. Khan. 2017. "Environmental Characteristics of Clay and Clay- Based Minerals." *Geology, Ecology, and Landscapes* 9508: 1–7. https://doi.org/10.1080/24749508.2017.1361128

Aizan, N., M. Zaini, H. Ismail, and A. Rusli. 2017. "A Short Review on Sepiolite Filled Polymer Nanocomposites." *Polymer-Plastics Technology and Engineering* 2559 (February): 1665–79. https://doi.org/10.1080/03602559.2017.1289395

Alghadi, A.M., S. Tirkes, and U. Tayfun. 2020. "Mechanical, Thermo-Mechanical and Morphological Characterization of ABS Based Composites Loaded with Perlite Mineral." *Materials Research Express* 7: 015301.

Alghamri, R., A. Kanellopoulos, C. Litina, and A. Al-Tabbaa. 2018. "Preparation and Polymeric Encapsulation of Powder Mineral Pellets for Self- Healing Cement Based Materials." *Construction and Building Materials* 186: 247–62.

Al-Oqla, F.M., S.M. Sapuan, M.R. Ishak, and A.A. Nuraini. 2015. "A Decision-Making Model for Selecting the Most Appropriate Natural Fiber – Polypropylene-Based Composites for Automotive Applications." *Journal of Composite Materials* 50 (4): 543–56. https://doi.org/10.1177/0021998315577233

Babilotte, J., V. Guduric, D.L. Nihouannen, A. Naveau, J.-C. Fricain, and S. Catros. 2019. "Review Article 3D Printed Polymer – Mineral Composite Biomaterials for Bone Tissue Engineering : Fabrication and Characterization." *Journal of Biomedical Material Research Part B*, 1–17. https://doi.org/10.1002/jbm.b.34348

Bommala, V.K., M.G. Krishna, and C.T. Rao. 2019. "Magnesium Matrix Composites for Biomedical Applications : A Review." *Journal of Magnesium and Alloys* 7 (1): 72–79. https://doi.org/10.1016/j.jma.2018.11.001

Bosi, F., C. Biagioni, and R. Oberti. 2019. "On the Chemical Identification and Classification of Minerals." *Minerals* 591 (5): 1–12.

Cao, M., X. Ming, K. He, L. Li, and S. Shen. 2019. "Effect of Macro-, Micro- and Nano-Calcium Carbonate on Properties of Cementitious Composites- A Review." *Materials* 781 (12): 1–20. https://doi.org/10.3390/ma12050781

Chauhan, A., R. Vaish, and C. Bowen. 2013. "Piezoelectric Material Selection for Ultrasonic Transducer and Actuator Applications." *Proceedings of the Institution of Mechanical Engineers, Part L: Journal of Materials: Design and Applications* 229 (1): 3–12. https://doi.org/10.1177/1464420713493591

Chen, Y.-L., S.-R. Wang, J. Ni, and T.M. Fernández-steeger. 2017. "An Experimental Study of the Mechanical Properties of Granite after High Temperature Exposure Based on Mineral Characteristics." *Engineering Geology* 220: 234–42. https://doi.org/10.1016/j.enggeo.2017.02.010

Chinchillas-chinchillas, M.J., A. Gaxiola, C.G. Alvarado-beltr, V.M. Orozco-Carmona, M.J. Pellegrini Cervantes, M. Rodriguez-Rodrigues, and A. Castro-Beltran. 2020. "A New Application of Recycled-PET/PAN Composite Nano Fi Bers to Cement e Based Materials." *Journal of Cleaner Production* 252: 119827. https://doi.org/10.1016/j.jclepro.2019.119827

Chothani, H.G., B.B. Kuchhadiya, and J.R. Solanki. 2015. "Selection of Material for Hacksaw Blade Using AHP-PROMETHEE Approach." *International Journal of Innovative Research in Advanced Engineering* 2 (1): 26–30.

Churchman, C.W., and R.L. Ackoff. 1954. "An Approximate Measure of Value." *Journal of Operations Research Society of America* 2 (1): 172–87.

Das, A., and A. Kumar. 2015. "Selection of Spring Material Using PROMETHEE Method." *Journal of Mechanical and Civil Engineering* 12 (5): 82–91. https://doi.org/10.9790/1684-12548291

Das, D., S. Bhattacharya, and B. Sarkar. 2016. "Decision-Based Design-Driven Material Selection: A Normative-Prescriptive Approach for Simultaneous Selection of Material and Geometric Variables in Gear Design." *Materials and Design* 92: 787–93. https://doi.org/10.1016/j.matdes.2015.12.064

Ferrara, G., B. Coppola, L. Di, L. Incarnato, and E. Martinelli. 2019. "Tensile Strength of Flax Fabrics to Be Used as Reinforcement in Cement-Based Composites : Experimental Tests under Different Environmental Exposures." *Composites Part B* 168 (March): 511–23. https://doi.org/10.1016/j.compositesb.2019.03.062

Gencer, C., and D. Gürpinar. 2007. "Analytic Network Process in Supplier Selection: A Case Study in an Electronic Firm." *Applied Mathematical Modelling* 31 (11): 2475–86. https://doi.org/10.1016/j.apm.2006.10.002

Hambali, A., S.M. Sapuan, N. Ismail, and Y. Nukman. 2009. "Composite Manufacturing Process Selection Using Analytical Hierarchy Process." *International Journal of Mechanical and Materials Engineering* 4 (1): 49–61.

Hambali, A, S.M. Sapuan, N. Ismail, and Y. Nukman. 2010. "Material Selection of Polymeric Composite Automotive Bumper Beam Using Analytical Hierarchy Process." *Journal of Central South University of Technology* 17: 244–56. https://doi.org/10.1007/s11771

Hambali, A., S.M. Sapuan, A.S. Rahim, N. Ismail, and Y. Nukman. 2011. "Concurrent Decisions on Design Concept and Material Using Analytical Hierarchy Process at the Conceptual Design Stage." In *Concurrent Engineering: Research and Applications* 19:111–21. https://doi.org/10.1177/1063293X11408138

Hasan, F., P.K. Jain, and D. Kumar. 2013. "Machine Reconfigurability Models Using Multi-Attribute Utility Theory and Power Function Approximation." *Procedia Engineering* 64: 1354–63. https://doi.org/10.1016/j.proeng.2013.09.217

Ho, W., X. Xu, and P.K. Dey. 2010. "Multi-Criteria Decision Making Approaches for Supplier Evaluation and Selection : A Literature Review." *European Journal of Operational Research* 202 (1): 16–24. https://doi.org/10.1016/j.ejor.2009.05.009

Hsu, C.-W., and A.H. Hu. 2009. "Applying Hazardous Substance Management to Supplier Selection Using Analytic Network Process." *Journal of Cleaner Production* 17 (2): 255–64. https://doi.org/10.1016/j.jclepro.2008.05.004

Jahan, A., M.Y. Ismail, S.M. Sapuan, and F. Mustapha. 2010. "Material Screening and Choosing Methods - A Review." *Materials and Design* 31 (2): 696–705. https://doi.org/10.1016/j.matdes.2009.08.013

Jahan, A., F. Mustapha, M.Y. Ismail, S.M. Sapuan, and M. Bahraminasab. 2011. "A Comprehensive VIKOR Method for Material Selection." *Materials and Design* 32 (3): 1215–21. https://doi.org/10.1016/j.matdes.2010.10.015

Jiao, Q., Y. Lan, Z. Guan, and Z. Li. 2011. "A New Material Selection Approach Using PROMETHEE Method." In *International Conference on Electronic & Mechanical Engineering and Information Technology*, Harbin, Heilongjang, China, 2950–54.

Kakhramanov, N.T., F.A. Mustafayeva, Kh.V. Allakhverdiyeva. 2019. "Technological Features of Extrusion of Composite Materials Based on Mixtures of High and Low Density Polyethylene and Mineral Fillers." *Azerbaijan Chemical Journal* 4 (1): 11–16.

Kashif, S., U. Rehman, S. Kumarova, and S.A. Memon. 2020. "A Review of Microscale, Rheological, Mechanical, Thermoelectrical and Piezoresistive Properties of Graphene Based Cement Composite." *Nanomaterials* 2076 (10): 1–42.

Khan, A.S., and M.R. Syed. 2019. "A Review of Bioceramics-Based Dental Restorative Materials." *Dental Materials Journal* 38 (2): 163–76. https://doi.org/10.4012/dmj.2018-039

Khouja, M. 1995. "The Use of Data Envelopment Analysis for Technology Selection." *Computers Ind. Engineering* 28 (I): 123–32.

Klozi, A., K. Skórczewska, M. Barczewski, K. Sa, J. Szulc, and A. Piasecki. 2018. "Application of the Basalt Powder as a Filler for Polypropylene Composites with Improved Thermo-Mechanical Stability and Reduced Flammability." *Polymer Engineering & Science* 59 (2): E71–79. https://doi.org/10.1002/pen.24962

Kuo, C.F.J., C.H. Lin, M.W. Hsu, and M.H. Li. 2017. "Evaluation of Intelligent Green Building Policies in Taiwan Using Fuzzy Analytic Hierarchical Process and Fuzzy Transformation Matrix." *Energy and Building* 139: 146–59. https://doi.org/10.1016/j.enbuild.2016.12.078

Li, C., B. Xie, J. Chen, Z. He, Z. Chen, and Y. Long. 2019. "Emerging Mineral-Coupled Composite Phase Change Materials for Thermal Energy Storage." *Energy Conversion and Management* 183 (January): 633–44. https://doi.org/10.1016/j.enconman.2019.01.021

Liu, J., F.-Y. Ding, and V. Lall. 2000. "Using Data Envelopment Analysis to Compare Suppliers for Supplier Selection and Performance Improvement." *Supply Chain Management: An International Journal* 5 (3): 143–50.

Long, W.J., J.-L. Tao, C. Lin, Y.-C. Gu, L. Mei, and H.-B. Duan. 2019. "Rheology and Buildability of Sustainable Cement-Based Composites Containing Micro-Crystalline Cellulose for 3D-Printing." *Journal of Cleaner Production* 239: 118054. https://doi.org/10.1016/j.jclepro.2019.118054

Malak, R.J., J.M. Aughenbaugh, and C.J.J. Paredis. 2009. "Multi-Attribute Utility Analysis in Set-Based Conceptual Design." *Computer-Aided Design* 41 (3): 214–27. https://doi.org/10.1016/j.cad.2008.06.004

Maniya, K., and M.G. Bhatt. 2010. "A Selection of Material Using a Novel Type Decision-Making Method: Preference Selection Index Method." *Materials and Design* 31 (4): 1785–89. https://doi.org/10.1016/j.matdes.2009.11.020

Mansor, M.R., S.M. Sapuan, A. Hambali, E.S. Zainudin, and A.A. Nuraini. 2014. "Materials Selection of Hybrid Bio-Composites Thermoset Matrix for Automotive Bumper Beam Application Using Topsis Method." *Advances in Environmental Biology* 8 (8): 3138–42.

Mansor, M.R., S.M. Sapuan, E.S. Zainudin, A.A. Nuraini, and A. Hambali. 2013. "Hybrid Natural and Glass Fibers Reinforced Polymer Composites Material Selection Using Analytical Hierarchy Process for Automotive Brake Lever Design." *Materials and Design* 51: 484–92. https://doi.org/10.1016/j.matdes.2013.04.072

Mastura, M.T., S.M. Sapuan, M.R. Mansor, and A.A. Nuraini. 2017a. "Conceptual Design of a Natural Fibre-Reinforced Composite Automotive Anti-Roll Bar Using a Hybrid Approach." *The International Journal of Advanced Manufacturing Technology* 91 (5): 2031–48. https://doi.org/10.1007/s00170-016-9882-8

Mastura, M.T., S.M. Sapuan, M.R. Mansor, & A.A. Nuraini. 2017b. "Environmentally Conscious Hybrid Bio-Composite Material Selection for Automotive Anti-Roll Bar." *International Journal of Advanced Manufacturing Technology* 89 (5–8): 2203–19. https://doi.org/10.1007/s00170-016-9217-9

Mathiyazhagan, K., S. Sudhakar, and A. Bhalotia. 2018. "Modeling the Criteria for Selection of Suppliers towards Green Aspect : A Case in Indian Automobile Industry." *OPSEARCH* 55: 65–84. https://doi.org/10.1007/s12597-017-0315-8

Mayyas, A., M.A. Omar, M.T. Hayajneh, A. Mayyas, M.A. Omar, and M.T. Hayajneh. 2016. "Eco-Material Selection Using Fuzzy TOPSIS Method." *International Journal of Sustainable Engineering* 9 (5): 292–304. https://doi.org/10.1080/19397038.2016.1153168

Mayyas, A., Q. Shen, A. Mayyas, M. Abdelhamid, D. Shan, A. Qattawi, and M. Omar. 2011. "Using Quality Function Deployment and Analytical Hierarchy Process for Material Selection of Body-In-White." *Materials & Design* 32 (5): 2771–82. https://doi.org/10.1016/j.matdes.2011.01.001

Mayyas, A.T., A. Qattawi, A.R. Mayyas, and M. Omar. 2013. "Quantifiable Measures of Sustainability: A Case Study of Materials Selection for Eco-Lightweight Auto-Bodies." *Journal of Cleaner Production* 40: 177–89. https://doi.org/10.1016/j.jclepro.2012.08.039

Mechtcherine, V., A. Michel, M. Liebscher, K. Schneider, and C. Großmann. 2020. "Automation in Construction Mineral-Impregnated Carbon Fi Ber Composites as Novel Reinforcement for Concrete Construction : Material and Automation Perspectives." *Automation in Construction* 110 (March 2019): 103002. https://doi.org/10.1016/j.autcon.2019.103002

Milani, A.S., A. Shanian, C. Lynam, and T. Scarinci. 2013. "An Application of the Analytic Network Process in Multiple Criteria Material Selection." *Materials and Design* 44: 622–32.

Mousavi-Nasab, S. H., and A. Sotoudeh-Anvai. 2017. "A Comprehensive MCDM-Based Approach Using TOPSIS, COPRAS and DEA as an Auxiliary Tool for Material Selection Problems." *Materials & Design* 121 (May): 237–53. https://doi.org/10.1016/j.matdes.2017.02.041

Narasimhan, R., S. Talluri, and D. Mendez. 2001. "Supplier Evaluation and Rationalization via Data Envelopment Analysis : An Empirical Examination." *The Journal of Supply Chain Management*, 37 (3): 28–37.

Nazar, S., J. Yang, B.S. Thomas, I. Azim, S. Kashif, and U. Rehman. 2020. "Rheological Properties of Cementitious Composites with and without Nano-Materials: A Comprehensive Review." *Journal of Cleaner Production* 272 (Nov.): 122701. https://doi.org/10.1016/j.jclepro.2020.122701

Noryani, M., S.M. Sapuan, and M.T. Mastura. 2018a. "Multi-Criteria Decision-Making Tools for Material Selection of Natural Fibre Composites: A Review." *Journal of Mechanical Engineering and Sciences* 12 (1): 3330–53.

Noryani, M., S.M. Sapuan, M.T. Mastura, M.Y.M. Zuhri, E.S. Edisyam. 2019. *"Regression Analysis Framework for Material Selection of Natural Fibre Reinforced Polymer Composites."* Edited by Universiti Putra Malaysia. Universiti Putra Malaysia.

Noryani, M., S.M. Sapuan, M.T. Mastura, M.Y. M. Zuhri, and E.S. Zainudin. 2018b. "A Statistical Framework for Selecting Natural Fibre Reinforced Polymer Composites Based on Regression Model." *Fibers and Polymers* 19 (5): 1039–49.

Noryani, M., S.M. Sapuan, M.T. Mastura, M.Y.M. Zuhri, and E.S. Zainudin. 2020. "Statistical Inferences in Material Selection of a Polymer Matrix for Natural Fiber Composites." *Polimery/Polymers* 65 (2): 105–14. https://doi.org/10.14314/POLIMERY.2020.2.4

Nur, S., H. Mohamad, H. Zuhailawati, and B.K. Dhindaw. 2019. "Mechanical and Degradation Behaviour of Biodegradable Magnesium – Zinc/Hydroxyapatite Composite with Different Powder Mixing Techniques." *Journal of Magnesium and Alloys* 7 (4): 566–76. https://doi.org/10.1016/j.jma.2019.11.003

Ogle, R.A., S.J. Dee, and B.L. Cox. 2015. "Resolving Inherently Safer Design Conflicts with Decision Analysis and Multi-Attribute Utility Theory." *Process Safety and Environmental Protection* 97: 61–69. https://doi.org/10.1016/j.psep.2015.03.009

Opricovic, S. 2011. "Fuzzy VIKOR with an Application to Water Resources Planning." *Expert Systems with Applications* 38 (10): 12983–90. https://doi.org/10.1016/j.eswa.2011.04.097

Patra, A., and P.K. Dan. 2013. "Selection of Facility Layout Design Using PROMETHEE and VIKOR." *International Journal of Mechanical and Production Engineering* 1 (2): 15–22.

Peng, A.-H., and X.-M. Xiao. 2013. "Material Selection Using PROMETHEE Combined with Analytic Network Process under Hybrid Environment." *Materials and Design* 47: 643–52. https://doi.org/10.1016/j.matdes.2012.12.058

Pennell, J.P, and R.I. Winner. 1989. "Concurrent Engineering: Practices and Prospects." *IEEE Global Telecommunications Conference and Exhibition "Communications Technology for the 1990s and Beyond,"* 647–55.

Prasad, B. 2014. *Concurrent Engineering Fundamentals, Volume II : Integrated Product Development.* Upper Saddle River, NJ: Prentice Hall. https://doi.org/10.13140/RG.2.1.4710.1527

San Cristóbal, J.R. 2011. "Multi-Criteria Decision-Making in the Selection of a Renewable Energy Project in Spain : The Vikor Method." *Renewable Energy* 36: 498–502. https://doi.org/10.1016/j.renene.2010.07.031

Saaty, T.L. 2008. "Decision Making with the Analytic Hierarchy Process." *International Journal of Services Science* 1 (1): 83–98. http://dx.doi.org/10.1504/IJSSCI.2008.017590

Sanayei, A., S.F. Mousavi, M.R. Abdi, and A. Mohaghar. 2008. "An Integrated Group Decision-Making Process for Supplier Selection and Order Allocation Using Multi-Attribute Utility Theory and Linear Programming." *Journal of the Franklin Institute* 345 (7): 731–47. https://doi.org/10.1016/j.jfranklin.2008.03.005

Sapuan, S.M. 2005. "A Conceptual Design of the Concurrent Engineering Design System for Polymeric-Based Composite Automotive Pedals." *American Journal of Applied Sciences* 2 (2): 514–25.

Sapuan, S.M. 2017. *Composite Materials: Concurrent Engineering Approach.* United Kingdom: Elsevier, Inc.

Sapuan, S.M., and H.S. Abdalla. 1998. "A Prototype Knowledge-Based System for the Material Selection of Polymeric-Based Composites for Automotive Components." *Composites Part A: Applied Science and Manufacturing* 29 (7): 731–42. https://doi.org/10.1016/S1359-835X(98)00049-9

Sathish, S.K. 2020. *"Clay Mineral Composite Powders for Use in Lithium Batteries."* Thesis, Technical University of Ostrava, Ostrava, Czech Republic.

Saw, L.T., F. Zainuddin, X.V. Cao, and D.N.U. Lan. 2020. "The Thermal-Mechanical Degradation of Mineral-Filled Polypropylene-Ethylene Copolymer Composites during Extrusion Process." *Polymer Composites*, 42 (1) 83–97. https://doi.org/10.1002/pc.25809

Schneider, K., A. Michel, M. Liebscher, L. Terreri, S. Hempel, and V. Mechtcherine. 2019. "Mineral-Impregnated Carbon Fibre Reinforcement for High Temperature Resistance of Thin-Walled Concrete Structures." *Cement and Concrete Composites* 97 (Mar): 68–77. https://doi.org/10.1016/j.cemconcomp.2018.12.006

Shackleton, V.J., and P.C. Spurgeon. 1982. The Relative Importance of Potential Outcomes of Occupational Guidance : An Assessment by Occupational Guidance Officers." *Journal of Occupational Psychology* 55: 191–95.

Shaharuzaman, M.A., S.M. Sapuan, M.R. Mansor, and M.Y.M. Zuhri. 2019a. "Decision Support Strategy in Selecting Natural Fiber Materials for Automotive Side-Door Impact Beam Composites." *Journal of Renewable Materials* 7 (10): 997–1010. https://doi.org/10.32604/jrm.2019.07529

Shaharuzaman, M.A., S.M. Sapuan, M.R. Mansor, and M.Y.M. Zuhri. 2019b. "The Weighting of Product Design Specification for a Composite Side-Door Impact Beam Using the Analytic Hierarchy Process Method." *International Journal of Materials and Product Technology* 59 (1): 63–80. https://doi.org/10.1504/IJMPT.2019.100833

Shanian, A., A.S. Milani, C. Carson, and R.C. Abeyaratne. 2008. "A New Application of ELECTRE III and Revised Simos' Procedure for Group Material Selection under Weighting Uncertainty." *Knowledge-Based Systems* 21 (7): 709–20. https://doi.org/10.1016/j.knosys.2008.03.028

Shanian, A., and O. Savadogo. 2006. "A Non-Compensatory Compromised Solution for Material Selection of Bipolar Plates for Polymer Electrolyte Membrane Fuel Cell (PEMFC) Using ELECTRE IV." *Electrochimica Acta* 51 (25): 5307–15. https://doi.org/10.1016/j.electacta.2006.01.055

Sheng, P., J. Zhang, Z. Ji, and S. Wang. 2018. "FEM Simulation and Optimization on the Elastic Modulus and Thermal Expansion Ratio of Polymer-Mineral Composite." *Construction and Building Materials* 167: 524–35. https://doi.org/10.1016/j.conbuildmat.2018.02.051

Sohlenius, G. 1992. "Concurrent Engineering." *CIRP Annals* 41: 645–55.

Sothornvit, R., S.I. Hong, D.J. An, and J.W. Rhim. 2010. "Effect of Clay Content on the Physical and Antimicrobial Properties of Whey Protein Isolate/Organo-Clay Composite Films." *LWT - Food Science and Technology* 4 (2): 279–84.

Stavitskaya, A., S. Batasheva, V. Vinokurov, G. Fakhrullina, V. Sangarov, Y. Lvov, and R. Fakhrullin. 2019. "Antimicrobial Applications of Clay Nanotube-Based Composites." *Nanomaterials* 9 (5): 708.

Sun, X., and V. Gollnick. 2014. "Intelligent Multicriteria Decision Support System for Systems Design." *Journal of Aircraft* 51 (1): 1–11. https://doi.org/10.2514/6.2010-9222

Taherian, R. 2014. "A Review of Composite and Metallic Bipolar Plates in Proton Exchange Membrane Fuel Cell: Materials, Fabrication, and Material Selection." *Journal of Power Sources* 265: 370–90.

Taherian, R., and M. Nasr. 2012. "Performance and Material Selection of Nanocomposite Bipolar Plate in Proton Exchange Membrane Fuel Cells." *International Journal of Energy Research* 33 (4): 23–40. https://doi.org/10.1002/er

Tramarico, C.L., V.A.P. Salomon, and F.A.S. Marins. 2015. "Analytic Hierarchy Process and Supply Chain Management: A Bibliometric Study." *Procedia Computer Science* 55: 441–50. https://doi.org/10.1016/j.procs.2015.07.005

Tzeng, G. and Huang, J. 2011. Multiple Attribute Decision Making Methods and Applications. New York: Sprinnger-Verlag. http://doi.org/10.1007/978-3-642-48318-9

Tzeng, G.H., and J.J. Huang. 2011a. "ELECTRE Method." In *Multiple Attribute Decision Making: Methods and Applications*, 81–93. Boca Raton, FL: CRC Press.

Tzeng, G. H., & Huang, J. J. 2011b. "TOPSIS and VIKOR." In *Multiple Attribute Decision Making: Methods and Applications*, 69–80. Boca Raton, FL: CRC Press.

Yousefpour, M., and A. Rahimi. 2014. "Characterization and Selection of Optimal Parameters to Achieve the Best Tribological Performance of the Electrodeposited Cr Nanocomposite Coating." *Materials and Design* 54: 382–89. https://doi.org/10.1016/j.matdes.2013.08.017

Zhang, D., M. Chen, S. Wu, Q. Liu, and J. Wan. 2018. "Preparation of Expanded Graphite/Polyethylene Glycol Composite Phase Change Material for Thermoregulation of Asphalt Binder." *Construction and Building Materials* 169: 513–21. https://doi.org/10.1016/j.conbuildmat.2018.02.167

3 Epoxy Resins for Interphase Strengthening of Textile-Reinforced Composites for Structural Applications

C. Signorini and A. Nobili
University of Modena and Reggio Emilia
Modena, Italy

CONTENTS

3.1 Introduction 45
3.2 Experimental Research on Epoxy Coatings of AR-Glass TRM 50
    3.2.1 The Technology of Fabric Pre-Impregnation 50
    3.2.2 Formulation Design of Epoxy Coatings for AR-Glass Fibers 51
    3.2.3 Approaches in Uniaxial Tensile Testing 54
3.3 Influence of the Coating Formulation in Epoxy-Coated TRM 55
3.4 Thermal Response of Epoxy-Coated TRM 57
3.5 Influence of Coating Viscosity in Epoxy-Coated TRM 59
3.6 Conclusions 62
References 63

3.1 INTRODUCTION

Externally bonded reinforcements (EBRs) designed for strengthening existing buildings have been extensively adopted since the early 1990s in the form of polymer-based fibrous composites, named fiber-reinforced polymers (FRPs). More specifically, high-strength fabrics made of synthetic fibers, impregnated by a polymeric resin laid on the substrate to be reinforced, impart enhanced resistance to structural members. In common practice, FRPs prove to be an extremely versatile reinforcing strategy, and are currently used to strengthen reinforced concrete (RC) elements, such as beams, columns, structural joints, panels and bridge girders and pillars (Oehlers and Seracino 2004). Also, FRP systems are regarded as an established technology to recover masonry buildings and to restore the correct structural behavior of walls and slabs, especially as a safeguard for the joints between structural elements (Angiolilli et al. 2020). Compared with traditional retrofitting strategies (e.g., steel brackets), FRPs allow for outstanding performance upgrades of the structural response of masonry structures with no significant addition of mass. This is an especially valuable property in seismic retrofitting. Commonly used fibers include carbon, glass or aramid (Kevlar®), although recently new promising materials have gained attention, such as poly(p-phenylene-2,6-benzobisoxazole), also known as PBO (Zylon®) and natural fibers, such as basalt, flax, hemp, sisal and others (Olivito, Cevallos, and Carrozzini 2014). In particular, natural fibers show great potential within the emerging concept of sustainable structural materials.

Epoxy resins are widely adopted as the embedding medium of FRP systems. Indeed, a synergic response is established between the epoxy matrix and the reinforcing fabric wherein the latter ultimately withstands to applied loading; whereas the former acts as a connection between multiple plies and a gateway with the support. The success of FRPs may be traced back to the liquid phase of the polymeric matrix, which allows uniform impregnation of the multifilaments and effective penetration of the substrate surface, thus creating a monolithic system (Figure 3.1). As a result, the conversion rate (that is the exploitation degree) of the fabric potential is near-optimal.

On the other hand, significant limitations are attached to the adoption of an organic binder. Indeed, polymers suffer from exhibiting a narrow range of thermal stability and combust in the presence of fire. In fact, thermosetting resins undergo dramatic performance losses beyond their fairly low glass-transition temperature (T_g), which is usually approximately 60°C–70°C. This behavior sets stringent limits for the adoption of FRPs to reinforce buildings susceptible to crowding, for instance, theaters, cinemas and museums (Spagnuolo et al. 2018). Moreover, organic binders offer little permeability to water vapor, which, in special conditions, might condensate within the substrate at the boundary with the EBR, eventually leading to support deterioration or even failure. This feature is extremely relevant for historical masonry, especially for frescoed vaults and walls.

In addition, organic binder cannot polymerize in the presence of water, which is a problem in wet applications and for the reinforcement of hydraulic infrastructures, such as pipes or dams. Consequently, significant efforts have been devoted to the development of novel reinforcing strategies wherein the polymeric binder is replaced by a mineral matrix.

The development of composite systems based on cementitious and/or lime-based matrices is currently a fast-paced research topic. Inorganic composites draw

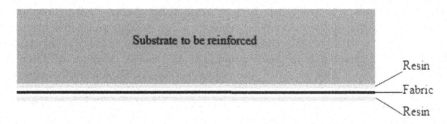

FIGURE 3.1 Schematic view of the reinforcement of an existing element through EBR composite laminate.

inspiration by the vast body of knowledge accumulated in the long tradition of adopting cement as a versatile, durable and cost-effective structural material. In fact, inorganic materials are compatible with most traditional substrates, both from a physical/chemical and a mechanical standpoint. This class of composite systems still lacks an agreed nomenclature, and it goes under the name of fiber-reinforced cementitious materials (FRCMs) or textile-reinforced mortar (TRM). The presence of the inorganic binder (i.e., lime or cement with inert mineral aggregates) has many advantages ranging from great temperature stability, inability to combust in the presence of fire, excellent water vapor permeability, resistance to aggressive environments (such as chemicals, UV rays, and explosions) and the ability to cure in water. For these reasons, TRM can be exploited to great advantage in historical buildings (Nobili and Falope 2017) and in processing plants of aggressive substances, in marine and underwater structures and infrastructures. However, this wealth of assets comes with a substantial performance price. It is important to emphasize that inorganic mortars come in a wide variety of compositions and are inhomogeneous by nature. Indeed, they feature a composite structure with a predominant solid phase due to the presence of aggregates, most commonly sand or fine gravel with variable diameters (generally up to a few millimeters, depending on the application). This composite structure is incapable of penetrating the inter-filament spacing and, consequently, the inner filaments cannot be reached by the surrounding matrix. This, in turn, accounts for inefficient load transfer from the matrix to the fabric, unlike what occurs in FRPs. The comparison is schematically illustrated in Figure 3.2.

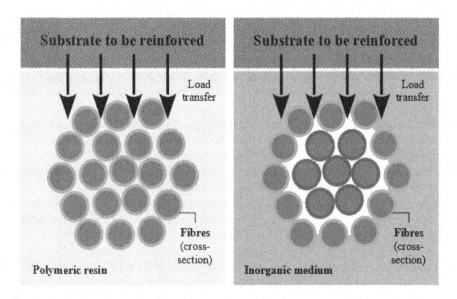

FIGURE 3.2 Schematic view of the impregnation mechanisms of FRP (left) and TRM systems (right). In the former resin is capable of strongly binding fibers in the yarn, and the resulting system is monolithic. In contrast, the inorganic binder of the TRM system is incapable of deep penetration, thereby it binds the exterior part of the yarn (the sleeve) and cannot reach the interior (the core). As a result, telescopic failure is likely to occur.

External fibers (called the *sleeve*) are effectively bonded by the hydration products of the binder to the surrounding matrix, which allows for good load transfer. However, inner fibers of the yarns (called the *core* or *bundle*) remain unaffected by the interphase bond and are in plain frictional contact with the sleeve filaments. For mild load levels, slippage occurs, which entails gradual debonding: although this mechanism significantly contributes to ductility, it also promotes inconsistent crack opening, stiffness loss and inability to fully exploit the reinforcement. Also, the result is often unacceptable for durability reasons.

Numerous possible solutions have been proposed to achieve greater conversion rates of the reinforcing fabric in TRM composites. For example, polymer-modified matrices incorporate a small polymer fraction (up to 5%, according to the prescriptions of the American Concrete Institute [ACI] guidelines) to enhance the bonding action of the embedding medium, with remarkable advantages in the bearing capacity and ductility of the whole composite (Elsanadedy et al. 2013). In a similar fashion, active nanomaterials may be added to the inorganic binder with remarkable success. For instance, inclusion of carbon nanotubes (CNTs) in the matrix greatly improves the flexural and compressive strength of the mortar, as well as the stiffness of beams reinforced with modified TRM (Irshidat and Al-Shannaq 2018). Albeit effective, this solution may be hardly considered on a large scale, given the cost of CNTs. An alternative promising approach targets the interphase directly, and it is unspecific to either the matrix or the reinforcement. It consists of fabric coating through functional materials that can modify the chemical and the physical interaction at the interphase. Both inorganic and organic coatings have been considered. To the former group belong efforts aimed at enhancing the chemical affinity at the interphase by surging the hydrophilicity of the fiber surface. In AR-glass (ARG) fabrics, silica-based functional nanofillers have been added to the multifilament bundle to induce a more controlled failure mechanism and to enhance durability. The efficiency of the treatment deeply depends on the type of the fillers (Cohen and Peled 2012). Amorphous nano-silica particles also have been proposed as a coating agent for adhesion with the hydration products of cement or lime-based mortars. Several literature contributions have witnessed the efficiency of the treatment, given the extremely elevated specific surface area (SSA) of the coatings, which ensures good hydrophilicity (Di Maida et al. 2015; Signorini et al. 2018; Lu et al. 2018; Signorini, Nobili, and Siligardi 2019a). An alternative approach relies on organic coatings and takes inspiration from FRP systems. Several studies document the remarkable performance gain that can be obtained by binding together individual filaments within yarns. This approach lends a twofold advantage: it prevents telescopic failure (Donnini, Corinaldesi, and Nanni 2016; Messori et al. 2018) and protects fibers from aggressive environments that may damage the long-term mechanical performance of the system (Scheffler et al. 2009; Nobili and Signorini 2017). Also, recent guidelines concerning TRM suggest adopting fabric coatings for handling, installation and durability against aggressive environments (ACI 549.4R-13 2013). Table 3.1 offers a literature overview of the state-of-the-art coating techniques.

In this chapter, we discuss recent findings concerning optimal design of epoxy coatings for ARG multifilament fabrics embedded in a lime-based mortar. For the sake of definiteness, we restrict attention to enhancing mechanical performance of

TABLE 3.1
Coating Techniques for Multifilament Fabrics in Textile-Reinforced Composite Materials: Literature Review

Reference(s)	Coating Material	Application	Summary
Fu, Lu, and Chung (1996)	Ozone treatment (and other oxidizing techniques)	Carbon fibers in cement (with several compositional modifications)	Oxidizing treatments, (and ozone in particular) improve the fiber-to-cement bond strength
Xu et al. (2004)	Epoxy resin	Coated carbon, aramid and ARG fiber in traditional and prestressed composite textile-reinforced concrete (TRC)	Epoxy coating combined with prestressing can significantly improve the fiber-to-matrix bond
Cohen and Peled (2012)	Pozzolanic (silica) and organic (polystyrene and styrene acrylic) particles	ARG multifilament bundles filled with nanoparticles and microparticles through wet and dry technologies in TRM and TRC	Mechanical performance and durability are best enhanced through large particle silica fume fillers
Yin, Xu, and Li (2013)	Epoxy resin	Coating of hybrid (E-glass/carbon) fabric plus sand overcoating within polypropylene (PP) fiber-reinforced concrete matrix in TRC	The influence of the concrete cover thickness is investigated; the coating strongly affects the bond and the superficial sand has a positive effect on crack propagation
Donnini, Corinaldesi, and Nanni (2016)	Epoxy resin	Coating of carbon fibers + overcoating with quarzitic sand in TRM composites	The mechanical capacity of FRCM systems (tensile strength and shear bond strength when applied to masonry) is enhanced; some difficulties are encountered concerning ease of application because of the rigidity of the coated yarn
Contamine and Si Larbi (2016)	Latex-based wet pre-impregnation compared with epoxy and polyester coating	Aramid, basalt, E-glass and ARG textiles in TRC composites	Latex pre-impregnation has positive effects on bonding, similar to what is obtained with epoxy or polyester
Nadiv et al. (2017)	Nano-silica and micro-silica particles (compared with epoxy)	Carbon multifilament fabrics in TRC	Micro-silica coating presents best performance (in pull-out tests), compared with nano-silica and epoxy coating
Signorini et al. (2018); Signorini, Nobili, and Siligardi (2019a,b)	Nano-silica and micro-silica particles	Carbon and ARG fibers coated with amorphous nano-silica through sol-gel synthesis and micro-silica from silica fume aqueous dispersion in TRM	A remarkable enhancement in the TRM bearing capacity and ductility is observed, especially for glass fibers, due to improved hydrophilicity at the interphase

TRM coupons assessed under comparative uniaxial tensile tests. Specifically, the effect of fabric coating on the overall response of the composite system is analyzed. Also, the role of resin formulation is discussed alongside its optimal viscosity. Because an organic coating is introduced in an essentially inorganic system, it is important to investigate to what extent the latter is capable of shielding the former from the damaging effect of exposure to high temperatures.

3.2 EXPERIMENTAL RESEARCH ON EPOXY COATINGS OF AR-GLASS TRM

The chapter critically discusses, in a systematic manner, some recent results concerning the effects of epoxy as coating agent for ARG multifilament fabrics. This section describes materials and methods of the investigation, the experimental set-up and compares our findings with relevant literature contributions.

To highlight the role of the coating, specimens employ a consistent set of materials, namely ARG fibers (FB-VAR320R12, FibreNet SpA, Udine, Italy) in a lime-base mortar (GeoCalce F Antisismico, Kerakoll SpA, Modena, Italy), whose properties are listed in Table 3.2.

The reinforcing phase consists of a balanced biaxial (0°/90°) ARG multifilament fabric, possessing an open square-grid mesh, whereas the embedding medium is made of natural hydraulic lime (NHL) and fine aggregates (up to a 1.4-mm diameter). The examined composite system is intended to act as EBR for masonry (brick, tuff or stone) and panels (Prota et al. 2006; Donnini et al. 2020).

3.2.1 THE TECHNOLOGY OF FABRIC PRE-IMPREGNATION

Numerous application procedures have been developed for EB FRP composite materials, although the most popular consists of manually laying the reinforcement onto the structural member whose surface has been pre-treated with the binder to

TABLE 3.2
Properties of the Lime Mortar and of the ARG Reinforcing Fabric, as Provided by the Producers (Mechanical Properties of the Mortar Refer to 28-Day Curing Time)

Mortar Properties			AR-Glass Fabric Properties		
Characteristic	**Unit**	**Value**	**Characteristic**	**Unit**	**Value**
Aggregate max. size	mm	1.4	Yarn count	tex	1200
Min. compressive strength	MPa	15.0	Weight per unit area	g/m^2	300
Min. flexural strength	MPa	3.4	Grid spacing (warp)	mm	12
Adhesion strength	MPa	1.0	Fabric cross-sectional area, A_f	mm^2/m	60
Water content	%	21	Ultimate strength	N/cm	720
Long. elastic modulus	GPa	1	Elastic modulus	GPa	74

trigger adhesion. This "wet lay-up" procedure carries over unaltered to the field of TRM, because it can be performed on-site by a qualified work force. The constituent materials are supplied to the building site and then assembled directly onto the substrate. Reinforcing fabrics hardly come dry, that is, without any surface treatment after weaving; instead, they most often are pre-impregnated (*pre-preg*), usually with silicon. Pre-preg is carried out on an industrial scale directly by the manufacturer and it is usually adopted for best processing and handling, although sometimes it is performed to deliver special properties (such as defect healing, durability etc.) to the fabric. In the latter case, concerns may arise in terms of storing and handling prescriptions, given that mistreatment may affect the coating quality and integrity. Specifically, when polymerization is adopted, temperature and humidity play a significant role. Occasionally, an appropriate thermal treatment may be necessary prior to lamination of the pre-preg fabric on-site. We conclude that pre-preg fabrics are currently widely used and indeed, along this trend, we move in the following sections, to focusing on specific treatments that require no further processing on-site. Because polymerization is reverted to, designing the response to high temperature becomes very important and, indeed, by careful resin selection, post-curing reactions may occur that improve the final performance.

3.2.2 Formulation Design of Epoxy Coatings for AR-Glass Fibers

In this section, we present two interesting formulations specifically addressed at coating ARG thermowelded fabrics, both based on a single high-purity bisphenol A diglycidyl ether epoxy precursor (DER® 332, Dow Chemical, USA), which acts as the embedding medium. These coatings differ by the curing agent, which presents different chemical structure. On the one hand, we consider an aliphatic amine, namely diethylenetriamine (DETA, Alfa Aesar, USA). DETA is obtained from the production of ethylenediamine from ethylene dichloride and it is commonly employed as a catalyst for thermoset resins, as well as epoxy. The result is a highly cross-linked structure, due to the presence of natrium (N), which reacts with epoxide groups. The thus formed OH groups provide the hardened resin with a strong binding capability. The structure of DETA is essentially linear; hence, the resulting resin is expected to exhibit a good degree of ductility under loading. Conversely, the thermal stability of the resin may be questionable. DETA comes in the form of a liquid compound. On the other hand, an aromatic amine is adopted, namely m-phenylenediamine (m-PDA, Acros Organics, USA), in the form of colorless flakes. m-PDA is a versatile compound that has many industrial applications. Apart from the use as a catalyst for epoxy, it is involved in the preparation of aramid fibers, which are particularly important in the military applications, due to their high dissipation capability. In addition, m-PDA is included in the manufacturing chain of various polymers, adhesives and dyes. The structure of this compound is characterized by the presence of benzene rings, which are expected to confer high thermal stability to the coating, together with a certain degree of brittleness. Both epoxy resins (especially the one cured with m-PDA) present an elevated viscosity, and this aspect should be thoroughly investigated to maximize the coating performance. Accordingly, diluting the resins by means of an organic solvent to reduce viscosity and thereby facilitate impregnation represents a viable solution, as described in the following sections. Indeed, highly viscous coatings shape as a thick layer surrounding the yarns and are incapable of penetrating among the filaments (Signorini et al. 2020b; Donnini, Corinaldesi, and Nanni 2016). In this form, the coating acts as an external sleeve with limited surface area available for interacting with the hydration products of the lime-based binder.

Limited affinity between the coating and the filaments also may be due to surface sizing. The latter is often a fundamental component, because the composition of ARG fibers is merely inorganic, characterized by the predominant presence of silica and zirconia. The latter, added in the molten glass in an adequate content (not less than 16%), warrants the typical resistance to alkaline environments. A pretreatment (silanization) of the fibers using a coupling agent is required to cause the affinity of the coating to the fibers. In the literature, several options are proposed, and the use of alkoxysilane molecules is regarded as the most effective solution. In particular, (3-aminopropyl)triethoxysilane (APTES) has exhibited a satisfactory coupling effect (Messori et al. 2018). Indeed, comparing failed TRM specimens after tensile tests proved that the sizing with APTES, prior to the embedment of the fibers in the epoxy resin, promotes a strong fiber-to-coating bond, as clearly highlighted by Figure 3.3, in which two specimens, without (a) and with (b) silanization, are compared.

In the paper by Messori et al. (2018), APTES is applied through fabric immersion in an aqueous solution at 2 vol%, taking care that the solution is homogenized through magnetic stirring. Water is chosen as the solvent to avoid the risk that organic solvents (which are the most obvious choice) might degrade the thermoplastic filaments (stitches) employed for thermowelding the textile (Hojo et al. 1994). Furthermore, aqueous solution presents lower environmental concerns and performs satisfactorily.

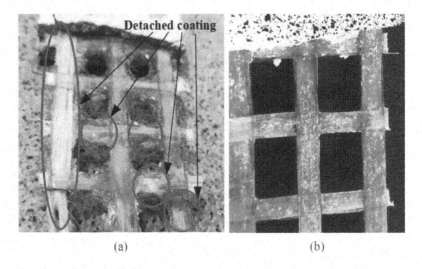

FIGURE 3.3 Effects of silanization on TRM specimens with ARG fabrics coated with aromatic-cured epoxy resin after tensile tests. In the absence of APTES sizing (a), coating patches detach from the fabric surface; in contrast, the coating remains firmly attached to fibers previously treated with APTES solution (b).

Epoxy Resins for Interphase Strengthening

FIGURE 3.4 Original ARG fabric (a) as it compares with the epoxy-coated specimens with aromatic (b) and aliphatic hardener (c).

After being completely dry, silanized fabrics are immersed in the epoxy resin. The epoxy precursor is pre-heated at 50°C to temporarily reduce its viscosity and facilitate the stirring process. The curing agent is then slowly added complying with the correct stoichiometric ratio and the resin is left stirring until a complete homogenization is attained (Zong et al. 2009). Then fabrics are immersed for a few seconds and eventually pressed to remove the excess of resin. The cross-linking reactions take place at room temperature. The appearance of the coated fabrics is shown in Figure 3.4b and c and may be compared to the original ARGs multifilament textile (see Figure 3.4a).

The images in Figure 3.4 show that the coating completely embeds the multifilament yarns, binding the fibers together. This outcome is expected to prevent telescopic failure during testing. Due to the elevated viscosity of the resin, the thickness of the coating is approximately 300–400 μm (Messori et al. 2018). The interphase is analyzed through environmental scanning electron microscope (E-SEM), as in Figures 3.5 and 3.6. The coating incorporates the filaments in the yarn and individual fibers are no longer visible. The coating viscosity favors the inclusion of air bubbles, which are incorporated during the stirring process. This outcome is more

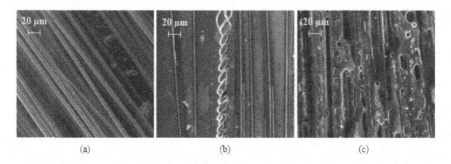

FIGURE 3.5 E-SEM magnifications of ARG fabric: uncoated (a), m-PDA-cured epoxy coated (b) and DETA-cured epoxy coated (c).

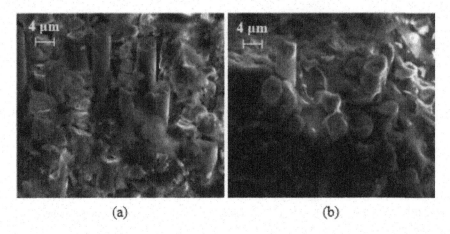

FIGURE 3.6 E-SEM magnification of the cross-section of coated fabric: m-PDA-cured epoxy (a) and DETA-cured epoxy (b).

evident for the aliphatic-cured resin (see Figure 3.5c) and it determines discontinuities in the coating, although roughness is introduced in the system, which benefits the mechanical grip with the mortar. The aromatic-cured coating exhibits its brittle nature in that polymerization triggers crack formation (see Figure 3.5b). Diffused cracks, absent when DETA-cured resin is used and are visible in the cross-sectional view of the yarn (see Figure 3.6b).

3.2.3 Approaches in Uniaxial Tensile Testing

To assess the mechanical behavior of TRM composites, direct tensile tests are performed. Although a few guidelines are now available, scientists have yet to agree on a standard procedure and setup. As mentioned and widely discussed in the paper by Contamine, Si Larbi and Hamelin (2011), the variables that should be carefully designed for testing are

- Shape of the specimens (prismatic or dumbbell),
- Dimensions (width, length, and aspect ratio),
- Displacement rate of the test, and
- Clamping system.

For each possible approach, advantages and drawbacks are discussed. In this chapter, we pick one protocol with no special claim except that we use it consistently. In particular, 1-ply unnotched prismatic samples with aspect ratio equal to 12 (length/width) are considered. Due to the particular manufacturing process, the prismatic rectangular shape is largely the easiest to implement. Indeed, the reinforcing fabric is placed between two layers of mortar, with a thickness of 3 mm each. Mortar is applied by a scraper and the constant thickness is ensured by the presence of polyethylene spacers. The wet lay-up procedure is explained in detail in several works and takes advantage of a modular mold (Nobili and Signorini 2017; Signorini et al. 2018).

Epoxy Resins for Interphase Strengthening

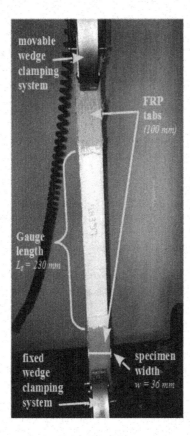

FIGURE 3.7 Testing setup and specimen dimensions.

Rigid wedges are used for the clamping system (Hartig et al. 2012). The edges of the samples are reinforced with FRP tabs to correctly transfer the load applied by the clamps and limit its impact on the specimen ends. The testing setup is shown in Figure 3.7 in which the specimen dimensions are also provided. A universal testing machine (UTM) equipped with a 30-kN load cell is adopted. The upper cross-bar moves at a controlled speed (displacement control), according to the prescriptions of the guideline by RILEM (RILEM Technical Committee 232-TDT 2016). Hereinafter, tests are conducted at a controlled strain rate of 2 mstrain/min. A minimum of five repetitions is warranted for each test group.

3.3 INFLUENCE OF THE COATING FORMULATION IN EPOXY-COATED TRM

The mechanical performance of TRM coupons in tension is compared in Figure 3.8, where stress-strain mean curves are presented. Stress conventionally normalizes the applied load to the cross-sectional area of the fabric, A_f. The performance of both epoxy coatings (with m-PDA and DETA as curing agents) is compared with

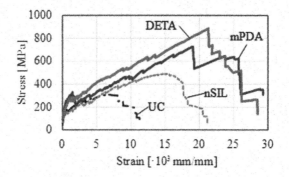

FIGURE 3.8 Strength curves of ARG TRM composite materials. Solid curves represent epoxy-coated TRM (Messori et al. 2018), the green dotted curve refers to ARG TRM specimens coated with nano-silica (Signorini, Nobili, and Siligardi 2019b) and the black dot-dashed curve pertains to uncoated (control) specimens.

nano-silica (nSIL) coating. By analyzing the mean curves with respect to uncoated specimens ([UC] control), the remarkable gain brought by surface modification is immediately apparent, both in terms of ultimate stress and ultimate elongation. Best performance is attached to the aliphatic resin, as a consequence of the superior ductility of the polymer structure of the curing agent.

Results in terms of ultimate strain (around 2.7%) are comparable with the findings by Dvorkin et al. (2013), although they refer to carbon fabric, which usually has less ductility (1.5%–2%). The influence of either epoxy coating is also remarkable when compared with nano-silica, which favors ductility. In terms of failure modes, the typical failure mechanism observed for uncoated ARG TRM consists of pull-out of the fabric from the matrix, after cracking occurs. As often pointed out, telescopic failure and internal delamination are associated with good ductility properties for the composite, although the bearing capacity and the exploitation index (EI), that is the efficiency to which the reinforcement is exploited, are poor (Carozzi et al. 2016). In contrast, both epoxy coatings are capable of switching the failure mode from delamination to the tensile rupture of the filaments. This failure mode is associated to full exploitation of the reinforcement, although it is intrinsically brittle. Nonetheless, in combination with the capacity of the mortar to crack progressively, the composite is able to attain high levels of deformability. The enhanced tenacity of the laminates develops consistent levels of ultimate stress and strain (see further details on the crack analysis given by Messori et al. 2018). Performance consistency is fundamental in as much as design considerations are concerned. Indeed, the significant reduction of the coefficient of variance for ultimate elongation (33% for UC vs. 13%–17% for epoxy coated) conveys sizeable results on characteristic values, which are often the basis of which to determine design values for the composite system. This reduction in data scattering is a direct consequence of the failure mode of the filaments, which, as shown in the bar chart in Figure 3.9a, occurs in close proximity of the expected characteristic elongation at failure of bare filaments (~2%). Characteristic values are determined according to Equation 1 of Appendix D (Table D1) in Eurocode "Basis of Structural Design. European committee for standardization (CEN)" There, the number of the test repetitions is considered through the

Epoxy Resins for Interphase Strengthening

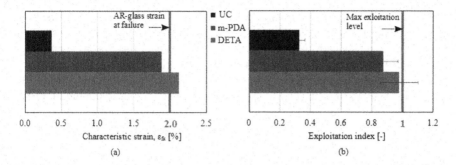

FIGURE 3.9 Characteristic elongation for each test group evaluated according to Eurocode 1 (a) and exploitation index in terms of strength (together with 1 standard deviation band) (b).

coefficient $Kn = 1.80$, relating characteristic and mean values for strain ε_{fk} and ε_{fm}, respectively, with ς being the standard deviation

$$\varepsilon_{fk} = \varepsilon_{fm} - 1.80 \, \varsigma(\varepsilon_{fm}) \qquad (3.1)$$

Figure 3.9b plots the EI for ARG fabrics, defined as the ultimate strength attained by TRM composites over the ultimate strength attained by the same fabric in FRP, which is the value customary regarded as the maximum exploitation exerted by the fabric. Although uncoated fabric deploys a small fraction of the potential strength of the fabric (approximately 35%), epoxy-coated specimens are able to maximize the mechanical performance of the TRM composite, surpassing 90% exploitation. Consequently, a remarkable improvement of the bearing capacity is achieved through epoxy coating. Still, concerns may arise about the behavior after exposure to high temperature considering the role played by the coating and of its vulnerability to high temperature. This concern is addressed in the next section.

3.4 THERMAL RESPONSE OF EPOXY-COATED TRM

When thermal stability of EB composites is considered, a vast body of literature is available concerning FRP systems that highlights the susceptibility of the organic matrix to high temperatures, see Cao, Zhis, and Wang (2009) and references therein. In TRM systems, however, the hydraulic nature of the binder significantly mitigates this weakness. Still, we saw that epoxy coating deeply affects performance and the question arises whether this improvement may hold after high temperature exposure. Only a handful of studies are available in the literature addressing the issue of the thermal stability of epoxy-coated fibers in TRM systems. Thermal properties (at different ranges of conditioning temperatures, up to 600°C) of carbon fibers with epoxy resin are investigated for textile-reinforced concrete (TRC) and FRCM composites in the contributions by Xu et al. (2014), Donnini et al. (2017) and de Andrade Silva et al. (2014). The detrimental effects associated with high temperature conditioning are assessed through bending tests, as well as direct tensile and shear bond tests.

These studies highlight performance decay associated with the damage of the polymer at the interphase. Indeed, long-term exposure to high temperature causes coating degradation and leads to early delamination (Xu et al. 2014). As an exception, de Andrade Silva et al. (2014) reported that heating specimens up to 150°C may favor interphase interlocking between the yarn and the matrix, which possibly justifies the increase in the bearing capacity of the composite. In addition, Rambo et al. (2015) investigated the role of thermal aging on basalt fabrics, up to 1000°C, in traction, when a styrene-acrylic latex is used as an adhesion promoter. Despite a refractory cementitious matrix, it appears that beyond 200°C damage is connected to the presence of fiber surface treatments and to its nature. Remarkably, only a few studies are available addressing thermal stability of ARG. The recent work by Maroudas and Papanicolaou (2017) provides evidence of performance decay for ARG-TRM laminates at temperatures exceeding 100°C. Authors ascribe such performance loss to damage to the adhesive capability at the interphase in combination with degradation of the bare fabric.

In this section, we discuss the major findings presented by Messori et al. (2019), with specific reference to the epoxy coatings described in the previous section, which differ according to the curing agent (i.e., DETA aliphatic amine and m-PDA aromatic amine). The spotlight is on assessing the outcomes of high temperature exposure up to 250°C. TRM coupons, manufactured as described in the previous sections, are air cured for 28 days (ICC AC434 2013). In contrast to Donnini et al. (2017), where hot testing is performed, tensile performance is assessed on room temperature specimens that have been previously exposed to one of four temperature levels (100°C, 150°C. 200°C and 250°C) for 120 minutes. It is found that exposure to temperatures higher than 150°C induce partial oxidization of the coating resin, which turns black, as shown in Figure 3.10. Conversely, no significant bearing on the lime mortar can be detected.

Interestingly, mortar embedment preserves resin from deterioration for temperatures up to 150°C.

Mechanical tests clearly show a great difference in the thermal behavior of the two coatings by virtue of their chemical composition. Indeed, by comparing ultimate tensile strength (UTS) data gathered in Figure 3.11, DETA epoxy-coated TRM composites (Figure 3.11a) exhibit a monotonic decreasing trend as a function of

FIGURE 3.10 Aromatic-cured epoxy coating after exposure for 120 minutes at high temperature (250°C). The coating is clearly black as a result of carbonization.

Epoxy Resins for Interphase Strengthening

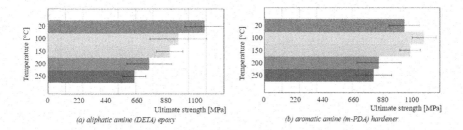

FIGURE 3.11 Mean tensile strength values for epoxy-coated ARG-TRM coupons subjected to high temperature with relevant 1 standard deviation band. (Results retrieved by Messori et al. 2019.)

the conditioning temperature. Remarkably, when the aromatic hardener is adopted (Figure 3.11b), a statistically significant *increase* of the UTS is observed at 100°C, which persists when conditioning at 150°C.

Finally, resin degradation prevails and performance decays at high temperature. The reason for this mixed behavior is illustrated by Messori et al. (2019) through differential scanning calorimetry (DSC) analysis of the bare resin. This reveals that, at ambient temperatures, m-PDA-cured resin is not yet completely polymerized and its conversion degree is approximately 67%. Conversely, when DETA is adopted as a curing agent, at ambient temperature the curing reaction approaches full conversion estimated at 96%. Therefore, m-PDA resin benefits from high temperature exposure up to 150°C as it leads to complete conversion. As a result, further cross-linking of the polymeric structure is achieved, which produces significant toughening of the composite system. However, this enhancement of the ultimate bearing capacity of the laminate is achieved at the expense of embrittlement, which is responsible for the reduction in the ultimate tensile elongation (UTE) capability. This analysis helps to understand that compositional differences in the coating agent formulation largely affect the final outcome of high temperature exposure. In fact, the embedding mortar shields the fabric from direct exposure and alters the mechanisms by which high temperature affects the organic coating, especially with regard to oxidation that is largely mitigated. This outcome combines with the expected fact that the aromatic hardener imparts greater thermal stability to the resin, due to the presence of the closed ring structures of benzene. Finally, albeit a reduction of both performance indices (UTS and UTE) is observed, unlike FRP it remains limited and, for UTS, does not exceed 22% and 40%, respectively, for m-PDA- and DETA-cured coatings, at 250°C. This suggests that epoxy coatings may be a valid option for enhancing structural performance of TRM systems, while still retaining the advantages connected to the inorganic binder and meanwhile mitigating its deficiencies (most notably performance scattering).

3.5 INFLUENCE OF COATING VISCOSITY IN EPOXY-COATED TRM

As discussed in some depth in the previous sections, epoxy coatings may be regarded as a powerful strategy to significantly improve the response of TRM composite materials. Coatings are capable of strengthening the interphase between multifilament fabrics and the embedding medium, which governs the bearing capacity of the whole composite system. However, as previously hinted, this outcome is antagonized by highly viscous epoxy resins, which fail to fully impregnate and bind the filaments together in yarn bundles. Resin composition should be engineered so that a very thin film is laid on each single filament. The advantages attached to reducing viscosity of DETA-cured epoxy coatings is well described in the experimental campaign recently presented by Signorini et al. (2020a), where resin dilution is adopted to fine-tune viscosity levels. Indeed, DETA-cured epoxy is diluted in acetone at different degrees, up to 90%, and then adopted as a coating agent for ARG fabric. This analysis specifically aims to reduce viscosity through a very simple and economical process. The epoxy Bisphenol A diglycidyl ether (DGEBA) precursor is preliminary diluted with acetone at 50°C in a covered beaker to favor the homogeneity of the solution, and the stoichiometric quantity of aliphatic amine is then added and thoroughly incorporated into the solution before embedding the fabrics.

As illustrated in Figure 3.12, the underlying idea is to favor impregnation of each single filament and thus take advantage of higher levels of specific surface in contact with the matrix. Textiles, once coated, polymerize at room temperature before being laid onto the mortar, according to the same procedure discussed in Section 3.3. The viscosity of the diluted resin is measured with a rheometer and correlated with mechanical performance of the TRM system, as assessed in uniaxial tensile tests.

The graph in Figure 3.13 superposes the EI of the coated textile, as defined in Section 3.3, onto the viscosity of the coating (presented on a decimal logarithmic scale), as a function of the dilution degree. Reasonably, the reduction of the epoxy content in the coating, due to dilution, weakens the interphase, and this is confirmed by the decreasing trend in the EI up to 25% dilution. However, beyond 25% dilution, mechanical performance takes an unexpected upturn that is ascribed to the enhanced capability of the coating to penetrate the inter-filament spacings in the yarn bundles. Indeed, in proximity of 50%–75% dilution, ultimate strength (and, of course, the EI) reaches performance levels comparable to the undiluted condition and then marginally surpasses them in correspondence with 75% dilution, which is associated to best performance. This outcome emerges as a compromise between two opposing trends: dilution reduces polymer content and thus negatively affects the binding strength,

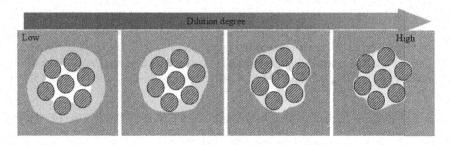

FIGURE 3.12 Schematic showing quality of the impregnation as a function of the dilution degree (i.e., viscosity) of the epoxy coating.

Epoxy Resins for Interphase Strengthening

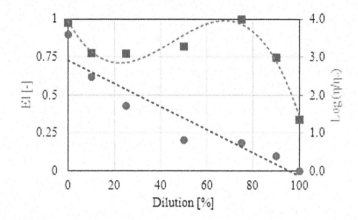

FIGURE 3.13 Exponential decay of epoxy coating viscosity (blue dots represent actual measurements and the blue dash line is the trend) superposed onto the EI (red) of the composite as a function of the dilution degree (DETA-cured resin).

and reduced viscosity favors thorough penetration of the resin within the multifilament yarns of the fabric, thereby largely enhancing the available adhesion surface for bond creation with the mortar. Overall, 75% dilution significantly reduces the polymer content in the TRM, thus favoring water vapor permeability and, in general, reducing all concerns attached to the organic content in the composite, not the least being its environmental impact (La Rosa et al. 2016). Interestingly, an economic benefit is also achieved in that dilution reduces the specific cost of the resin per unit weight of the composite, as estimated by Signorini et al. (2020a) through a simple economic analysis. In terms of economic ranking of high-performance composite materials, an index combining mechanical performance (in terms of dissipated energy) with the unit cost of raw materials is determined and compared across different systems. The results are given in Table 3.3.

Due to the negligible cost of the solvent with respect to epoxy resin, dilution produces a notable advantage in terms of cost, whereas the mechanical response is almost identical to that of undiluted specimens. This analysis retrieves data from the literature, and it is intended for illustrative purposes, because different test methods and performance measures may be considered instead, while material costs are extremely variable in time and space. Still, the comparison is meaningful and explains some well-established facts, such as the great success of rebar and epoxy-glass (such as fiberglass) systems. It also shows that strongly diluted epoxy-coated ARG-TRM systems are extremely competitive with comparable strengthening solutions, tailing FRP and well in front of any inorganic binder system. Indeed, with optimal dilution, the specific cost of coated ARG-TRM and net of application costs (which, presumably, are similar for coating occurs at the manufacturing stage) are comparable with carbon FRP (C-FRP), which is traditionally regarded among the best optimized strengthening systems, as well as the most commonly adopted in current practice.

TABLE 3.3
Cost/Performance Index Across Different Composite Systems (the Cost Is Referred Only to the Raw Materials, Such As Fabrics, Coatings and Embedding Media), While Performance Refers to Dissipated Energy of Similar-Size Coupons Tested in Uniaxial Tensile Tests)

Technology	Description	Cost/Dissipated Energy (€/MJ)	Source(s)
Steel bar	-	0.06	Camera di Commercio di Modena (2018)
C-FRP	High tenacity/high modulus carbon uniaxial fabric with epoxy	23.58/24.93	CNR TD200-R1 (2013)
G-FRP	E-glass uniaxial fabric with epoxy	4.41	
A-FRP	Aramid (Kevlar) uniaxial fabric with epoxy	13.27	
C-TRM (impregnated)	High tenacity carbon biaxial fabric impregnated (wet) with water-based latex embedded in lime mortar	40.73	Nobili and Signorini (2017)
C-TRM (dry)	High tenacity carbon biaxial fabric with cementitious mortar	360.92	Signorini and Nobili (2021)
B-TRM	Basalt biaxial fabric with cementitious mortar	117.67	
P-TRM	Zylon (PBO) biaxial fabric with cementitious mortar	652.21	
ARG-TRM (uncoated)	ARG biaxial fabric with lime-based mortar	280.07	Signorini, Nobili, and Siligardi (2019a)
ARG-TRM (DETA coated)	ARG biaxial fabric coated with DETA-cured epoxy resin embedded in lime-based mortar	92.64	Messori et al. (2018)
ARG-TRM (m-PDA coated)	ARG biaxial fabric coated with m-PDA-cured epoxy resin embedded in lime-based mortar	112.05	
ARG-TRM (75% diluted DETA coated)	ARG biaxial fabric coated with DETA-cured epoxy resin diluted in acetone at 75% embedded in lime-based mortar	33.42	Signorini et al. (2020a)

Source: Signorini et al. (2020a).

3.6 CONCLUSIONS

In this chapter, we critically review some recent studies concerning interphase strengthening of TRM composite systems for structural applications. Specifically, the interphase between multifilament fabrics and the embedding inorganic medium is targeted by epoxy-based engineered coatings to maximize the degree of exploitation of the reinforcing fabric. In consideration of recent studies in the field, we conclude the following:

- Yarn pre-impregnation with epoxy thin films greatly increases the load bearing capacity of the composite system, with a conversion rate close to optimal for glass fiber (up to 97%).
- Interestingly, load levels are increased without compromising ductility, as a consequence of the diffuse crack pattern that emerges and promotes dissipation of mechanical energy.
- High temperature exposure, up to 250°C, of the composite system slightly impairs performance despite the presence of the organic coating. Indeed, the presence of the inorganic embedding medium shields the epoxy coating from direct oxidation and consequent damage to the resin is considerably mitigated, despite the glass transition temperature having been well exceeded. This stands in marked contrast to the experimental findings concerning FRP systems, which operate successfully on a limited temperature range.
- The coating formulation is very important, and it may be engineered so that the damage induced by high temperature exposure, as mitigated by the embedding mortar, is greatly reduced. In fact, aromatic resins, although more brittle by nature, lead to improved temperature response, which goes through a stage of temperature-induced post-cross-linking (post-curing) with increased performance.
- Coating viscosity deeply affects final performance. Indeed, coating dilution proves best performing in that (1) it better penetrates the intra-filament spacings and thereby greatly magnifies the active surface area available for bond formation; (2) it reduces the amount of organic binder and the disadvantages connected to it, such as permeability and environmental impact and finally (3) it is advantageous in terms of cost reduction.
- A simple economical exercise, in which material costs are weighted against energy dissipated at failure in uniaxial tensile tests, shows that highly diluted epoxy-coated ARG-TRM systems perform comparably to the well-established class of C-FRP composites and better than any inorganic binder-based solution.

REFERENCES

ACI 549.4R-13. 2013. Guide to Design and Construction of Externally Bonded Fabric-Reinforced Cementitious Matrix (FRCM) Systems for Repair and Strengthening Concrete and Masonry Structures. Farmington Hills, MI: American Concrete Institute.

Angiolilli, Michele, Amedeo Gregori, Madura Pathirage, and Gianluca Cusatis. 2020. "Fiber Reinforced Cementitious Matrix (FRCM) for Strengthening Historical Stone Masonry Structures: Experiments and Computations." *Engineering Structures* 224 (December): 111102. https://doi.org/10.1016/j.engstruct.2020.111102

Camera di Commercio di Modena. 2018. "Building Materials Price Datasheet 2018 (Prezziario Opere Edili 2018)."

Cao, Shenghu, Zhis Wu, and Xin Wang. 2009. "Tensile Properties of CFRP and Hybrid FRP Composites at Elevated Temperatures." *Journal of Composite Materials* 43 (4): 315–30.

Carozzi, Francesca Giulia, Pierluigi Colombi, Giulia Fava, and Carlo Poggi. 2016. "A Cohesive Interface Crack Model for the Matrix-Textile Debonding in FRCM Composites." *Composite Structures* 143 (May): 230–41. https://doi.org/10.1016/j.compstruct.2016.02.019

CNR TD200-R1. 2013. "Guide for the Design and Construction of an Externally Bonded FRP System for Strengthening Existing Structures." Advisory Committee on Technical Recommendations for Construction.

Cohen, Zvi, and Alva Peled. 2012. "Effect of Nanofillers and Production Methods to Control the Interfacial Characteristics of Glass Bundles in Textile Fabric Cement-Based Composites." *Composites Part A: Applied Science and Manufacturing* 43 (6): 962–72. https://doi.org/10.1016/j.compositesa.2012.01.022

Contamine, Raphaël, and Amir Si Larbi. 2016. "Development of a Textile Reinforced Concrete (TRC) to Retrofit Reinforced Concrete Structures." *European Journal of Environmental and Civil Engineering* 20 (6): 626–42. https://doi.org/10.1080/19648189.2015.1030089

Contamine, Raphaël, Amir Si Larbi, and Patrice Hamelin. 2011. "Contribution to Direct Tensile Testing of Textile Reinforced Concrete (TRC) Composites." *Materials Science and Engineering A* 528 (29–30): 8589–98. https://doi.org/10.1016/j.msea.2011.08.009

de Andrade Silva, Flávio, Marko Butler, Simone Hempel, Romildo Dias Toledo Filho, Viktor Mechtcherine, Flávio de Andrade Silva, Marko Butler, Simone Hempel, Romildo Dias Toledo Filho, and Viktor Mechtcherine. 2014. "Effects of Elevated Temperatures on the Interface Properties of Carbon Textile-Reinforced Concrete." *Cement and Concrete Composites* 48 (April): 26–34. https://doi.org/10.1016/J.CEMCONCOMP.2014.01.007

Di Maida, P., E. Radi, C. Sciancalepore, and F. Bondioli. 2015. "Pullout Behavior of Polypropylene Macro-Synthetic Fibers Treated with Nano-Silica." *Construction and Building Materials* 82: 39–44.

Donnini, Jacopo, Valeria Corinaldesi, and Antonio Nanni. 2016. "Mechanical Properties of FRCM Using Carbon Fabrics with Different Coating Treatments." *Composites Part B: Engineering* 88: 220–28. https://doi.org/10.1016/j.compositesb.2015.11.012.

Donnini, Jacopo, Francisco De Caso y Basalo, Valeria Corinaldesi, Giovanni Lancioni, Antonio Nanni, Francisco De Caso y Basalo, Valeria Corinaldesi, Giovanni Lancioni, and Antonio Nanni. 2017. "Fabric-Reinforced Cementitious Matrix Behavior at High-Temperature: Experimental and Numerical Results." *Composites Part B: Engineering* 108 (January): 108–21. https://doi.org/10.1016/J.COMPOSITESB.2016.10.004

Donnini, Jacopo, Gianluca Maracchini, Stefano Lenci, Valeria Corinaldesi, and Enrico Quagliarini. 2020. "TRM Reinforced Tuff and Fired Clay Brick Masonry: Experimental and Analytical Investigation on Their in-Plane and out-of-Plane Behavior." *Construction and Building Materials* 272 (November): 121643. https://doi.org/10.1016/j.conbuildmat.2020.121643

Dvorkin, D., Amir Poursaee, Alva Peled, and William Jason Weiss. 2013. "Influence of Bundle Coating on the Tensile Behavior, Bonding, Cracking and Fluid Transport of Fabric Cement-Based Composites." *Cement and Concrete Composites* 42: 9–19.

Elsanadedy, Hussein M., Tarek H. Almusallam, Saleh H. Alsayed, and Yousef A. Al-Salloum. 2013. "Flexural Strengthening of RC Beams Using Textile Reinforced Mortar – Experimental and Numerical Study." *Composite Structures* 97 (March): 40–55. https://doi.org/10.1016/j.compstruct.2012.09.053

Fu, X., W. Lu, and D. D. L. Chung. 1996. "Improving the Bond Strength between Carbon Fiber and Cement by Fiber Surface Treatment and Polymer Addition to Cement Mix." *Cement Concrete Res* 26 (7): 1007–12.

Hartig, J., F. Jesse, K. Schicktanz, and U. Häußler-Combe. 2012. "Influence of Experimental Setups on the Apparent Uniaxial Tensile Load-Bearing Capacity of Textile Reinforced Concrete Specimens." *Materials and Structures* 45 (3): 433–46. https://doi.org/10.1617/s11527-011-9775-0

Hojo, H., K. Ogasawara, W. L. Chang, and K. Tsuda. 1994. "Degradation Behavior of Unsaturated Polyester Resin in Alcohols." *Advanced Composite Materials* 3 (4): 341–53. https://doi.org/10.1163/156855194X00213

ICC AC434. 2013. "Acceptance Criteria for Masonry and Concrete Strengthening Using Fiber-Reinforced Cementitious Matrix (FRCM) Composite Systems." Whittier, CA.

Irshidat, Mohammad R., and Ammar Al-Shannaq. 2018. "Using Textile Reinforced Mortar Modified with Carbon Nano Tubes to Improve Flexural Performance of RC Beams." *Composite Structures* 200 (September): 127–34. https://doi.org/10.1016/j.compstruct.2018.05.088

La Rosa, A. D., D. R. Banatao, S. J. Pastine, A. Latteri, and G. Cicala. 2016. "Recycling Treatment of Carbon Fibre/Epoxy Composites: Materials Recovery and Characterization and Environmental Impacts through Life Cycle Assessment." *Composites Part B: Engineering* 104 (November): 17–25. https://doi.org/10.1016/j.compositesb.2016.08.015

Lu, Mengyuan, Huigang Xiao, Min Liu, Xiaojiao Li, Hui Li, and Li Sun. 2018. "Improved Interfacial Strength of SiO2 Coated Carbon Fiber in Cement Matrix." *Cement and Concrete Composites* 91 (August): 21–28. https://doi.org/10.1016/j.cemconcomp.2018.04.007

Maroudas, S. R., and C. G. Papanicolaou. 2017. "Effect of High Temperatures on the TRM-to-Masonry Bond." *Key Engineering Materials* 747: 533–41.

Messori, Massimo, Andrea Nobili, Cesare Signorini, and Antonella Sola. 2018. "Mechanical Performance of Epoxy Coated AR-Glass Fabric Textile Reinforced Mortar: Influence of Coating Thickness and Formulation." *Composites Part B: Engineering* 149 (September): 135–43. https://doi.org/10.1016/j.compositesb.2018.05.023

Messori, Massimo, Andrea Nobili, Cesare Signorini, and Antonella Sola. 2019. "Effect of High Temperature Exposure on Epoxy-Coated Glass Textile Reinforced Mortar (GTRM) Composites." *Construction and Building Materials* 212 (July): 765–74. https://doi.org/10.1016/j.conbuildmat.2019.04.026

Nadiv, Roey, Alva Peled, Viktor Mechtcherine, Simone Hempel, and Christof Schroefl. 2017. "Micro- and Nanoparticle Mineral Coating for Enhanced Properties of Carbon Multifilament Yarn Cement-Based Composites." *Composites Part B: Engineering* 111 (February): 179–89. https://doi.org/10.1016/j.compositesb.2016.12.005

Nobili, Andrea, and Federico O. Falope. 2017. "Impregnated Carbon Fabric–Reinforced Cementitious Matrix Composite for Rehabilitation of the Finale Emilia Hospital Roofs: Case Study." *Journal of Composites for Construction* 21 (4): 05017001. https://doi.org/10.1061/(ASCE)CC.1943-5614.0000780

Nobili, Andrea, and Cesare Signorini. 2017. "On the Effect of Curing Time and Environmental Exposure on Impregnated Carbon Fabric Reinforced Cementitious Matrix (CFRCM) Composite with Design Considerations." *Composites Part B: Engineering* 112: 300–313. https://doi.org/10.1016/j.compositesb.2016.12.022

Oehlers, D., and R. Seracino. 2004. *Design of FRP and Steel Plated RC Structures: Retrofitting Beams and Slabs for Strength, Stiffness and Ductility*. Oxford, UK: Elsevier.

Olivito, R. S., O. A. Cevallos, and A. Carrozzini. 2014. "Development of Durable Cementitious Composites Using Sisal and Flax Fabrics for Reinforcement of Masonry Structures." *Materials and Design* 57 (May): 258–68. https://doi.org/10.1016/j.matdes.2013.11.023

Prota, A., G. Marcari, G. Fabbrocino, G. Manfredi, and C. Aldea. 2006. "Experimental In-Plane Behavior of Tuff Masonry Strengthened with Cementitious Matrix-Grid Composites." *Journal of Composites for Construction* 10 (3): 223–33.

Rambo, Dimas Alan Strauss, Flávio de Andrade Silva, Romildo Dias Toledo Filho, and Otávio da Fonseca Martins Gomes. 2015. "Effect of Elevated Temperatures on the Mechanical Behavior of Basalt Textile Reinforced Refractory Concrete." *Materials Design* 65: 24–33.

RILEM Technical Committee 232-TDT. 2016. "Test Methods and Design of Textile Reinforced Concrete." *Materials and Structures* 49: 4923–27. https://doi.org/10.1617/s11527-016-0839-z

Scheffler, C., S. L. Gao, R. Plonka, E. Mäder, S. Hempel, M. Butler, and V. Mechtcherine. 2009. "Interphase Modification of Alkali-Resistant Glass Fibres and Carbon Fibres for Textile Reinforced Concrete I: Fibre Properties and Durability." *Composites Science and Technology* 69 (3–4): 531–38. https://doi.org/10.1016/j.compscitech.2008.11.027

Signorini, C., and A. Nobili. 2021. "Comparing Durability of Steel Reinforced Grout (SRG) and Textile Reinforced Mortar (TRM) for Structural Retrofitting." *Materials and Structures* 54: 131.

Signorini, C., A. Sola, A. Nobili, and C. Siligardi. 2019a. "Lime-Cement Textile Reinforced Mortar (TRM) with Modified Interphase." *Journal of Applied Biomaterials and Functional Materials* 17 (1). https://doi.org/10.1177/2280800019827823

Signorini, Cesare, Andrea Nobili, Erika Iveth Cedillo González, and Cristina Siligardi. 2018. "Silica Coating for Interphase Bond Enhancement of Carbon and AR-Glass Textile Reinforced Mortar (TRM)." *Composites Part B: Engineering* 141: 191–202. https://doi.org/10.1016/j.compositesb.2017.12.045

Signorini, Cesare, Andrea Nobili, and Cristina Siligardi. 2019b. "Sustainable Mineral Coating of Alkali-Resistant Glass Fibres in Textile-Reinforced Mortar Composites for Structural Purposes." *Journal of Composite Materials* 53 (28–30): 0021998319855765.

Signorini, Cesare, Andrea Nobili, Antonella Sola, and Massimo Messori. 2020a. "Designing Epoxy Viscosity for Optimal Mechanical Performance of Coated Glass Textile Reinforced Mortar (GTRM) Composites." *Construction and Building Materials* 233 (February): 117325. https://doi.org/10.1016/j.conbuildmat.2019.117325

Signorini, Cesare, Andrea Nobili, Antonella Sola, and Massimo Messori. 2020b. "Optimal Epoxy Dilution for Epoxy-Coated Textile Reinforced Mortar (TRM): An Experimental Perspective." In *Lecture Notes in Mechanical Engineering*, 499–511. Springer. https://doi.org/10.1007/978-3-030-41057-5_41

Spagnuolo, Simone, Alberto Meda, Zila Rinaldi, and Antonio Nanni. 2018. "Residual Behaviour of Glass FRP Bars Subjected to High Temperatures." *Composite Structures* 203: 886–93. https://doi.org/10.1016/j.compstruct.2018.07.077

Xu, S., L. Shen, J. Wang, and Y. Fu. 2014. "High Temperature Mechanical Performance and Micro Interfacial Adhesive Failure of Textile Reinforced Concrete Thin-Plate." *Journal of Zhejiang University SCIENCE A* 15 (1): 31–38.

Xu, Shilang, Markus Krüger, Hans-Wolf Reinhardt, and Joško Ožbolt. 2004. "Bond Characteristics of Carbon, Alkali Resistant Glass, and Aramid Textiles in Mortar." *Journal of Materials in Civil Engineering* 16 (4): 356–64. https://doi.org/10.1061/(ASCE)0899-1561(2004)16:4(356)

Yin, Shiping, Shilang Xu, and Hedong Li. 2013. "Improved Mechanical Properties of Textile Reinforced Concrete Thin Plate." *Journal Wuhan University of Technology, Materials Science Edition* 28 (1): 92–98. https://doi.org/10.1007/s11595-013-0647-z

Zong, Liming, Martin C. Hawley, Rensheng Sun, and Leo C. Kempel. 2009. "Dielectric Relaxation of Curing DGEBA/MPDA System at 2.45 GHz." *Journal of Thermoplastic Composite Materials* 22 (3): 249–57. https://doi.org/10.1177/0892705708093501

4 Recent Advances in Nanofillers for Multidisciplinary Applications of Polymer Nanocomposites

Dang Mao Nguyen, Patrick Perré
Laboratoire Innovation Matériau Bois Habitat Apprentissage (LIMBHA), Ecole Supérieure du Bois, Nantes, France

Thi Phuong Thao Nguyen
The University of Danang
Danang City, Vietnam

Quoc Bao Bui
Ton Duc Thang University
Ho Chi Minh City, Vietnam

DongQuy Hoang
University of Science, Vietnam National University
Ho Chi Minh, Vietnam

CONTENTS

4.1 Introduction 68
4.2 Preparation of Nanofillers 69
    4.2.1 Montmorillonite (MMT) 69
    4.2.2 Silica Nanoparticles (SiO_2 NPs) 70
    4.2.3 Cellulose Nanocrystals (CNCs) 71
4.3 Filler-Reinforced Polymer Nanocomposites 72
    4.3.1 Mechanical Properties 73
    4.3.2 Barrier Properties 75
    4.3.3 Thermal Stability 79
    4.3.4 Flame Retardancy 81
    4.3.5 Biomedical Applications 83

DOI: 10.1201/9781003221012-4

4.4 Conclusions 87
Acknowledgments 87
References 87

4.1 INTRODUCTION

The discovery and development of nanotechnology was a breakthrough in the field of nanoscience and materials science. Nano-reinforced polymer composites were discovered in the early 1990s (Kojima et al., 2011; Usuki et al., 2011) and created revolutionary combinations of nanoscale fillers and polymers to expand significant properties for polymer nanocomposites. The fabrication of polymers nanocomposites was based on a common principle using polymer or polymer blends that are commonly reinforced by various sized and concentrations of fillers via different technologies. These technologies include solution and melting methods to significantly improve the limitations of the polymer matrix, expanding the applications. Nanocomposites bring attractive opportunities for various applications in various industries, such as food packaging (Attaran et al., 2015; Youssef et al., 2015), automotive (Naskar et al., 2016) and biomedical (Mondal, 2017; Scaffaro et al., 2018) because of their light weight and excellent rheological, thermal, mechanical, barrier and biodegradation properties compared with pure polymer matrices (Kargarzadeh et al., 2017). These performances are explained by the reinforcement behavior of fillers at the nanoscale particles (<100 nm), which significantly influences the properties of polymer nanocomposites including surface interactions, adhesion, morphology particle motion, dispersion and interfaces. Thus, the range of applications and dominant properties of the polymer nanocomposites are highly dependent on the filler characteristics including size, shape, volume fraction and state of dispersion of the nanofillers (Pfaendner, 2010; Cividanes et al., 2017), which enable applications in different fields such as energy storage, automotive, aerospace, packaging, electronic and tribology applications (Zhang et al., 2006; Chang et al., 2007).

In the literature, nanofillers were mainly classified into three categories based on their dimensions: one-dimensional (1D), two-dimensional (2D) and three-dimensional (3D) (Vengatesan, 2016). The 1D nanofillers, usually in the form of sheets, have one of their dimensions less than 100 nm. They are widely used in microelectronics, biomedical, biosensors, sensors and coatings because of their excellent magnetic, electrical and optic properties (Li et al., 2017). Examples of nanofillers belonging to the 1D category include montmorillonite (MMT), graphite platelets, ZnO platelets, carbon wall and amphiphilic graphene platelets. The 2D nanofillers exist in the form of fibers, tubes and filaments. They have two dimensions less than 100 nm. They are used in various applications, such as electronics, optoelectronics, energy, catalysis, photocatalysts and nanoreactors. Their flame-retardant property is most effective compared with 1D and 3D nanofillers (Isitman et al., 2012), and present better reinforcement properties compared with 3D nanofillers (Brune & Bicerano, 2002). The 2D nanofillers are used for carbon nanotubes (CNTs), cellulose whiskers, gold or silver nanotubes, 2D graphene and clay nanotubes. Some 2D nanofillers are used for polymer nanocomposites, such as clay fibers (Can et al., 2015; Gupta et al., 2017), cellulose fibers (Fahmy & Mobarak, 2008), nanotubes, natural fibers and silica. The 3D nanofillers have all three dimensions one the nanometer scale. They exist in cubical and spherical shapes, which are generally called nanoparticles (NPs), nanogranules or nanocrystals. They are used to reinforce polymer nanocomposites to improve certain critical properties including good stability, excellent transparency to visible light, ultraviolet (UV) resistance, biomedicine (Di Carlo et al., 2012; Matos et al., 2015), nontoxicity and high photocatalytic activity (Vengatesan, 2016). There are 3D nanofillers for nano-silica, nano-titanium oxide, carbon black and nano-silver.

However, despite the variety and outstanding advantages of nanofillers and polymer nanocomposites, the available and wide popularity of these materials are still far from expectations (Pfaendner, 2010). Thus, the following key evidence is provided to explain for expected delay in development and applications of these materials. Some nanofillers are expensive, have environmental concerns and present limitations in large-scale production. The limitations of the manufacturing process and materials technology, including surface modification of nanofillers, to reach the intended goal also hinder the development of these materials (Natterodt et al., 2017; Scaffaro et al., 2012). The suitability between the nanofillers and the polymer matrix must be carefully considered regarding their application. Therefore, the limitation of polymer matrix choices regarding environmental concerns and reusability also contributes to the unmet expectations(Geyer et al., 2017). Finally, there are limits to the understanding of the relationships between processing and final performance, particularly about how nanofillers could improve some properties of final products.

This chapter presents the preparations, characterizations and reinforcement properties of certain inorganic minerals, such as MMT and silicon dioxide (SiO_2) as well as organic nanofillers, such as cellulose nanocrystals (CNCs), from natural sources to expand the final application for polymer nanocomposites. These nanofillers are purified and extracted from agriculture waste products. They are used as effective renewable reinforcers for polymer nanocomposites because they are low cost, there is a good trade-off between barrier effects and mechanical properties and their use in medical applications. Also, these nanofillers are expected to improve the physicochemical properties, such as rheological, thermal and biodegradation, of those materials.

4.2 PREPARATION OF NANOFILLERS

4.2.1 MONTMORILLONITE (MMT)

Clays are well known to cumulate the following features: low cost, available in large quantities, environmentally friendly and exceptional mechanical properties at a single layer compared with other fillers (Nguyen & Baird, 2006; Thuc et al., 2010). MMT can be purified and separated from clay minerals through different approaches to obtain MMT with particle sizes ranging from 0.1 to 2 μm and an average particle diameter of about 0.5 μm. Some approaches were proposed to obtain the MMT fraction <2 μm, such as magnetic separation and separation based on settling velocity, etc. Some techniques were applied to reduce the MMT particle size, such as ultrasonic treatment (Lapides & Yariv, 2004), centrifugation methods

(Chipera & Bish, 2001) and separation of the coarsest grains from MMT particles (Pacuła et al., 2006). MMT usually exists in a layered structure and is composed of many superimposed layered structures with regular spacing within consecutive layers (d_{001}-spacing) of approximately 10 Å. The d_{001}-spacing between the MMT layers swells in the presence of water and can be enlarged by polar molecules, which are linked to the polarizing surface of the MMT. When d_{001}-spacing is significantly increased, the layers structure breaks to form intercalation/exfoliation structures in polymer nanocomposites, resulting in improvements in their properties (Tombácz et al., 1998; Shen et al., 2007). This is the expected objective of polymer nanocomposites reinforced by MMT or clay minerals to create the 1D nanofillers. However, with hydrophilic polymers, the polymer chains cannot interfere with the inner layer structures of MMT due to immiscibility. MMTs tend to agglomerate due to higher surface energy compared with a polymer matrix (Kádár et al., 2006). To increase the interaction between polymers and MMT, the surface of MMT, or polymers or both should be modified. However, the modification of the MMT surface was reported as the most effective. Accordingly, many modifying agents are selected to modify MMT surfaces, depending on the intended use, with the goal of expanding the d_{001}-spacing of MMT layers, leading to separate layers and dispersion into individual layers (exfoliated). These agents reduce the interlayer cohesive energy and make the interface between MMT and polymers more compatible (Móczó & Pukánszky, 2008). After modifying, the functional groups attached on the MMT surfaces act as effective agents to improve the compatibility and physicochemical properties of polymer nanocomposites (Li et al., 2009; Aghjeh et al., 2016). Therefore, MMT attracted increasing interest for polymer nanocomposites for applications both in academia and industry during the last decade. MMT is still a potential agent for cosmetic, organic removal in wastewater and to reinforce polymer nanocomposites. However, MMT is usually modified by low-molecular-weight agents, which are thermally decomposed first during processing or affect the thermal stability of MMT-reinforced nanocomposites.

4.2.2 Silica Nanoparticles (SiO_2 NPs)

SiO_2, also known as silica, is a compound of silicic acid with interconnected tetrahedral SiO_4 units. SiO_2 can be found naturally and synthesized with amorphous and crystals structures (Martin, 2007; Mallakpour & Marefatpour, 2015a). SiO_2 NPs can be prepared in a relatively simple and cost-effective way with more hydroxyl groups on their surface. They exist in various shapes such as cubes, tubes, meso/micro porous spheres and hollow spheres with a high surface area. SiO_2 NPs have a wide range of emerging applications, and they were used to reinforce polymer nanocomposites and ceramic materials and to gain and improve some properties such as mechanical, biocompatibility, optical UV filtering, abrasion and luminescence (Lin et al., 2010; Kango et al., 2013). The mechanical properties were improved, including rigidity, yield strength and elongation at break of polymer nanocomposites reinforced with SiO_2 NPs (Wang et al., 2014). They could be used as an insulator due to their sizeable band gap energy without electrical conductivity and improvement for strength and durability to cement (Singh et al., 2011). In addition, SiO_2 NPs could be combined with several other metal oxides with photocatalytic activity to remove dyes in wastewater (Haghjoo et al., 2017). Amorphous SiO_2 could be applied in the food and drug industry easily (Gazzano et al., 2012; Pavan et al., 2013) as a contrast agents and as a carrier for drug delivery (Yang et al., 2020).

In previous studies, there are various methods to synthesize SiO_2 NPs, such as sol-gel processing, microemulsion (micelle), flame spray pyrolysis process and others (Mallakpour & Naghdi, 2018). Among these methods, sol-gel is the most used to prepare the SiO_2 NPs because of its low cost, simplicity and versatile ability for controlling particle size, morphology and reaction parameters. For example, SiO_2 NPs were synthesized from tetramethoxysilane (TMOS) and tetraethyl orthosilicate (TEOS) but at the cost of toxicity. Also, SiO_2 NPs were synthesized from agricultural biomass (Adam et al., 2011), rice husk (Le et al., 2013) and fly ash (Mao et al., 2018) using the sol-gel method. However, to increase the extraction efficiency of SiO_2 NPs with uniform size and high surface area through the sol-gel method, certain surfactants are used during the reaction to limit the accumulation of SiO_2 NPs (Mao et al., 2018).

4.2.3 CELLULOSE NANOCRYSTALS (CNCS)

Cellulose is a sustainable and renewable polymer that is derived from plants (Moon et al., 2011), algae (Klemm et al., 2005) and some bacteria (Pacheco et al., 2017; de Lima Fontes et al., 2018). CNCs are well known for their highly crystalline structure and lightweight products with a density of about 1.5–1.6 g·cm^{-3}. They have significant mechanical properties with a Young's modulus of approximately 150 GPa, tensile strength up to 7.5 GPa and bending strength of approximately 10 GPa (Azizi Samir et al., 2004; Jonoobi et al., 2015). CNCs present other very interesting features such as high specific surface, high aspect ratio and low thermal expansion coefficient (Lu et al., 2013). The nanoscale size of cellulose particles induces important changes. The more it decreases, the more specific surface area there is and the total surface energy increases, which, consequently, makes for a good reinforcing material in composite matrices (Mariano et al., 2016). The CNCs possess a rod-like and spherical structure with abundant active hydroxyl groups. Also, these groups can generate a rigid network called a "percolation network" by forming strong hydrogen bonds between them. The different arrangement of the molecules affects not only the surface properties, but also the physical and thermodynamic properties, such as thermal conductivity, solubility, melting point and mechanical (Braga et al., 2009).

In the literature, four methods could be used to synthesize the CNCs: the mechanical process, the chemical process of hydrolysis, the biological process of hydrolysis and the combination of all of these methods (Yang et al., 2019). Among them, the chemical process of hydrolysis is the most common method used to synthesize CNCs. This includes alkali hydrolysis, acid hydrolysis, oxidation degradation and the biological process of hydrolysis. The aim of the hydrolysis process is to break the β-1,4-glucosidic bond connected between the monomers of the cellulose. They strongly attract hydrogen via the covalent modification and break the hydrogen bonds between cellulose macromolecules to form CNCs. The acid hydrolysis is broadly applied internationally (Habibi et al., 2010). However, this method was deemed environmentally unfriendly due to the environmental threat caused by terrible wastes of concentrated acid, water and residual. Therefore, hydrolysis using weak organic acids, including formic acid, oxalic acid and maleic acid, have been used instead to extract CNCs (Wang et al., 2017). Although they regenerate CNCs with a low yield due to the weak acidity of organic acid, this process is more environmentally friendly.

The biological process of hydrolysis was proposed as a revolutionary alternative way to hydrolyze chemicals, in response to the inconveniences caused by chemical hydrolysis. The process is based on enzymatic hydrolysis. Cellulase, which can be secreted by bacteria, could catalyze the degradation of cellulose by cleaving the internal bonds of this polysaccharide chain. It is a mixture of different enzymes with different specificities. Some bacteria have been used in the preparation of the CNCs, such as *Acetobacter*, *Azotobacter*, *Achromobacter* and *Aerobacter* (Shi et al., 2013).

Today, bacteria are increasingly demonstrating their capacity to synthesize CNCs effectively. Depending on the type of bacteria, the characteristics and size of the microcellulose are different. For example, spherical CNCs obtained by catalytic hydrolysis with *Trichoderma viride* G were 2.5–10 nm in diameter (Kar et al., 2015), whereas CNCs obtained from *Gluconacetobacter xylinus* revealed an average length of 325 nm and average diameter of 25 nm. Although the enzymatic hydrolysis requires a long amount of time, this method has increasingly earned researchers' interest all over the world because of its low-cost production and its exceptional physical and chemical properties, including irreplaceable biodegradability.

The source and preparation method strongly influence the size, crystallinity and, in turn, impact the physical and chemical properties of CNCs. For example, the width of CNCs made from wood pulp by acid hydrolysis has a different morphology than wood pulp obtained from alkali hydrolysis (5.7–10.7 nm and 10–100 nm, respectively) (Jasmani & Adnan, 2017). The CNCs from wood pulp and cotton were obtained by acid hydrolysis, and the CNCs cotton width (7 nm) is larger than that of wood pulp (5.7–10.7 nm) (Jasmani & Adnan, 2017). Having an incredible source of raw material, likewise, possessing a large number of interesting properties, CNCs have shown good potential for applications in many fields, such as regenerative medicine, optics and the food industry. More than that, they continue to attract researchers' attention for sustainability, low cost and availability. Interesting CNC properties including biocompatibility and high strength. The biodegradability of this filler is being strongly exploited to invent a large number of basic and advanced products. In conclusion, CNCs have many potential applications in a wide range of areas that would create precious value for society.

4.3 FILLER-REINFORCED POLYMER NANOCOMPOSITES

In general, the polymer nanocomposite-based nanofillers are prepared using different methods, such as solution blending, sol-gel, in situ polymerization and the melting process (Mallakpour & Naghdi, 2018). The nanofillers have a high mechanical strength that possesses impressive mechanical properties and reinforcing capability, making these viable microparticles candidates for the processing of polymer nanocomposites (Habibi et al., 2010). When nanofillers are included in the polymer matrix, their surface can interact with functional groups of polymers, creating a rigid percolation network. However, to design a typical matrix-nanofiller network, there are some requirements (Miao & Hamad, 2016a): (1) nanofillers must be uniformly dispersed in the polymer matrix as individual NPs, (2) the content of nanofillers in the nanocomposite must be above the threshold value to allow the formation of a percolated network of polymer-nanofillers and (3) the formation of a nanofiller network cannot be affected by other factors such as morphology and chemistry of the polymer matrix.

Otherwise, the nanofiller surfaces can be absorbed or grafted with other agents via covalent bonds. The modified nanofillers demonstrated an improvement in polymer nanocomposite properties, which allows researchers to develop novel materials to serve people's needs without damaging the environment.

4.3.1 MECHANICAL PROPERTIES

Mineral nanofillers are well known as a reinforcer for polymer nanocomposites. In general, they improve one of the most important properties of materials, mechanical properties, in a certain concentration. Thus, the mechanical properties of polymer nanocomposite-reinforced CNCs, SiO_2 NPs and MMT are summarized in Table 4.1.

In the last decades, CNCs emerged as renewable and sustainable reinforcers for polymer matrices because of their outstanding mechanical strength and stiffness. In particular, the aggregation effect of CNCs has demonstrated its role in the stiffness of the nanocomposite materials determination. Actually, the stiffness of the materials mainly relates to the percolated CNC network due to strong hydrogen bonding interactions between CNC NPs. Knowing that, this 3D network develops when the content of CNCs is above the percolation threshold. This behavior is totally different from one NP to another, providing different mechanical properties. The second hypothesis was experimentally proved due to tensile strength tests performed on films prepared by water evaporation of nanocrystals (Bras et al., 2011). Results showed a range of obtained values from approximately 1 to 15 GPa; these are fully correlated with the ratio length/diameter (L/D) of nanocrystals. To conclude, any parameter that affects the percolating nanocrystal network formation would also affect the mechanical performance of the composite (Dufresne, 2006). As mentioned above, morphology and dimensions of the micro-NPs can effectively influence the formation because of the difference in the number of free hydroxyl groups presented on their surfaces. These two characteristics sequentially depend on the sources of raw materials and the preparation process of the nanocrystals. The microstructure of the matrix and matrix/filler interactions would also favorably impact the percolation network, and form by chemical coupling.

The reinforcement effects of MMT to polymer nanocomposites are widely reported in the literature. Published results show that the mechanical properties could be remarkably improved when exfoliated MMT nanolayers were homogeneously dispersed in the polymer matrix (Behniafar et al., 2016; Zabihi et al., 2017), which was usually recognized as an explanation of the high stiffness. The reinforcement extent of MMT significantly depends on the MMT nanolayer states in the polymer matrix including exfoliation, intercalation or cluster. The reinforcement is

TABLE 4.1
The Influence of CNCs, SiO$_2$, and MMT on Mechanical Properties of Polymer Nanocomposites

Filler	Matrix	Content (%)	E (GPa)	σ (MPa)	E (%)	Reference
SiO$_2$	Nylon-6	4.1		68.6–102		Alexandre and Dubois (2000)
SiO$_2$	PMMA	12.6		59.0–62.0		Alexandre and Dubois (2000)
SiO$_2$	PP	5.0		31.4–29.5		Alexandre and Dubois (2000)
SiO$_2$	PS	11.3		28.7–21.7		Alexandre and Dubois (2000)
SiO$_2$	PLA	1	1.07–0.88	33.5–38.3	5.8–7.5	Régibeau et al.(2020)
Modified SiO$_2$	PLA	1	1.07–1.33	33.5–53.7	5.8–7.5	Régibeau et al. (2020)
Modified SiO$_2$	PLA	5	1.07–1.25	33.5–42.1	5.8–5.8	Régibeau et al. (2020)
CNCs	PLA	2.5	-	40–51	4.3–5.6	Espino-Pérez et al. (2013)
CNCs	PLA	5	2400–4000	43–46	90–18	Fortunati et al. (2012)
CNCs	PLLA	2	1.1–1.4	48.3–58.6	31.1–8.3	Pei et al. (2010)
CNCs	PHB	5	1.4–1.8	25–23	4–3	Gårdebjer et al. (2015)
CNCs	PLA	5	1.3–1.6	55–54	9–7	Gårdebjer et al. (2015)
CNCs	PBS	0.5	42.1–54.3	0.69–0.83	230–357	Kim et al. (2018)
CNCs	PBAT	10	0.06–0.12	6.3–7.2	10.2–5.8	Morelli et al. (2016)
CNCs	SPS	56.8			-	Ilyas et al. (2020a)
CNCs	SPS	0.1–1.0	0.05–0.18	4.8–11.7		Ilyas, Sapuan, Ishak, and Zainudin (2018)
CNCs	PS	1	0.229	1103	-	Ilyas et al. (2020b)
CNCs	SPS	1	0.12	10.7	-	Ilyas et al. (2019)
CNCs	PP			134		Sabaruddin et al. (2020)
CNCs	AgNPs	4	98E-6	0.4		Rozilah et al. (2020)
CNCs	SBF	1	0.082	2.5		Asrofi et al. (2020)
MMT	ABS/NB	1	1320–1600	25–32	-	Nguyen et al., 2016)
MMT	LDPE/ starch	1	320–510	17–18	750–650	Nguyen et al. (2016)
MMT	PU/PEO	3	3.12–4.28	-	-	Ha Thuc et al. (2014)
MMT	PU/PVA	3	3.12–4.85	-	-	Ha Thuc et al. (2014)

Note: The first value is dedicated to mechanical properties of the polymer matrix and the second one is dedicated to nanocomposites.

most significant when the MMT layers are in the exfoliation state with individual MMT nanolayers and well dispersion in the polymer matrix (Nikolaidis et al., 2012). The exfoliated MMT nanolayers could hinder the motion of the polymer chains, resulting in the enhancement of mechanical properties of polymer nanocomposites. However, it was noted that MMT significantly effects the elongation at break, as this is often opposite to stiffness. The interfacial interactions between MMT nanolayers and functional groups of polymer molecules also improve the mechanical properties of polymer nanocomposites. The good interfacial interactions lead to the effective transfer of interfacial force, resulting in significant improvement of mechanical properties. Therefore, the surface of MMT could be modified to enhance the compatibility between MMT nanofillers and the polymer matrix. For example, the surface of MMT was modified with chitosan to form the covalent bonds and hydrogen bonding with the epoxy matrix (Park & Jana, 2003). When the MMT content was increased significantly, it tended to agglomerate and disperse heterogeneously in the matrix polymer, reducing the mechanical properties of the polymer nanocomposites (Sharma et al., 2017). In particular, the tensile strength of polypropylene (PP)/MMT nanocomposites with 3 wt% MMT reached 49.6 MPa compared with 42.3 MPa for pure PP. However, when the MMT loading was increased above 3 wt%, the tensile strength was reduced due to the agglomeration of MMT, which was weak and acted as initial points for crack propagation (Zhang et al., 2017).

One of the most remarkable properties of nanocomposites incorporated with SiO_2 NPs is the improvement of their mechanical properties compared with matrix polymers. The presence of SiO_2 NPs achieves mechanical property equilibrium, including strength, stiffness and toughness possibly because SiO_2 NPs are in an inorganic phase with a higher mechanical strength than the polymer phase. Therefore, nanocomposites filled by SiO_2 NPs show higher mechanical performance than matrix polymers. In addition, the mechanism of improvement of mechanical properties was proposed with a three-step mechanism, including stress concentration, debonding and shear yielding. Thus, the external force can be absorbed by SiO_2 NPs and transferred to SiO_2 particle neighbors before destroying the materials. The mechanical properties of nanocomposites were also dependent on certain factors, including compatibility between polymers and SiO_2 NPs, concentration, particle size and dispersion state of SiO_2 NPs. The internal interfaces between the polymer and SiO_2 NPs were the most important because they induced the reduction of mechanical performance due to the weakness of connections and immiscibility. In addition, the SiO_2 NP surface could be modified via the sol-gel method for better compatibility and good dispersion into the matrix polymer to enhance the mechanical properties.

4.3.2 Barrier Properties

In the literature, the nanofillers could be used to significantly improve the barrier performance of polymer nanocomposites. Thus, the barrier properties of materials reinforced with CNCs, SiO_2 NPs and MMT are summarized and explained in Table 4.2.

Despite the hydrophilic or hydrophobic character of the polymer matrix, CNCs showed great impact on water resistance of nanocomposite film. For hydrophilic matrices, adding CNCs showed strong hydrogen bonding interactions between CNC surface and functional groups of polymer matrices, which inhibits the diffusion of water molecule diffusion and induces a decrease in water uptake. This was confirmed by studies on different matrices such as plasticized glycerin, plasticized starch and chitosan. For hydrophobic matrices, the behavior is well indicated for polyvinyl acetate or natural rubber. Moreover, the negatively charged surface group resulting from sulfuric acid hydrolysis interestingly sets up permselective properties of the nanocomposite. Logically, as the opposite charge attracts one to another, positive-charged agents are absorbed by the films, and negative-charged molecules are inhibited to transfer through the membranes. This behavior can be applied to the

TABLE 4.2
The Barrier Performances of Polymer Nanocomposite Incorporation with CNCs, SiO$_2$ NPs and MMT

Nanofiller	Matrix	Results and Conclusions	References
CNCs	PLA film	The barrier properties of CNC-PLA films significantly improved compared with pure PLA due to good compatibility and dispersion of CNCs. The films with 1 wt% CNC could improve the oxygen and moisture barrier performance of CNC-PLA films closer to those of PET, PVC, LDPE and HDPE	Miao and Hamad (2016b)
Modified CNCs	PLA	CNCs act as blocking agents in polymers, promoting a tortuous path to permeation of water and gas molecules, improving the barrier performance	Ambrosio-Martín, Fabra et al. (2015)
CNCs	PCL film	Good dispersion of CNCs within the PCL film leads to higher tortuosity effects, improving the barrier properties	Follain et al. (2013)
CNCs	PLA	Water permeability decreased by 82% and oxygen permeability reduced by 90% when adding CNC in PLA	Sanchez-Garcia and Lagaron (2010)
Modified CNCs	PLA	O$_2$ permeability was not reduced after the addition of modified CNCs into PLA; this can be related to the permeability value of the neat polymer	Gunatillake and Adhikari (2003)
CNCs	PLA	Improvements in barrier properties with increased crystallinity due to the addition of CNCs	Fortunati et al. (2013)
CNCs	PBS and PBSA	The improvement of barrier properties of the polymer was related to the changes in its crystallinity due to the addition of the CNCs	Charlon et al. (2015)
Modified CNCs	PLA	The tortuosity effect of CNC on the oxygen barrier properties is limited, but there was significant improvement in the water vapor barrier properties	Espino-Pérez et al. (2018)
Modified CNC	PCL	The permeability and diffusivity of the gases N$_2$, O$_2$ and CO$_2$ were increased because of structural defects in the interface between PCL and CNCs, facilitating the gas transfer	Follain et al. (2018)
SiO$_2$ NPs		Unoccupied areas at the border of the SiO$_2$ surface and the polymer phase caused the passing of gases. This was solved by improving interfacial interaction by using a coupling agent for SiO$_2$ and the polymer	Goh et al. (2011)
SiO$_2$ NPs	Ethylene-vinyl acetate	A significant increase in permeability of N$_2$, O$_2$, and CH$_4$ gases and an increase in the selectivity of CO$_2$ when increasing the SiO$_2$ content. Thus, increasing SiO$_2$ content, leads to an increase in the available sorption sites and pathways at the interfaces and in the SiO$_2$ domains for the polar gases	Sadeghi et al. (2008)
SiO$_2$ NPs	polyether-PU membranes	The permeability of membranes for CO$_2$, CH$_4$, N$_2$ and O$_2$ was decreased by increasing the content of SiO$_2$ NPs, but it increases in CO$_2$/N$_2$ and CO$_2$/CH$_4$ selectivity	Sadeghi et al. (2011)

Nanofiller	Matrix	Observations	Reference
SiO$_2$ NPs	Polybenzimidazole (PBI) membrane	The diffusivity of the gases in the nanocomposite membrane was decreased due to the obstructions induced by SiO$_2$ NPs. However, 20 wt% SiO$_2$ NPs were added into membrane, and the permeability of CO$_2$ increased 4.5 times and selectivity of CO$_2$/N$_2$ increased 20 times	Sadeghi et al. (2009)
SiO$_2$ NPs	PU membranes	The PU membranes were reinforced by SiO$_2$ NPs, leading to an increase in CO$_2$/N$_2$ selectivity and the potential for commercial applications	Favvas et al. (2007)
SiO$_2$ NPs	Epoxy and polydimethylsiloxane coatings	The superior barrier performances of nanocomposite coatings incorporated with SiO$_2$ NPs were obtained due to the hydrophobic character and excellent intercalated structure of matrix and nanofillers	Ammar et al. (2017)
MMT	Polymer matrix	MMT nanolayers were considered as large 2D platy inorganic particles that could act against the penetration of gases and water, leading to the barrier performance of polymer matrix	Zhu et al. (2019)
MMT	Epoxy/glass fibers	The MMT was used to reinforce the epoxy/glass fiber composite; the water resistance performance of the composites was increased by providing the tortuous pathways with the presence of MMT nanofillers	Mohammed and Issa (2016)
Silicate	Polyimide	The nanocomposite films with exfoliated structure produced with high aspect ratio layered silicates have the capacity to reduce gas permeability	Lan et al. (1994)
Silicate platelets	Polymer matrices	The barrier performance of nanocomposites is related to the intercalation or exfoliation structure, namely the orientation and dispersion of silicate platelets at nanometer sizes in the polymer matrix	Lu and Mai (2005)
Clay	Carboxymethylcellulose films	The addition of nanoclays dramatically improves the water vapor barrier properties of carboxymethyl/cellulose films: there was up to a fivefold decrease in permeability. The potential films can be used as food packaging materials, including edible applications	de Melo Fiori et al. (2019)
MMT	SBR	The gas permeability of modified clay nanofiller-filled SBR nanocomposites showed the best barrier properties due to high aspect ratio and good dispersion, leading to an increase in tortuosity and reduction in free volume	Bhattacharya et al. (2011)
Rectorite (clay)	NR	The gas barrier properties of the nanocomposites with rectorite-clay were remarkably improved compared with pure NR. This was attributed to the reduction of the permeable amorphous rubber portion and the increase in tortuosity of the diffusion path for penetrant molecules	Wang et al. (2005)
MMT	Polymer matrix	MMT nanolayers were considered as large 2D platy inorganic particles that could act against the penetration of gases and water, leading to the barrier performance of polymer matrix	Zhu et al. (2019)

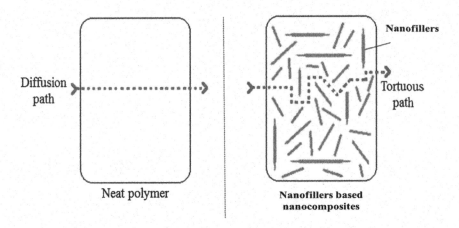

FIGURE 4.1 Schematic of the tortuous path for gas and water molecules to diffuse through polymer matrix due to the addition of nanofillers. (Reproduced with copyright permission from Ferreira et al. 2018.)

water purification industry (Ma et al., 2011). Thus, the CNCs act as blocking agents in polymers, promoting a tortuous path to permeating water and gas molecules, improving the barrier performance as described in Figure 4.1. The good dispersion of CNCs within the polymer matrix also leads to changes in crystallinity of polymers, leading to improved barrier properties.

In addition, the natural impermeability of MMT increases the barrier performances of polymer nanocomposites by providing a tortuous path that delays the diffusion of the gas and water molecules by the polymer matrix. In addition, the large layered inorganic clays are usually impermeable to water and gases across the layer thickness, which provide an excellent barrier for polymer nanocomposites. The addition of exfoliated MMT nanolayers into the polymers matrix also contributes to the increase of diffusion length pathways, for both gas and water, and decreases the permeability of the nanocomposites.

The barrier performances of MMT-nanocomposites are significantly dependent on MMT concentrations, the dispersion extent of MMT and the intercalation or exfoliated structure of MMT in polymer nanocomposites. In the previous studies, it was reported that the exfoliated nanocomposite-based poly(lactic acid) (PLA) and poly(butylene succinate) (PBS) and 7 wt% MMT had permeability reduced by 40% for O_2 and by 50% for the water vapor (Risse et al., 2014). The oxygen permeability of nanocomposite-based high-density polyethylene (HDPE) films was decreased as MMT concentration increased at 15wt% (Horst et al., 2012). The exfoliation of modified MMT/poly(3-hydroxybutyrate-co-3-hydroxyvalerate) nanocomposites showed a low water vapor transmission rate (WVTR) value at 26.4 g/m²/day, which was suitable for green-based packaging (Farmahini-Farahani et al., 2015). The modified MMT was used to reinforce canola protein to improve barrier properties and adhesion strength. It could also act as an anticorrosive coating (Bandara et al., 2017).

Similarly, to CNCs and MMT, SiO_2 NPs were also used to improve the barrier properties of polymer nanocomposites, particularly permeability and selectivity. In addition, the surface modification of NPs using coupling agents to enhance the interfacial interaction between the polymer matrix and SiO_2 was proposed to improve the barrier performance of SiO_2-nanocomposites. However, increase in the voids (free volumes) through the interaction between the hydroxyl groups of the SiO_2 surface was also reported. Consequently, polar gases such as CO_2 and SO_2 tend to penetrate the gas within the nanocomposite membranes (Mallakpour & Naghdi, 2018).

4.3.3 Thermal Stability

The nanofillers were reported as agents that increase the thermal stability of polymer nanocomposites. Thus, the influence of CNCs, SiO_2 NPs and MMT on thermal decomposition of polymer nanocomposites was highlighted in Table 4.3.

TABLE 4.3
The Influence of CNCs, SiO_2 NPs and MMT on Thermal Decomposition of Polymer Nanocomposites

Nanofiller	Matrix	Results and Comments	References
CNCs	Polyether sulfone (PES)	The thermal stability of PES/CNC nanocomposite membrane was reduced compared with pure PES membrane. This is due to the lower thermal decomposition of CNCs	Zhang et al. (2018)
CNCs	Starch	Thermal stability of starch/CNC nanocomposites did not change compared with pure starch film	de Souza Coelho et al. (2020)
SiO_2	PVA	PVA nanocomposites with different modified SiO_2 NP contents showed an improvement of thermal stability due to high dispersion of the modified SiO_2 in the PVA, and the creation of the hydrogen bonds between hydroxyl groups in the PVA matrix and functional groups on the SiO_2 surface	Mallakpour and Marefatpour (2015b)
SiO_2	LDPE	The thermal decomposition of nanocomposites-based LDPE with 3% modified SiO_2 NPs was delayed compared with that of unmodified SiO_2 due to the higher thermo-oxidative stability of modified SiO_2 NPs, which act as a barrier for thermo-oxidative degradation of the nanocomposites	Liu et al. (2017)
SiO_2	PCL	An improvement of thermal stability of nanocomposites-based PCL was reported as a good dispersion of the SiO_2 NPs in the PCL matrix and hydrogen bonds between the functional groups of the PCL and surface-modified SiO_2, and it enhanced temperature degradation of the nanocomposite films	Mallakpour and Khani (2018)
SiO_2	PVA	Thermal stability of PVA-based nanocomposites with 9 wt% SiO_2 NPs was observed and attributed to partial agglomerations and less homogeneity of SiO_2.	Mallakpour and Nazari (2018)

(Continued)

TABLE 4.3 (*Continued*)
The Influence of CNCs, SiO$_2$ NPs and MMT on Thermal Decomposition of Polymer Nanocomposites

Nanofiller	Matrix	Results and Comments	References
SiO$_2$	PMMA/PVA	The thermal stability of synthesized nanocomposite film PMMA/PVA/SiO$_2$ NPs was found below 110°C. This finding provides a pathway for the application of optical and optoelectronic devices	Alsaad et al. (2020)
MMT	Acrylic polymer	The weight (%) of the thermal decomposition of clay/polymer nanocomposites was decreased with clay incorporation, especially at the second stage of degradation over the range of 75%–34%	Serge et al. (2019)
MMT	Poly(propylene carbonate)	The thermal stability of nanofiller nanocomposites was remarkably improved compared with polymer matrix because the uniform dispersion of nanofillers and the inhibition heat transfer of nanofillers in the matrix	Wang et al. (2020)
MMT	Chitosan	The higher thermal stability of chitosan/MMT composites was attributed to the high thermal stability of MMT and the interaction between the MMT particles and chitosan	Han et al. (2010)
MMT	Chitosan/lactic acid films	The highest thermal decomposition of MMT-Na/chitosan-g-lactic acid films was observed with 5 and 10 wt% clay contents. This is because clay is a superior insulator and a barrier to mass transport during decomposition. Then, thermal stability was reduced as clay loads increased	Depan et al. (2006)
MMT	Poly(butyl acrylate)/chitosan	The TRIAB-modified MMT was reported to have inherently excellent thermal and barrier properties. It prevents rapid heat transmission, limiting the continuous decomposition of the poly(butyl acrylate)/chitosan nanocomposites.	Yu et al. (2004)
MMT	Plasticized thermoplastic starch	The thermal stability of glycerol-plasticized thermoplastic starch (GTPS) was significantly improved with 30 wt% MMT. This is attributed to the homogeneous dispersion of silicate layers in the GTPS matrix	Huang et al. (2004)
MMT	Thermoplastic starch (TPS)	The improvement of thermal stability of nanocomposites is attributed to the barrier effect of the high aspect ratio of the clay platelets dispersed, resulting in delaying the escape of volatile degradation products from the nanocomposites	Schlemmer et al. (2010)
Clay	Starch/glycerol films	The thermal stability of Cara starch/glycerol/clays platelets films did not change	Wilhelm et al. (2003)
Clay	Starch	No significant change in thermal stabilities was observed for starch with pure and modified nanoclays	Zeppa et al. (2009)

Accordingly, the intermolecular bonding between the nanocellulose crystals and the polymer matrix actively influences the thermal stability of the materials by enhancing the dissociation energy needed for cleavage of the linking. By adding CNCs to the poly(alcohol vinylique) matrix, the nanocomposites showed an improvement in terms of thermal stability due to the hydrogen bonds created through the complexes (Mandal & Chakrabarty, 2014). This result was also obtained in the previous study (Mondragon et al., 2015) when the authors added the nanocrystals in the gelatin matrix with an augmentation of the degradation temperature by 7°C–9°C. However, different trends have been found in other experiments (Nagalakshmaiah, 2016), in which a diminution in thermal stability in CNC/PVOH nanocomposites was observed. This fact can be attributed to the surface sulfation of CNCs through sulfuric acid hydrolysis. They compared the sulfate group effects on the sulfated and desulfated CNCs incorporated into the polymer for thermal stability. The sulfated nanocellulose demonstrated a lower decomposition temperature than nanocellulose without sulfates. The sulfate groups are therefore considered as a catalyst in degrading nanocellulose, leading to the lower decomposition temperature. On the other hand, when blending CNCs with hydrophobic matrices such as polylactic acid (PLA) and polyethylene (PE), the nanocellulose tends to agglomerate due to the lack of functional groups for binding. This agglomeration is in turn responsible for the poor interfacial adhesion and inhomogeneous dispersion of CNCs in the matrices, and, consequently, decreases the thermal stability of the nanocomposites. A clear example of this is the decreased thermal stability in CNCs incorporated into Cariflex isoprene rubber latex, which is revealed in the study by Nagalakshmaiah et al. (2016).

4.3.4 Flame Retardancy

In terms of safety problems, the flame retardancy of the materials is always a serious issue for researchers. Polymers such as PP, PE, polystyrene (PS), etc., are highly flammable. Flame retardants are commonly added to the matrices inducing low fire prevention capacity. The most widely useful flame retardants are inorganic reactive fillers and halogenated compounds. Inorganic fillers decrease the mechanical properties of the materials, while halogenated compounds release toxic gases to the environment. The CNCs could not act as an effective flame retardant for the polymer matrix. However, even though CNCs are not good as a flame-reducing agent, their capacity to combine with other chemical molecules allows them to provide flame retardancy. The CNCs were coated with ZnO NPs into the HDPE matrix at different concentrations changing from 0.4% to 10%. Results showed that CNC-grafted ZnO was able to slow down the fire burning and performed as a flame retardant, which is verified by decreasing the average mass loss, peak heat release rate and total smoke release compared with pure polymer (Bajwa et al., 2019). On the other hand, nanocomposite-incorporated CNCs coated with graphene oxide or clay can act as flame-blocking materials (Wicklein et al., 2015). CNCs that were treated by silylation boosted the production of char, which can block propagation of fire (Liu & Berglund, 2013).

In addition, the CNCs were incorporated with skeleton to synthesize a nanofibrous flame retardant (Feng et al., 2017), which increased flame resistance for PLA to achieve a V-0 with only 10% of flame retardant. The CNCs were also combined with polyphosphate (APP) to create novel flame retardant, which improved flame retardancy of PLA to achieve the UL-94 V-0 rating with a high limiting oxygen index (LOI) of 27.5% (Yin et al., 2018). This was attributed to the interaction between ammonium polyphosphate and CNCs and good dispersion of ammonium polyphosphate/CNCs in the PLA matrix. In conclusion, CNCs are not flame retardant, but they can be combined with other partners to create novel green flame retardants. This demonstrates that CNCs can be used as a promising agent for developing flame-retardant polymer nanocomposites. The functionalized CNCs are synthesized and used as flame retardants for polymers; however, the functionalized CNTs showed an insignificant improvement at a very low content of approximately 1 wt%. Thus, the synthesis and flame-retardant mechanism of the flame retardants based on CNCs are presented in Figure 4.2.

MMT is well known to be an effective flame retardant in forms of layered silicates or nanoclay for polymer nanocomposites. It was reported that the incorporation of layered silicates into the polymer matrix gained good flame retardance nanocomposites (Ma et al., 2007; Kiliaris & Papaspyrides, 2010). In fact, because the MMT surface is not polar, it is usually modified with low-molecular substances to improve the interfacial compatibility with the polymer matrix (Pavlidou & Papaspyrides, 2008).

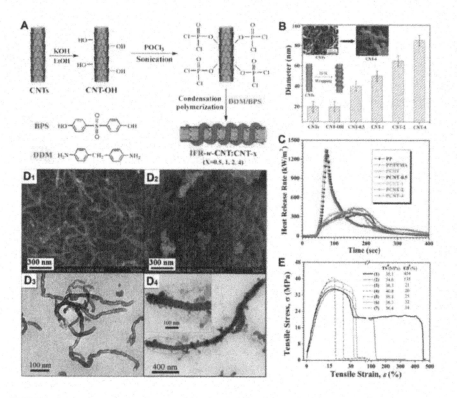

FIGURE 4.2 The approaches of synthetic functionalized CNCs (CNCs-x), characterization and its application of fire retardancy of the polymer matrix with 1 wt% CNT or CNT-x. (Reproduced with copyright permission from He et al. 2020.)

Unfortunately, these agents are highly flammable, which negatively affected the flame resistance of nanocomposites based on modified MMT. The flame-retardant mechanism of MMT in nanocomposites was reported to be tied to its physical barrier effect. This means that during the burning process the layered MMT forms a thermally insulated protection layer, which significantly slows down the burning process of the polymer (Fina et al. 2012). Along with the physical barrier effect, it was found that the flame-retardant mechanism of MMT is achieved by the dripping of molten MMT/nanocomposites during combustion. In addition, to improve the fire resistance of nanocomposites, MMT has been combined with several compounds to create new flame retardants with high activity, including halogenated compounds (Chen et al., 2009), metal hydroxides (Beyer, 2001), etc. Thus, the synergistic effect of MMT and its partners on flame retardancy of nanocomposites was to form a char barrier during burning, which was responsible for enhancing flame retardancy for nanocomposites.

The SiO_2 NPs have flame-retardant ability when they are added into the polymer matrix (Masjedi-Arani et al., 2016). The flame-retardant mechanism of SiO_2 NPs/nanocomposites was analyzed as the role of Si-O-Si layers, which act as an obstacle against flame and oxygen approaches. The Si-O-Si network layers are formed at the middle and later stages during the burning of nanocomposites. These layers are responsible for the fire resistance of nanocomposites (Wang et al., 2010). The fire resistance of SiO_2 NPs has been significantly enhanced through their surface modifications. The SiO_2 surface was doped with H_3PO_4 or H_2SO_4 and then, they were used as flame retardants for epoxy resins (Gu et al., 2013). At 5 wt% of modified SiO_2 NPs, the flame retardancy and the thermal stability of nanocomposite-based epoxy was significantly increased by 37°C–72°C in both air and nitrogen atmospheres. In addition, the SiO_2 NP surface was immobilized using bis (4-aminophenoxy) phenyl phosphine oxide to form the novel flame retardant to increase the char layer yield during burning (Kawahara et al., 2013). The SiO_2 surface was also modified using 2,3,4,5-tetrabromo-6-[(4-hydroxyphenyl) carbamoyl] benzoic acid as an effective flame retardant for the poly(amide-imide) (PAI) matrix (Chigwada & Wilkie, 2003). The thermal stability of nanocomposite-based PAI was significantly enhanced compared with pure PAI, and the nanocomposite was classified as the self-extinguishing materials through the fire test method (LOI values).

4.3.5 BIOMEDICAL APPLICATIONS

Apart from applications as biomaterials and in the sectors of the food industry, wastewater treatment or energy and electronics, CNCs have also been modified for biomedical applications. Countless research and development has confirmed its effectiveness in the biomedical sectors. Here are some of the promising applications for the recent use of CNCs in health protection. By binding directly or indirectly with drugs, such as hydrophobic interactions, covalent modifications or encapsulating drugs or even ionic bonds, CNCs are known as the drug carrier in pharmaceutical applications. Research shows that CNCs facilitate drug delivery. Binding with tetracycline and doxorubicin via ionic interactions improve the complete release of a drug in one day (Jackson et al., 2011). In the study, the grafted CNCs/chitosan oligosaccharides utilized for loading procaine hydrochloride released the drug within 1 hour at pH 8 (Akhlaghi et al., 2013). In the case of cetyltrimethylammonium bromide (CTAB), when this agent neutralized its positive charge with negatively charged CNCs, the hydrophobic binding with the anticancer drugs, e.g., docetaxel, paclitaxel and etoposide, is enhanced. Consequently, these drugs could increase the release time over 2 days. The study also indicated that the complexes were able to bind to KU-7 cells and strengthen the drug uptake (Wicklein et al., 2015). CNCs improve not only the delivery of drugs, by inducing a fast response, but also their activity. Compared with pure curcumin, complexes of b-cyclodextrin-modified CNCs can become hydrophobic curcumin, which demonstrated enhanced cytotoxic effects against colorectal and prostatic cancer cell lines (García-García et al., 2018). In addition, CNCs are grafted with poly(ethyl ethylene phosphate) for the loading of the antitumor drug doxorubicin (DOX) and delivered it to cancer cells. The result shows that as the complexes circulated within the body, their anticancer activity was at LC_{50} of 9.95 mg doxorubicin equiv. L^{-1} for HeLa cells compared with 6.38 mg doxorubicin equiv. L^{-1} for free doxorubicin (Wang et al., 2015).

For decades, silver NPs (AgNPs) have been well known for their antibacterial properties by killing both gram-negative and gram-positive bacteria, but their trend to form aggregation in aqueous solutions limits their applications. Therefore, immobilizing AgNPs on a stable substrate is the optimal solution to enhance their antibacterial characteristics. A study of immobilization of AgNPs on polydopamine-coated CNCs (PD-CNCs) demonstrated that the minimum inhibitory concentration (MIC) for *Escherichia coli* (gram-negative) and *Bacillus subtilis* (gram-positive) of AgNP-PD-CNCs was four times lower than its AgNPs. In other words, PD-CNCs improve the AgNPs ability to inhibit bacterial growth. This occurs when polydopamine is bound with CNCs and these complexes improve their adhesion to the surface of bacteria and reduce the aggregation of AgNPs simultaneously. The antibacterial activity is thereby ameliorated. CNCs can also attach to many other agents, such as polymers, porphyrin, lectin or functional groups that inhibit viral infection. The antiviral activity of CNCs was strongly expressed in the previous experiment (Zoppe et al., 2014). The authors first tested the activity of CNCs decorated with anionic sulfate groups to inhibit alphavirus infectivity in Vero (B) cells. The results depicted a strong inhibitory effect up to 100% for cotton CNCs and 88% for Whatman CNCs. Moreover, the viral inhibition was significantly better when sulfate groups were exchanged for tyrosine sulfate mimetic groups. To ensure CNCs were not harmful for the body, the cytotoxicity test was conducted using the CellTiter Blue assay demonstrating a negligible effect.

CNCs have been exploited in several applications for tissue engineering, including bone tissue regeneration, improving bone-implant adhesion and injectable tissue scaffolds. In a previous experiment (Yang et al., 2013), the authors successfully developed hydrogels containing CNCs modified with pristine and aldehyde and adipic acid dihydrazide-modified carboxymethyl cellulose and aldehyde-modified dextran. With the presence of CNCs, the elastic moduli of hydrogels were improved by 140%. Beyond that, as their duration for water resistance is 60 days, and the cytotoxic effect to 3T3 fibroblast cells was tested to be insignificant, the hydrogels are suitable for applying to tissue scaffolds. CNCs were also used to produce Nano-(HAp)/CNC/silk fibroin by chemical grafting or coated with bioactive glass to regenerate a calvarial bone defect in rats. Also, the bioactive glass-modified CNCs are indicated to enhance adhesion and proliferation of MC313-E1 cells throughout cell culture tests, making them a good candidate for bone implant adhesion.

In another field, biosensors have been widely used in medical diagnostics for a long time. For CNCs, due to the reactive hydroxyl groups on their surface, they can consequently adhere to selective nanomaterials providing sensing capabilities. For instance, CNCs synthesized by TEMPO are used in CNCs/L-Cys/Au electrodes that detect enantiomers of Phe, Leu and Val amino acids. The electrodes with CNCs showed higher adsorption capacities for D-amino acids compared with L-amino acids. The sensor is of practical use for detecting type 2 diabetes serum, especially due to the prevalent availability of these three amino acids in the serum of patients with the disease. Furthermore, Ag-Pd/carboxylated CNCs are used as a trademark for electrical detection of DNA hybridization, or as labeled DNA probes, to identify the complementary target DNA sequence. Fluorescent dye-modified CNCs are developed and demonstrated as biomarkers in immunocompetent mice. This can be explained by the migration of modified CNCs to the bones in limbs because of the electrostatic interaction with Ca^{2+} in the bone matrix, making the bone a target for the detection of related disease.

On the other hand, clay mineral is an available natural resource and was used in medical applications a long time ago, including drug delivery, protecting drugs against chemical and enzymes attack and extending the drug release process. Thus, drugs were encapsulated in clay minerals, which allowed the rate and the drug release process to be controlled (Lazzara et al., 2017), increasing the product shelf-life and reduction of side effects (Aguzzi et al., 2007). Clay is modified with non-toxic agents, especially of biological origins, like lecithin and chitosan, to produce appropriate organo-clay for environmental and biomedical applications such as tissue scaffolds, drug delivery vehicles and vaccine adjuvants. It was proven that clay minerals are non-toxic for oral administration and transdermal application (Lvov et al., 2016). They could also be used to cure wounds and as antiseptics and anti-inflammatory agents (Lazzara et al., 2017). In addition, clay minerals could be used as delivery systems in clinical medicine, as potential drug carriers and as commercialized pharmaceutical products (Ariga et al., 2017). Some popular clay minerals including MMT, kaolin and sepiolite are usually used for medical application because of their particle's colloidal dimensions, high surface areas and an empty cavity that can encapsulate drug molecules. Halloysite clay nanotubes (HNTs) are effective in the drug loading process compared with clay minerals and MMT because their aluminosilicate kaolin sheets are rolled 15–20 times (Lvov et al., 2016). The mechanism of drug loading and release of this material is based on opposing charges inside and outside the lumen and they act as nanocarriers. Moreover, the anticancer drug DOX was produced from kaolin to reduce toxicity and enhance the efficiency of drug release. The clay-DOX reaction was based on the negative charge on clays and the positive charge on DOX (Lazzara et al., 2017).

Similar to CNCs and clay, SiO_2 NPs are also of interest for their applications in drug delivery, cosmetics and medical applications. It was reported that SiO_2 NPs have unique properties such as porous structure, surface functionality, controllable particle size, high surface area, chemical stability and biocompatibility (Kilpeläinen et al., 2009; Wang et al., 2013). In the application of drug delivery, the drug release of SiO_2 NPs could be controlled by the microenvironment such as by pH or oxidation. The SiO_2 NP surface was modified to enhance applications such as the

DOX-modified silica NPs combined through a hydrazone linkage and used as drug delivery system for anticancer medications (Zhang & Kong, 2015). The incorporation of SiO$_2$ NP-protein was also developed to provide more efficient drug delivery systems for disease treatment (Mirshafiee et al., 2016). Mesoporous silica NPs have been developed due to their significant benefits such as no considerable toxicity, biocompatibility and use as organic drug carriers (Ghosh et al., 2021). Recently, polymer nanocomposites incorporated with SiO$_2$ NPs were widely studied for anticancer drugs and drug delivery applications (Hao et al., 2015) due to their negative surface potential, which could be easily coated with a positive charged anticancer drug (Blanco et al., 2015). Additionally, SiO$_2$ NPs have been able to combine with other potential agents to increase antibacterial and anticancer abilities. Thus, the asymmetric mesoporous silica NPs Fe$_3$O$_4$@SiO$_2$&EPMO are successfully developed via an anisotropic epitaxial growth; the incorporation was significantly efficient for killing cancer cells and exhibited an excellent antibacterial activity (Figure 4.3).

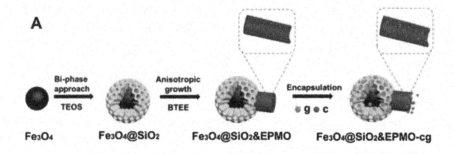

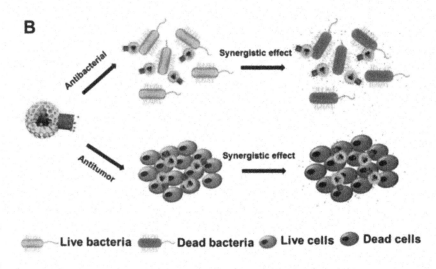

FIGURE 4.3 Synthesis of asymmetric mesoporous silica nanoparticles Fe$_3$O$_4$@SiO$_2$&EPMO for antibacterial and anticancer dual drugs. (Reproduced with copyright permission from Cheng et al., 2020.)

4.4 CONCLUSIONS

This chapter presents an overview of the applications of naturally derived NPs, including inorganic minerals such as MMT, SiO$_2$ NPs and organic NPs such as CNCs. The NPs are synthesized from agricultural by-products through facile approaches. They have the potential for wide application in polymer nanocomposites compared with polymer matrices to significantly improve many properties, such as mechanical, fire resistance, gas and water barrier, thermal stability and medical and anticancer and antibacterial applications.

ACKNOWLEDGMENTS

This research is funded by Vietnam National University HoChiMinh City (VNU-HCM) under grant number GEN 2019-48- 02.

REFERENCES

Adam, F., Chew, T.-S., and Andas, J. 2011. "A simple template-free sol–gel synthesis of spherical nanosilica from agricultural biomass." *Journal of Sol-Gel Science and Technology* 59(3): 580–583. https://doi.org/10.1007/s10971-011-2531-7

Aghjeh, M. R., Asadi, V., Mehdijabbar, P., Khonakdar, H. A., and Jafari, S. H. 2016. "Application of linear rheology in determination of nanoclay localization in PLA/EVA/Clay nanocomposites: Correlation with microstructure and thermal properties." *Composites Part B: Engineering* 86: 273–284. https://doi.org/10.1016/j.compositesb.2015.09.064

Aguzzi, C., Cerezo, P., Viseras, C., and Caramella, C. 2007. "Use of clays as drug delivery systems: Possibilities and limitations." *Applied Clay Science* 36(1): 22–36. https://doi.org/10.1016/j.clay.2006.06.015

Akhlaghi, S. P., Berry, R. C., and Tam, K. C. 2013. "Surface modification of cellulose nanocrystal with chitosan oligosaccharide for drug delivery applications." *Cellulose* 20(4): 1747–1764. https://doi.org/10.1007/s10570-013-9954-y

Alexandre, M., and Dubois, P. 2000. "Polymer-layered silicate nanocomposites: preparation, properties and uses of a new class of materials." *Materials Science and Engineering: R: Reports* 28(1): 1–63. https://doi.org/10.1016/S0927-796X(00)00012-7

Alsaad, A. M., Ahmad, A. A., Dairy, A. R. A., Al-anbar, A. S., and Al-Bataineh, Q. M. 2020. "Spectroscopic characterization of optical and thermal properties of (PMMA-PVA) hybrid thin films doped with SiO2 nanoparticles." *Results in Physics* 19: 103463. https://doi.org/10.1016/j.rinp.2020.103463

Ambrosio-Martín, J., Fabra, M. J., Lopez-Rubio, A., and Lagaron, J. M. 2015. "Melt polycondensation to improve the dispersion of bacterial cellulose into polylactide via melt compounding: enhanced barrier and mechanical properties." *Cellulose* 22(2): 1201–1226. https://doi.org/10.1007/s10570-014-0523-9

Ammar, S., Ramesh, K., Ma, I. A. W., Farah, Z., Vengadaesvaran, B., Ramesh, S., and Arof, A. K. 2017. "Studies on SiO$_2$-hybrid polymeric nanocomposite coatings with superior corrosion protection and hydrophobicity." *Surface and Coatings Technology* 324: 536–545. https://doi.org/10.1016/j.surfcoat.2017.06.014

Ariga, K., Abe, H., Ji, Q., and Lvov, Y. M. 2017. "Chapter 7 Halloysite and related mesoporous carriers for advanced catalysis and drug delivery." In *Functional Polymer Composites with Nanoclays*, pp. 207–222. The Royal Society of Chemistry. https://doi.org/10.1039/9781782626725-00207

Asrofi, M., Sapuan, S. M., Ilyas, R. A., and Ramesh, M. 2020. "Characteristic of composite bioplastics from tapioca starch and sugarcane bagasse fiber: effect of time duration of ultrasonication (bath-type)." *Materials Today: Proceedings* 46: 1626–1630. https://doi.org/10.1016/j.matpr.2020.07.254

Attaran, S. A., Hassan, A., and Wahit, M. U. 2015. "Materials for food packaging applications based on bio-based polymer nanocomposites: A review." *Journal of Thermoplastic Composite Materials* 30(2): 143–173. https://doi.org/10.1177/0892705715588801

Azizi Samir, M. A. S., Alloin, F., Sanchez, J.-Y., El Kissi, N., and Dufresne, A. 2004. "Preparation of cellulose whiskers reinforced nanocomposites from an organic medium suspension." *Macromolecules* 37(4):1386–1393. https://doi.org/10.1021/ma030532a

Bajwa, D. S., Rehovsky, C., Shojaeiarani, J., Stark, N., Bajwa, S., and Dietenberger, M. A. 2019. "Functionalized cellulose nanocrystals: a potential fire retardant for polymer composites." *Polymers (Basel)* 11(8): 1361. https://doi.org/10.3390/polym11081361

Bandara, N., Esparza, Y., and Wu, J. 2017. "Exfoliating nanomaterials in canola protein derived adhesive improves strength and water resistance." *RSC Advances* 7(11): 6743–6752. https://doi.org/10.1039/C6RA27470F

Behniafar, H., Ahmadi-khaneghah, A., and Yazdi, M. 2016. "Enhanced heat stability and storage modulus in novel PTMO-intercalated clay platelets/PTMO-based polyurethane nanocomposites." *Journal of Polymer Research* 23(9): 202. https://doi.org/10.1007/s10965-016-1097-z

Beyer, G. 2001. "Flame retardant properties of EVA-nanocomposites and improvements by combination of nanofillers with aluminium trihydrate." *Fire and Materials* 25(5): 193–197. https://doi.org/10.1002/fam.776

Bhattacharya, M., Biswas, S., and Bhowmick, A. K. 2011. "Permeation characteristics and modeling of barrier properties of multifunctional rubber nanocomposites." *Polymer* 52(7): 1562–1576. https://doi.org/10.1016/j.polymer.2011.01.055

Blanco, E., Shen, H., and Ferrari, M. 2015. "Principles of nanoparticle design for overcoming biological barriers to drug delivery." *Nature Biotechnology* 33(9): 941–951. https://doi.org/10.1038/nbt.3330

Braga, D., Grepioni, F., Maini, L., and Polito, M. 2009. "Crystal polymorphism and multiple crystal forms." In *Molecular Networks*, edited by M. W. Hosseini, pp. 87–95. Berlin, Heidelberg: Springer Berlin. doi: 10.1007/430_2008_7

Bras, J., Viet, D., Bruzzese, C., and Dufresne, A. 2011. "Correlation between stiffness of sheets prepared from cellulose whiskers and nanoparticles dimensions." *Carbohydrate Polymers* 84(1): 211–215. https://doi.org/10.1016/j.carbpol.2010.11.022

Brune, D. A., and Bicerano, J. 2002. "Micromechanics of nanocomposites: comparison of tensile and compressive elastic moduli, and prediction of effects of incomplete exfoliation and imperfect alignment on modulus." *Polymer* 43(2): 369–387. https://doi.org/10.1016/S0032-3861(01)00543-2

Can, M. F., Avdan, L., and Bedeloglu, A. C. 2015. "Properties of biodegradable PVA/sepiolite-based nanocomposite fiber mats." *Polymer Composites* 36(12): 2334–2342. https://doi.org/10.1002/pc.23147

Chang, L., Zhang, Z., Ye, L., and Friedrich, K. 2007. "Tribological properties of epoxy nanocomposites: III. Characteristics of transfer films." *Wear* 262(5): 699–706. https://doi.org/10.1016/j.wear.2006.08.002

Charlon, S., Follain, N., Chappey, C., Dargent, E., Soulestin, J., Sclavons, M., and Marais, S. 2015. "Improvement of barrier properties of bio-based polyester nanocomposite membranes by water-assisted extrusion." *Journal of Membrane Science* 496: 185–198. https://doi.org/10.1016/j.memsci.2015.08.043

Chen, X.-S., Yu, Z.-Z., Liu, W., and Zhang, S. 2009. "Synergistic effect of decabromodiphenyl ethane and montmorillonite on flame retardancy of polypropylene." *Polymer Degradation and Stability* 94(9): 1520–1525. https://doi.org/10.1016/j.polymdegradstab.2009.04.031

Cheng, Y., Zhang, Y., Deng, W., and Hu, J. 2020. "Antibacterial and anticancer activities of asymmetric lollipop-like mesoporous silica nanoparticles loaded with curcumin and gentamicin sulfate." *Colloids and Surfaces B: Biointerfaces* 186: 110744. https://doi.org/10.1016/j.colsurfb.2019.110744

Chigwada, G., and Wilkie, C. A. 2003. "Synergy between conventional phosphorus fire retardants and organically-modified clays can lead to fire retardancy of styrenics." *Polymer Degradation and Stability* 81(3): 551–557. https://doi.org/10.1016/S0141-3910(03)00156-3

Chipera, S. J., and Bish, D. L. 2001. "Baseline studies of the clay minerals society source clays: powder x-ray diffraction analyses." *Clays and Clay Minerals* 49(5): 398–409. doi: 10.1346/CCMN.2001.0490507

Cividanes, L. S., Franceschi, W., Ferreira, F. V., Menezes, B. R. C., Sales, R. C. M., and Thim, G. P. 2017. "How Do CNT affect the branch and crosslink reactions in CNT-epoxy." *Materials Research Express* 4(10): 105101.

de Lima Fontes, M., Meneguin, A. B., Tercjak, A., Gutierrez, J., Cury, B. S. F., dos Santos, A. M., ... Barud, H. S. 2018. "Effect of in situ modification of bacterial cellulose with carboxymethylcellulose on its nano/microstructure and methotrexate release properties." *Carbohydrate Polymers* 179: 126–134. https://doi.org/10.1016/j.carbpol.2017.09.061

de Melo Fiori, A. P. S., Camani, P. H., dos Santos Rosa, D., and Carastan, D. J. 2019. "Combined effects of clay minerals and polyethylene glycol in the mechanical and water barrier properties of carboxymethylcellulose films." *Industrial Crops and Products* 140: 111644. https://doi.org/10.1016/j.indcrop.2019.111644

de Souza Coelho, C. C., Silva, R. B. S., Carvalho, C. W. P., Rossi, A. L., Teixeira, J. A., Freitas-Silva, O., and Cabral, L. M. C. 2020."Cellulose nanocrystals from grape pomace and their use for the development of starch-based nanocomposite films." *International Journal of Biological Macromolecules* 159: 1048–1061. https://doi.org/10.1016/j.ijbiomac.2020.05.046

Depan, D., Kumar, A. P., and Singh, R. P. 2006. "Preparation and characterization of novel hybrid of chitosan-g-lactic acid and montmorillonite." *Journal of Biomedical Material Research Part A* 78(2): 372–382. doi: 10.1002/jbm.a.30738

Di Carlo, G., Curulli, A., Toro, R. G., Bianchini, C., De Caro, T., Padeletti, G., ... Ingo, G. M. 2012. "Green synthesis of gold–chitosan nanocomposites for caffeic acid sensing." *Langmuir* 28(12): 5471–5479. https://doi.org/10.1021/la204924d

Dufresne, A. 2006. "Comparing the mechanical properties of high performances polymer nanocomposites from biological sources." *Journal of Nanoscience and Nanotechnology* 6(2), 322–330. doi: 10.1166/jnn.2006.906

Espino-Pérez, E., Bras, J., Almeida, G., Plessis, C., Belgacem, N., Perré, P., and Domenek, S. 2018. "Designed cellulose nanocrystal surface properties for improving barrier properties in polylactide nanocomposites." *Carbohydrate Polymers* 183: 267–277. https://doi.org/10.1016/j.carbpol.2017.12.005

Espino-Pérez, E., Bras, J., Ducruet, V., Guinault, A., Dufresne, A., and Domenek, S. 2013. "Influence of chemical surface modification of cellulose nanowhiskers on thermal, mechanical, and barrier properties of poly(lactide) based bionanocomposites." *European Polymer Journal* 49(10): 3144–3154. https://doi.org/10.1016/j.eurpolymj.2013.07.017

Fahmy, T. Y. A., and Mobarak, F. 2008. "Nanocomposites from natural cellulose fibers filled with kaolin in presence of sucrose." *Carbohydrate Polymers* 72(4), 751–755. https://doi.org/10.1016/j.carbpol.2008.01.008

Farmahini-Farahani, M., Xiao, H., Khan, A., Pan, Y., and Yang, Y. 2015. "Preparation and characterization of exfoliated PHBV nanocomposites to enhance water vapor barriers of calendared paper." *Industrial & Engineering Chemistry Research* 54(45): 11277–11284. https://doi.org/10.1021/acs.iecr.5b02734

Favvas, E. P., Kapantaidakis, G. C., Nolan, J. W., Mitropoulos, A. C., and Kanellopoulos, N. K. 2007. "Preparation, characterization and gas permeation properties of carbon hollow fiber membranes based on Matrimid® 5218 precursor." *Journal of Materials Processing Technology* 186(1): 102–110. https://doi.org/10.1016/j.jmatprotec.2006.12.024

Feng, J., Sun, Y., Song, P., Lei, W., Wu, Q., Liu, L., ... Wang, H. 2017. "Fire-resistant, strong, and green polymer nanocomposites based on poly(lactic acid) and core–shell nanofibrous flame retardants." *ACS Sustainable Chemistry & Engineering* 5(9): 7894–7904. https://doi.org/10.1021/acssuschemeng.7b01430

Ferreira, F. V., Dufresne, A., Pinheiro, I. F., Souza, D. H. S., Gouveia, R. F., Mei, L. H. I., and Lona, L. M. F. 2018. "How do cellulose nanocrystals affect the overall properties of biodegradable polymer nanocomposites: a comprehensive review." *European Polymer Journal* 108: 274–285. https://doi.org/10.1016/j.eurpolymj.2018.08.045

Fina, A., Cuttica, F., and Camino, G. 2012. "Ignition of polypropylene/montmorillonite nanocomposites." *Polymer Degradation and Stability* 97(12): 2619–2626. https://doi.org/10.1016/j.polymdegradstab.2012.07.017

Follain, N., Belbekhouche, S., Bras, J., Siqueira, G., Chappey, C., Marais, S., and Dufresne, A. 2018. "Tunable gas barrier properties of filled-PCL film by forming percolating cellulose network." *Colloids and Surfaces A: Physicochemical and Engineering Aspects* 545: 26–30. https://doi.org/10.1016/j.colsurfa.2018.02.040

Follain, N., Belbekhouche, S., Bras, J., Siqueira, G., Marais, S., and Dufresne, A. 2013. "Water transport properties of bio-nanocomposites reinforced by Luffa cylindrica cellulose nanocrystals." *Journal of Membrane Science* 427: 218–229. https://doi.org/10.1016/j.memsci.2012.09.048

Fortunati, E., Armentano, I., Zhou, Q., Iannoni, A., Saino, E., Visai, L., ... Kenny, J. M. 2012. "Multifunctional bionanocomposite films of poly(lactic acid), cellulose nanocrystals and silver nanoparticles." *Carbohydrate Polymers* 87(2): 1596–1605. https://doi.org/10.1016/j.carbpol.2011.09.066

Fortunati, E., Peltzer, M., Armentano, I., Jiménez, A., and Kenny, J. M. 2013. "Combined effects of cellulose nanocrystals and silver nanoparticles on the barrier and migration properties of PLA nano-biocomposites." *Journal of Food Engineering* 118(1): 117–124. https://doi.org/10.1016/j.jfoodeng.2013.03.025

García-García, D., Balart, R., Lopez-Martinez, J., Ek, M., and Moriana, R. 2018. "Optimizing the yield and physico-chemical properties of pine cone cellulose nanocrystals by different hydrolysis time." *Cellulose* 25(5): 2925–2938. https://doi.org/10.1007/s10570-018-1760-0

Gårdebjer, S., Bergstrand, A., Idström, A., Börstell, C., Naana, S., Nordstierna, L., and Larsson, A. 2015. "Solid-state NMR to quantify surface coverage and chain length of lactic acid modified cellulose nanocrystals, used as fillers in biodegradable composites." *Composites Science and Technology* 107: 1–9. https://doi.org/10.1016/j.compscitech.2014.11.014

Gazzano, E., Ghiazza, M., Polimeni, M., Bolis, V., Fenoglio, I., Attanasio, A., ... Ghigo, D. 2012. "Physicochemical determinants in the cellular responses to nanostructured amorphous silicas." *Toxicological Sciences* 128(1): 158–170. doi: 10.1093/toxsci/kfs128

Geyer, R., Jambeck, J. R., and Law, K. L. 2017. "Production, use, and fate of all plastics ever made." *Science Advances* 3(7): e1700782. doi: 10.1126/sciadv.1700782

Ghosh, S., Dutta, S., Sarkar, A., Kundu, M., and Sil, P. C. 2021. "Targeted delivery of curcumin in breast cancer cells via hyaluronic acid modified mesoporous silica nanoparticle to enhance anticancer efficiency." *Colloids and Surfaces B: Biointerfaces* 197: 111404. https://doi.org/10.1016/j.colsurfb.2020.111404

Goh, P. S., Ismail, A. F., Sanip, S. M., Ng, B. C., and Aziz, M. 2011. "Recent advances of inorganic fillers in mixed matrix membrane for gas separation." *Separation and Purification Technology* 81(3): 243–264. https://doi.org/10.1016/j.seppur.2011.07.042

Gu, H., Guo, J., He, Q., Tadakamalla, S., Zhang, X., Yan, X., ... Guo, Z. 2013. "Flame-retardant epoxy resin nanocomposites reinforced with polyaniline-stabilized silica nanoparticles." *Industrial & Engineering Chemistry Research* 52(23): 7718–7728. https://doi.org/10.1021/ie400275n

Gunatillake, P. A., and Adhikari, R. 2003. "Biodegradable synthetic polymers for tissue engineering." *European Cells & Materials* 5: 1–16; discussion 16. doi: 10.22203/ecm. v005a01

Gupta, P., Bera, M., and Maji, P. K. 2017. "Nanotailoring of sepiolite clay with poly [styrene-b-(ethylene-co-butylene)-b-styrene]: structure–property correlation." *Polymers for Advanced Technologies* 28(11): 1428–1437. https://doi.org/10.1002/pat.4019

Ha Thuc, C. N., Cao, H. T., Nguyen, D. M., Tran, M. A., Duclaux, L., Grillet, A. C., and Ha Thuc, H. 2014. "Preparation and characterization of polyurethane nanocomposites using Vietnamese montmorillonite modified by polyol surfactants." *Journal of Nanomaterials* 2014: 302735. https://doi.org/10.1155/2014/302735

Habibi, Y., Lucia, L. A., and Rojas, O. J. 2010. "Cellulose nanocrystals: chemistry, self-assembly, and applications." *Chemical Reviews* 110(6): 3479–3500. https://doi.org/10.1021/cr900339w

Haghjoo, H., Sangsefidi, F. S., and Salavati-Niasari, M. 2017. "Study on the optical, magnetic, and photocatalytic activities of the synthesized Mn_2O_3-SiO_2 nanocomposites by microwave method." *Journal of Molecular Liquids* 242: 779–788. https://doi.org/10.1016/j.molliq.2017.07.068

Han, Y.-S., Lee, S.-H., Choi, K. H., and Park, I. 2010. "Preparation and characterization of chitosan–clay nanocomposites with antimicrobial activity." *Journal of Physics and Chemistry of Solids* 71(4): 464–467. https://doi.org/10.1016/j.jpcs.2009.12.012

Hao, N., Jayawardana, K. W., Chen, X., and Yan, M. 2015. "One-step synthesis of amine-functionalized hollow mesoporous silica nanoparticles as efficient antibacterial and anticancer materials." *ACS Applied Materials & Interfaces* 7(2): 1040–1045. https://doi.org/10.1021/am508219g

He, W., Song, P., Yu, B., Fang, Z., and Wang, H. 2020. "Flame retardant polymeric nanocomposites through the combination of nanomaterials and conventional flame retardants." *Progress in Materials Science* 114: 100687. https://doi.org/10.1016/j.pmatsci.2020.100687

Horst, M. F., Quinzani, L. M., and Failla, M. D. 2012. "Rheological and barrier properties of nanocomposites of HDPE and exfoliated montmorillonite." *Journal of Thermoplastic Composite Materials* 27(1): 106–125. https://doi.org/10.1177/0892705712443248

Huang, M.-F., Yu, J.-G., and Ma, X.-F. 2004. "Studies on the properties of Montmorillonite-reinforced thermoplastic starch composites." *Polymer* 45(20): 7017–7023. https://doi.org/10.1016/j.polymer.2004.07.068

Ilyas, R. A., Sapuan, S. M., Atikah, M. S. N., Asyraf, M. R. M., Rafiqah, S. A., Aisyah, H. A., … Norrrahim, M. N. F. 2020a. "Effect of hydrolysis time on the morphological, physical, chemical, and thermal behavior of sugar palm nanocrystalline cellulose (Arenga pinnata (Wurmb.) Merr)." *Textile Research Journal* 91(1–2): 152–167. https://doi.org/10.1177/0040517520932393

Ilyas, R. A., Sapuan, S. M., Ibrahim, R., Abral, H., Ishak, M., Zainudin, E. S., … Jumaidin, R. 2019. "Effect of sugar palm nanofibrillated cellulose concentrations on morphological, mechanical and physical properties of biodegradable films based on agro-waste sugar palm (Arenga pinnata (Wurmb.) Merr) starch." *Journal of Materials Research and Technology* 8: 4819–4830. doi:10.1016/j.jmrt.2019.08.028

Ilyas, R. A., Sapuan, S. M., Ibrahim, R., Abral, H., Ishak, M. R., Zainudin, E. S., … Jumaidin, R. 2020b. "Thermal, biodegradability and water barrier properties of bio-nanocomposites based on plasticised sugar palm starch and nanofibrillated celluloses from sugar palm fibres." *Journal of Biobased Materials and Bioenergy* 14(2): 234–248(215). https://doi.org/10.1166/jbmb.2020.1951

Ilyas, R. A., Sapuan, S. M., Ishak, M. R., and Zainudin, E. S. 2018. "Development and characterization of sugar palm nanocrystalline cellulose reinforced sugar palm starch bionanocomposites." *Carbohydrate Polymers* 202: 186–202. https://doi.org/10.1016/j.carbpol.2018.09.002

Isitman, N. A., Dogan, M., Bayramli, E., and Kaynak, C. 2012. "The role of nanoparticle geometry in flame retardancy of polylactide nanocomposites containing aluminium phosphinate." *Polymer Degradation and Stability* 97(8): 1285–1296. https://doi.org/10.1016/j.polymdegradstab.2012.05.028

Jackson, J. K., Letchford, K., Wasserman, B. Z., Ye, L., Hamad, W. Y., and Burt, H. M. 2011. "The use of nanocrystalline cellulose for the binding and controlled release of drugs." *International Journal of Nanomedicine* 6: 321–330. doi: 10.2147/IJN.S16749

Jasmani, L., and Adnan, S. 2017. "Preparation and characterization of nanocrystalline cellulose from Acacia mangium and its reinforcement potential." *Carbohydrate Polymers* 161: 166–171. https://doi.org/10.1016/j.carbpol.2016.12.061

Jonoobi, M., Oladi, R., Davoudpour, Y., Oksman, K., Dufresne, A., Hamzeh, Y., and Davoodi, R. 2015. "Different preparation methods and properties of nanostructured cellulose from various natural resources and residues: a review." *Cellulose* 22(2): 935–969. https://doi.org/10.1007/s10570-015-0551-0

Kádár, F., Százdi, L., Fekete, E., and Pukánszky, B. 2006. "Surface characteristics of layered silicates: influence on the properties of clay/polymer nanocomposites." *Langmuir* 22(18): 7848–7854. https://doi.org/10.1021/la060144c

Kango, S., Kalia, S., Celli, A., Njuguna, J., Habibi, Y., and Kumar, R. 2013. "Surface modification of inorganic nanoparticles for development of organic–inorganic nanocomposites—A review." *Progress in Polymer Science* 38(8): 1232–1261. https://doi.org/10.1016/j.progpolymsci.2013.02.003

Kar, K. K., Rana, S., and Pandey, J. 2015. *Handbook of Polymer Nanocomposites Processing, Performance and Application*. Springer. doi:10.1007/978-3-642-45229-1

Kargarzadeh, H., Mariano, M., Huang, J., Lin, N., Ahmad, I., Dufresne, A., and Thomas, S. 2017. "Recent developments on nanocellulose reinforced polymer nanocomposites: a review." *Polymer* 132: 368–393. https://doi.org/10.1016/j.polymer.2017.09.043

Kawahara, T., Yuuki, A., Hashimoto, K., Fujiki, K., Yamauchi, T., and Tsubokawa, N. 2013. "Immobilization of flame-retardant onto silica nanoparticle surface and properties of epoxy resin filled with the flame-retardant-immobilized silica (2)." *Reactive and Functional Polymers* 73(3): 613–618. https://doi.org/10.1016/j.reactfunctpolym.2013.01.001

Kiliaris, P., and Papaspyrides, C. D. 2010. "Polymer/layered silicate (clay) nanocomposites: An overview of flame retardancy." *Progress in Polymer Science* 35(7): 902–958. https://doi.org/10.1016/j.progpolymsci.2010.03.001

Kilpeläinen, M., Riikonen, J., Vlasova, M. A., Huotari, A., Lehto, V. P., Salonen, J., ... Järvinen, K. 2009. "In vivo delivery of a peptide, ghrelin antagonist, with mesoporous silicon microparticles." *Journal of Controlled Release* 137(2): 166–170. doi: 10.1016/j.jconrel.2009.03.017

Kim, T., Jeon, H., Jegal, J., Kim, J. H., Yang, H., Park, J., ... Hwang, S.Y. 2018. "Trans crystallization behavior and strong reinforcement effect of cellulose nanocrystals on reinforced poly(butylene succinate) nanocomposites." *RSC Advances* 8: 15389–15398. https://doi.org/10.1039/C8RA01868E

Klemm, D., Heublein, B., Fink, H. P., and Bohn, A. 2005. "Cellulose: fascinating biopolymer and sustainable raw material." *Angewandte Chemie International Edition* 44(22): 3358–3393. https://doi.org/10.1002/anie.200460587

Kojima, Y., Usuki, A., Kawasumi, M., Okada, A., Fukushima, Y., Kurauchi, T., and Kamigaito, O. 2011. "Mechanical properties of nylon 6-clay hybrid." *Journal of Materials Research* 8(5): 1185–1189. https://doi.org/10.1557/JMR.1993.1185

Lan, T., Kaviratna, P. D., and Pinnavaia, T. J. 1994. "On the nature of polyimide-clay hybrid composites." *Chemistry of Materials* 6(5): 573–575. https://doi.org/10.1021/cm00041a002

Lapides, I., and Yariv, S. 2004. "The effect of ultrasound treatment on the particle-size of Wyoming bentonite in aqueous suspensions." *Journal of Materials Science* 39(16): 5209–5212. https://doi.org/10.1023/B:JMSC.0000039211.80605.c5

Lazzara, G., Riela, S., and Fakhrullin, R. F. 2017. "Clay-based drug-delivery systems: what does the future hold?" *Therapeutic Delivery* 8(8): 633–646. doi: 10.4155/tde-2017-0041

Le, V. H., Thuc, C. N. H., and Thuc, H. H. 2013. "Synthesis of silica nanoparticles from Vietnamese rice husk by sol–gel method." *Nanoscale Research Letters* 8(1): 58. https://doi.org/10.1186/1556-276X-8-58

Li, B. L., Setyawati, M. I., Chen, L., Xie, J., Ariga, K., Lim, C.-T., ... Leong, D. T. 2017. "Directing assembly and disassembly of 2D MoS$_2$ nanosheets with DNA for drug delivery." *ACS Applied Materials & Interfaces* 9(18): 15286–15296. https://doi.org/10.1021/acsami.7b02529

Li, P., Kim, N. H., Siddaramaiah, and Lee, J. H. 2009. "Swelling behavior of polyacrylamide/laponite clay nanocomposite hydrogels: pH-sensitive property." *Composites Part B: Engineering* 40(4): 275–283. https://doi.org/10.1016/j.compositesb.2009.01.001

Lin, J., Chen, H., and Yao, L. 2010. "Surface tailoring of SiO2 nanoparticles by mechanochemical method based on simple milling." *Applied Surface Science* 256(20): 5978–5984. https://doi.org/10.1016/j.apsusc.2010.03.105

Liu, A., and Berglund, L. A. 2013. "Fire-retardant and ductile clay nanopaper biocomposites based on montmorillonite in matrix of cellulose nanofibers and carboxymethyl cellulose." *European Polymer Journal* 49(4): 940–949. https://doi.org/10.1016/j.eurpolymj.2012.12.017

Liu, P., Tang, H., Lu, M., Gao, C., Wang, F., Ding, Y., ... Yang, M. 2017. "Preparation of nanosilica-immobilized antioxidant and the antioxidative behavior in low density polyethylene." *Polymer Degradation and Stability* 135: 1–7. https://doi.org/10.1016/j.polymdegradstab.2016.10.013

Lu, C., and Mai, Y.-W. 2005. "Influence of aspect ratio on barrier properties of polymer-clay nanocomposites." *Physical Review Letters* 95(8): 088303. https://doi.org/10.1103/PhysRevLett.95.088303

Lu, Z., Fan, L., Zheng, H., Lu, Q., Liao, Y., and Huang, B. 2013. "Preparation, characterization and optimization of nanocellulose whiskers by simultaneously ultrasonic wave and microwave assisted." *Bioresource Technology* 146: 82–88. https://doi.org/10.1016/j.biortech.2013.07.047

Lvov, Y., Wang, W., Zhang, L., and Fakhrullin, R. 2016. "Halloysite clay nanotubes for loading and sustained release of functional compounds." *Advanced Materials* 28(6): 1227–1250. https://doi.org/10.1002/adma.201502341

Ma, H., Burger, C., Hsiao, B. S., and Chu, B. 2011. "Ultrafine polysaccharide nanofibrous membranes for water purification." *Biomacromolecules* 12(4): 970–976. https://doi.org/10.1021/bm1013316

Ma, H., Tong, L., Xu, Z., and Fang, Z. 2007. "Clay network in ABS-graft-MAH nanocomposites: rheology and flammability." *Polymer Degradation and Stability* 92(8): 1439–1445. https://doi.org/10.1016/j.polymdegradstab.2007.05.013

Mallakpour, S., and Khani, Z. 2018. "Surface modified SiO2 nanoparticles by thiamine and ultrasonication synthesis of PCL/SiO$_2$-VB1 NCs: morphology, thermal, mechanical and bioactivity investigations." *Ultrasonics Sonochemistry* 41: 527–537. https://doi.org/10.1016/j.ultsonch.2017.10.015

Mallakpour, S., and Marefatpour, F. 2015a. "An effective and environmentally friendly method for surface modification of amorphous silica nanoparticles by biodegradable diacids derived from different amino acids." *Synthesis and Reactivity in Inorganic, Metal-Organic, and Nano-Metal Chemistry* 45(3): 376–380. https://doi.org/10.1080/15533174.2013.831899

Mallakpour, S., and Marefatpour, F. 2015b. "The utilization of poly(amide-imide)/SiO$_2$ nanocomposite as nanofiller for strengthening of mechanical and thermal properties of poly(vinyl alcohol) nanocomposite films." *Progress in Organic Coatings* 85: 60–67. https://doi.org/10.1016/j.porgcoat.2015.03.003

Mallakpour, S., and Naghdi, M. 2018. "Polymer/SiO$_2$ nanocomposites: production and applications." *Progress in Materials Science* 97: 409–447. https://doi.org/10.1016/j.pmatsci.2018.04.002

Mallakpour, S., and Nazari, H. Y. 2018. "The influence of bovine serum albumin-modified silica on the physicochemical properties of poly(vinyl alcohol) nanocomposites synthesized by ultrasonication technique." *Ultrasonics Sonochemistry* 41: 1–10. https://doi.org/10.1016/j.ultsonch.2017.09.017

Mandal, A., and Chakrabarty, D. 2014. "Studies on the mechanical, thermal, morphological and barrier properties of nanocomposites based on poly(vinyl alcohol) and nanocellulose from sugarcane bagasse." *Journal of Industrial and Engineering Chemistry* 20(2): 462–473. https://doi.org/10.1016/j.jiec.2013.05.003

Mao, N. D., Lee, S. Y., Shin, H. J., Kwac, L. K., Ko, S. C., Kim, H. G., and Jeong, H. 2018. "Biomass fly ash as an alternative approach for synthesis of amorphous silica nanoparticles with high surface area." *Journal of Nanoscience and Nanotechnology* 18(5): 3329–3334. doi: 10.1166/jnn.2018.14548

Mariano, M., Chirat, C., El Kissi, N., and Dufresne, A. 2016. "Impact of cellulose nanocrystal aspect ratio on crystallization and reinforcement of poly(butylene adipate-co-terephthalate)." *Journal of Polymer Science Part B: Polymer Physics* 54(22): 2284–2297. https://doi.org/10.1002/polb.24139

Martin, K. R. 2007. "The chemistry of silica and its potential health benefits." *Journal of Nutrition, Health & Aging* 11(2): 94–97.

Masjedi-Arani, M., Ghanbari, D., Salavati-Niasari, M., and Bagheri, S. 2016. "Sonochemical synthesis of spherical silica nanoparticles and polymeric nanocomposites." *Journal of Cluster Science* 27(1): 39–53. https://doi.org/10.1007/s10876-015-0897-3

Matos, A. C., Marques, C. F., Pinto, R. V., Ribeiro, I. A. C., Gonçalves, L. M., Vaz, M. A., ... Bettencourt, A. F. 2015. "Novel doped calcium phosphate-PMMA bone cement composites as levofloxacin delivery systems." *International Journal of Pharmaceutics* 490(1): 200–208. https://doi.org/10.1016/j.ijpharm.2015.05.038

Miao, C., and Hamad, W. Y. 2016a. "Alkenylation of cellulose nanocrystals (CNC) and their applications." *Polymer* 101: 338–346. https://doi.org/10.1016/j.polymer.2016.08.099

Miao, C., and Hamad, W. Y. 2016b. "In-situ polymerized cellulose nanocrystals (CNC)—poly(l-lactide) (PLLA) nanomaterials and applications in nanocomposite processing." *Carbohydrate Polymers* 153: 549–558. https://doi.org/10.1016/j.carbpol.2016.08.012

Mirshafiee, V., Kim, R., Mahmoudi, M., and Kraft, M. L. 2016. "The importance of selecting a proper biological milieu for protein corona analysis in vitro: human plasma versus human serum." *International Journal of Biochemistry & Cell Biology* 75: 188–195. doi: 10.1016/j.biocel.2015.11.019

Móczó, J., and Pukánszky, B. 2008. "Polymer micro and nanocomposites: Structure, interactions, properties." *Journal of Industrial and Engineering Chemistry* 14(5): 535–563. https://doi.org/10.1016/j.jiec.2008.06.011

Mohammed, A. A., and Issa, T. T. 2016. "The water absorption effect on the hardness of composites polyester." *AIP Conference Proceedings* 1727(1): 020016. https://doi.org/10.1063/1.4945971

Mondal, S. 2017. "Preparation, properties and applications of nanocellulosic materials." *Carbohydrate Polymers* 163: 301–316. https://doi.org/10.1016/j.carbpol.2016.12.050

Mondragon, G., Peña-Rodriguez, C., González, A., Eceiza, A., and Arbelaiz, A. 2015. "Bionanocomposites based on gelatin matrix and nanocellulose." *European Polymer Journal* 62:1–9. https://doi.org/10.1016/j.eurpolymj.2014.11.003

Moon, Robert J., Martini, Ashlie, Nairn, J., Simonsen, J., and Youngblood, J. 2011. "Cellulose nanomaterials review: structure, properties and nanocomposites." *Chemical Society Reviews* 40: 3941–3994. https://doi.org/10.1039/C0CS00108B

Morelli, C. L., Belgacem, M. N., Branciforti, M. C., Bretas, R. E. S., Crisci, A., and Bras, J. 2016. "Supramolecular aromatic interactions to enhance biodegradable film properties through incorporation of functionalized cellulose nanocrystals." *Composites Part A: Applied Science and Manufacturing* 83: 80–88. https://doi.org/10.1016/j.compositesa.2015.10.038

Nagalakshmaiah, M., El Kissi, N., Mortha, G., and Dufresne, A. 2016. "Structural investigation of cellulose nanocrystals extracted from chili leftover and their reinforcement in cariflex-IR rubber latex." *Carbohydrate Polymers* 136: 945–954. https://doi.org/10.1016/j.carbpol.2015.09.096

Naskar, A. K., Keum, J. K., and Boeman, R. G. 2016. "Polymer matrix nanocomposites for automotive structural components." *Nature Nanotechnology* 11(12): 1026–1030. https://doi.org/10.1038/nnano.2016.262

Natterodt, J. C., Sapkota, J., Foster, E. J., and Weder, C. 2017. "Polymer nanocomposites with cellulose nanocrystals featuring adaptive surface groups." *Biomacromolecules* 18(2): 517–525. https://doi.org/10.1021/acs.biomac.6b01639

Nguyen, D.M., Thanh, D.T., Thuong, T.T., Grillet, A.-C., Kim, N.H., and Lee, J.H. 2016. "Enhanced mechanicam and thermal properties of recycled ABS/nitrile rubber/nanofil N15 nanocomposites." Composites Part B: Engineering 9: 280–288. https://doi.org/10.1016/j.compositesb.2016.03.039

Nguyen, D. M., Vu, T. T., Grillet, A.-C., Ha Thuc, H., and Ha Thuc, C. N. 2016. "Effect of organoclay on morphology and properties of linear low density polyethylene and Vietnamese cassava starch biobased blend." *Carbohydrate Polymers* 136: 163–170. https://doi.org/10.1016/j.carbpol.2015.09.020

Nguyen, Q. T., and Baird, D. G. 2006. "Preparation of polymer–clay nanocomposites and their properties." *Advances in Polymer Technology* 25(4): 270–285. https://doi.org/10.1002/adv.20079

Nikolaidis, A. K., Achilias, D. S., and Karayannidis, G. P. 2012. "Effect of the type of organic modifier on the polymerization kinetics and the properties of poly(methyl methacrylate)/organomodified montmorillonite nanocomposites." *European Polymer Journal* 48(2): 240–251. https://doi.org/10.3390/polym12020364

Pacheco, G., Nogueira, C. R., Meneguin, A. B., Trovatti, E., Silva, M. C. C., Machado, R. T. A., ... da S. Barud, H. 2017. "Development and characterization of bacterial cellulose produced by cashew tree residues as alternative carbon source." *Industrial Crops and Products* 107: 13–19. https://doi.org/10.1016/j.indcrop.2017.05.026

Pacuła, A., Bielańska, E., Gaweł, A., Bahranowski, K., and Serwicka, E. M. 2006. "Textural effects in powdered montmorillonite induced by freeze-drying and ultrasound pretreatment." *Applied Clay Science* 32(1): 64–72. https://doi.org/10.1016/j.clay.2005.10.002

Park, J. H., and Jana, S. C. 2003. "Mechanism of exfoliation of nanoclay particles in epoxy-clay nanocomposites." *Macromolecules* 36(8): 2758–2768. https://doi.org/10.1021/ma021509c

Pavan, C., Tomatis, M., Ghiazza, M., Rabolli, V., Bolis, V., Lison, D., and Fubini, B. 2013. "In search of the chemical basis of the hemolytic potential of silicas." *Chemical Research in Toxicology* 26(8): 1188–1198. https://doi.org/10.1021/tx400105f

Pavlidou, S., and Papaspyrides, C. D. 2008. "A review on polymer–layered silicate nanocomposites." *Progress in Polymer Science* 33(12): 1119–1198. https://doi.org/10.1016/j.progpolymsci.2008.07.008

Pei, A., Zhou, Q., and Berglund, L. A. 2010. "Functionalized cellulose nanocrystals as biobased nucleation agents in poly(l-lactide) (PLLA) – Crystallization and mechanical property effects." *Composites Science and Technology* 70(5): 815–821. https://doi.org/10.1016/j.compscitech.2010.01.018

Pfaendner, R. 2010. "Nanocomposites: Industrial opportunity or challenge." *Polymer Degradation and Stability* 95(3): 369–373. https://doi.org/10.1016/J.polymdegradstab.2009.11.019

Régibeau, N., Tilkin, R. G., Compère, P., Heinrichs, B., and Grandfils, C. 2020. "Preparation of PDLLA based nanocomposites with modified silica by in situ polymerization: Study of molecular, morphological, and mechanical properties." *Materials Today Communications* 25: 101610. https://doi.org/10.1016/j.mtcomm.2020.101610

Risse, S., Tighzert, L., Berzin, F., and Vergnes, B. 2014."Microstructure, rheological behavior, and properties of poly(lactic acid)/poly(butylene succinate)/organoclay nanocomposites." *Journal of Applied Polymer Science* 131(12). https://doi.org/10.1002/app.40364

Rozilah, A., Jaafar, C. N. A., Sapuan, S. M., Zainol, I., and Ilyas, R. A. 2020. "The effects of silver nanoparticles compositions on the mechanical, physiochemical, antibacterial, and morphology properties of sugar palm starch biocomposites for antibacterial coating." *Polymers (Basel)* 12(11). https://doi.org/10.3390/polym12112605

Sabaruddin, F. A., Paridah, M. T., Sapuan, S. M., Ilyas, R. A., Lee, S. H., Abdan, K., … Abdul Khalil, H. P. S. 2020. "The effects of unbleached and bleached nanocellulose on the thermal and flammability of polypropylene-reinforced kenaf core hybrid polymer bionanocomposites." *Polymers (Basel)* 13(1): 116. https://doi.org/10.3390/polym13010116

Sadeghi, M., Khanbabaei, G., Dehaghani, A. H. S., Sadeghi, M., Aravand, M. A., Akbarzade, M., and Khatti, S. 2008. "Gas permeation properties of ethylene vinyl acetate–silica nanocomposite membranes." *Journal of Membrane Science* 322(2): 423–428. https://doi.org/10.1016/j.memsci.2008.05.077

Sadeghi, M., Semsarzadeh, M. A., Barikani, M., and Pourafshari Chenar, M. 2011. "Gas separation properties of polyether-based polyurethane–silica nanocomposite membranes." *Journal of Membrane Science* 376(1): 188–195. https://doi.org/10.1016/j.memsci.2011.04.021

Sadeghi, M., Semsarzadeh, M. A., and Moadel, H. 2009. "Enhancement of the gas separation properties of polybenzimidazole (PBI) membrane by incorporation of silica nano particles." *Journal of Membrane Science* 331(1): 21–30. https://doi.org/10.1016/j.memsci.2008.12.073

Sanchez-Garcia, M. D., and Lagaron, J. M. 2010. "On the use of plant cellulose nanowhiskers to enhance the barrier properties of polylactic acid." *Cellulose* 17(5): 987–1004. https://doi.org/10.1007/s10570-010-9430-x

Scaffaro, R., Lopresti, F., D'Arrigo, M., Marino, A., and Nostro, A. 2018. "Efficacy of poly(lactic acid)/carvacrol electrospun membranes against Staphylococcus aureus and Candida albicans in single and mixed cultures." *Applied Microbial and Biotechnology* 102(9): 4171–4181. https://doi.org/10.1007/s00253-018-8879-7

Scaffaro, R., Maio, A., Agnello, S., and Glisenti, A. 2012. "Plasma functionalization of multiwalled carbon nanotubes and their use in the preparation of nylon 6-based nanohybrids." *Plasma Processes and Polymers* 9(5): 503–512. https://doi.org/10.1002/ppap.201100140

Schlemmer, D., Angélica, R. S., and Sales, M. J. A. 2010. "Morphological and thermomechanical characterization of thermoplastic starch/montmorillonite nanocomposites." *Composite Structures* 92(9): 2066–2070. https://doi.org/10.1016/j.compstruct.2009.10.034

Serge, E.J., Alla, J. P., Belibi, P. D. B., Mbadcam, K. J., and Fathima, N. N. 2019. "Clay/polymer nanocomposites as filler materials for leather." *Journal of Cleaner Production* 237: 117837. https://doi.org/10.1016/j.jclepro.2019.117837

Sharma, S., Kumar Poddar, M., and Moholkar, V. S. 2017. "Enhancement of thermal and mechanical properties of poly(MMA-co-BA)/Cloisite 30B nanocomposites by ultrasound-assisted in-situ emulsion polymerization." *Ultrasonics Sonochemistry* 36: 212–225. https://doi.org/10.1016/j.ultsonch.2016.11.029

Shen, W., He, H., Zhu, J., Yuan, P., and Frost, R. L. 2007. "Grafting of montmorillonite with different functional silanes via two different reaction systems." *Journal of Colloid and Interface Science* 313(1): 268–273. https://doi.org/10.1016/j.jcis.2007.04.029

Shi, Z., Phillips, G. O., and Yang, G. 2013. "Nanocellulose electroconductive composites." *Nanoscale* 5(8): 3194–3201. https://doi.org/10.1039/C3NR00408B

Singh, L. P., Agarwal, S. K., Bhattacharyya, S. K., Sharma, U., and Ahalawat, S. 2011. "Preparation of silica nanoparticles and its beneficial role in cementitious materials." *Nanomaterials and Nanotechnology* 1: 9. https://doi.org/10.5772/50950

Thuc, C.-N. H., Grillet, A.-C., Reinert, L., Ohashi, F., Thuc, H. H., and Duclaux, L. 2010. "Separation and purification of montmorillonite and polyethylene oxide modified montmorillonite from Vietnamese bentonites." *Applied Clay Science* 49(3): 229–238. https://doi.org/10.1016/j.clay.2010.05.011

Tombácz, E., Szekeres, M., Baranyi, L., and Michéli, E. 1998. "Surface modification of clay minerals by organic polyions." *Colloids and Surfaces A: Physicochemical and Engineering Aspects* 141(3): 379–384. https://doi.org/10.1016/S0927-7757(98)00241-6

Usuki, A., Kojima, Y., Kawasumi, M., Okada, A., Fukushima, Y., Kurauchi, T., and Kamigaito, O. 2011. "Synthesis of nylon 6-clay hybrid." *Journal of Materials Research* 8(5): 1179–1184. https://doi.org/10.1557/JMR.1993.1179

Vengatesan, M. R., and MittalV. 2016. "Nanoparticle- and nanofiber-based polymer nanocomposites: an overview" In *Spherical and Fibrous Filler Composites*, pp. 1–38. Berlin, Wiley-VCH Verlag. https://doi.org/10.1002/9783527670222.ch1

Wang, D., Li, J., Zhang, X., Zhang, J., Yu, J., and Zhang, J. 2020. "Poly(propylene carbonate)/clay nanocomposites with enhanced mechanical property, thermal stability and oxygen barrier property." *Composites Communications* 22: 100520. https://doi.org/10.1016/j.coco.2020.100520

Wang, H., He, J., Zhang, M., Tam, K. C., and Ni, P. 2015. "A new pathway towards polymer modified cellulose nanocrystals via a "grafting onto" process for drug delivery." *Polymer Chemistry* 6(23): 4206–4209. https://doi.org/10.1039/C5PY00466G

Wang, R., Chen, L., Zhu, J. Y., and Yang, R. 2017. "Tailored and integrated production of carboxylated cellulose nanocrystals (CNC) with nanofibrils (CNF) through maleic acid hydrolysis." *ChemNanoMat* 3(5): 328–335. https://doi.org/10.1002/cnma.201700015

Wang, X., Wang, P., Jiang, Y., Su, Q., and Zheng, J. 2014. "Facile surface modification of silica nanoparticles with a combination of noncovalent and covalent methods for composites application." *Composites Science and Technology* 104: 1–8. https://doi.org/10.1016/j.compscitech.2014.08.027

Wang, Y., Zhang, H., Wu, Y., Yang, J., and Zhang, L. 2005. "Preparation and properties of natural rubber/rectorite nanocomposites." *European Polymer Journal* 41(11): 2776–2783. https://doi.org/10.1016/j.eurpolymj.2005.05.019

Wang, Y., Zhao, Q., Hu, Y., Sun, L., Bai, L., Jiang, T., and Wang, S. 2013. "Ordered nanoporous silica as carriers for improved delivery of water insoluble drugs: a comparative study between three dimensional and two dimensional macroporous silica." *International Journal of Nanomedicine* 8: 4015–4031. https://doi.org/10.2147/IJN.S52605

Wang, Z., Han, E., Liu, F., and Ke, W. 2010. "Fire and corrosion resistances of intumescent nano-coating containing nano-sio2 in salt spray condition." *Journal of Materials Science & Technology* 26(1): 75–81. https://doi.org/10.1016/S1005-0302(10)60012-6

Wicklein, B., Kocjan, A., Salazar-Alvarez, G., Carosio, F., Camino, G., Antonietti, M., and Bergström, L. 2015. "Thermally insulating and fire-retardant lightweight anisotropic foams based on nanocellulose and graphene oxide." *Nature Nanotechnology* 10(3): 277–283. https://doi.org/10.1038/nnano.2014.248

Wilhelm, H. M., Sierakowski, M. R., Souza, G. P., and Wypych, F. 2003. "Starch films reinforced with mineral clay." *Carbohydrate Polymers* 52(2): 101–110. https://doi.org/10.1016/S0144-8617(02)00239-4

Yang, X., Bakaic, E., Hoare, T., and Cranston, E. D. 2013. "Injectable polysaccharide hydrogels reinforced with cellulose nanocrystals: morphology, rheology, degradation, and cytotoxicity." *Biomacromolecules* 14(12): 4447–4455. https://doi.org/10.1021/bm401364z

Yang, Y., Chen, Z., Zhang, J., Wang, G., Zhang, R., and Suo, D. 2019. "Preparation and applications of the cellulose nanocrystal." *International Journal of Polymer Science* 2019: 1767028. https://doi.org/10.1155/2019/1767028

Yang, Y., Zhang, M., Song, H., and Yu, C. 2020. "Silica-based nanoparticles for biomedical applications: from nanocarriers to biomodulators." *Accounts of Chemical Research* 53(8), 1545–1556. https://doi.org/10.1021/acs.accounts.0c00280

Yin, W., Chen, L., Lu, F., Song, P., Dai, J., and Meng, L. 2018. "Mechanically robust, flame-retardant poly(lactic acid) biocomposites via combining cellulose nanofibers and ammonium polyphosphate." *ACS Omega* 3(5): 5615–5626. https://doi.org/10.1021/acsomega.8b00540

Youssef, A. M., El-Sayed, S. M., Salama, H. H., El-Sayed, H. S., and Dufresne, A. 2015. "Evaluation of bionanocomposites as packaging material on properties of soft white cheese during storage period." *Carbohydrate Polymers* 132: 274–285. https://doi.org/10.1016/j.carbpol.2015.06.075

Yu, L., Li, L., Wei'an, Z., and Yue'e, F. 2004. "A new hybrid nanocomposite prepared by graft copolymerization of butyl acrylate onto chitosan in the presence of organophilic montmorillonite." *Radiation Physics and Chemistry* 69(6): 467–471. https://doi.org/10.1016/j.radphyschem.2003.10.012

Zabihi, O., Ahmadi, M., and Naebe, M. 2017. "Self-assembly of quaternized chitosan nanoparticles within nanoclay layers for enhancement of interfacial properties in toughened polymer nanocomposites." *Materials & Design* 119: 277–289. https://doi.org/10.1016/j.matdes.2017.01.079

Zeppa, C., Gouanvé, F., and Espuche, E. 2009. "Effect of a plasticizer on the structure of biodegradable starch/clay nanocomposites: thermal, water-sorption, and oxygen-barrier properties." *Journal of Applied Polymer Science* 112(4): 2044–2056. https://doi.org/10.1002/app.29588

Zhang, D., Karkooti, A., Liu, L., Sadrzadeh, M., Thundat, T., Liu, Y., and Narain, R. 2018. "Fabrication of antifouling and antibacterial polyethersulfone (PES)/cellulose nanocrystals (CNC) nanocomposite membranes." *Journal of Membrane Science* 549: 350–356. https://doi.org/10.1016/j.memsci.2017.12.034

Zhang, G., Wu, T., Lin, W., Tan, Y., Chen, R., Huang, Z., ... Qu, J. 2017. "Preparation of polymer/clay nanocomposites via melt intercalation under continuous elongation flow." *Composites Science and Technology* 145: 157–164. https://doi.org/10.1016/j.compscitech.2017.04.005

Zhang, M. Q., Rong, M. Z., and Friedrich, K. 2006. "20 - Wear resisting polymer nanocomposites: preparation and properties." In *Polymer Nanocomposites*, edited by Y.-W. Mai and Z.-Z. Yu, pp. 540–577). Woodhead Publishing. https://doi.org/10.1533/9781845691127.2.540

Zhang, P., and Kong, J. 2015. "Doxorubicin-tethered fluorescent silica nanoparticles for pH-responsive anticancer drug delivery." *Talanta* 134: 501–507. https://doi.org/10.1016/j.talanta.2014.09.041

Zhu, T. T., Zhou, C. H., Kabwe, F. B., Wu, Q. Q., Li, C. S., and Zhang, J. R. 2019. "Exfoliation of montmorillonite and related properties of clay/polymer nanocomposites." *Applied Clay Science* 169: 48–66. https://doi.org/10.1016/j.clay.2018.12.006

Zoppe, J. O., Ruottinen, V., Ruotsalainen, J., Rönkkö, S., Johansson, L.-S., Hinkkanen, A., ... Seppälä, J. 2014. "Synthesis of cellulose nanocrystals carrying tyrosine sulfate mimetic ligands and inhibition of alphavirus infection." *Biomacromolecules* 15(4): 1534–1542. https://doi.org/10.1021/bm500229d

5 Utilization of Natural Zeolite as Filler in Improving the Mechanical Properties of Unsaturated Polyester Composite

H. Nasution, H. Harahap, and D.M. Putra, Winny
Universitas Sumatera Utara
Medan, Indonesia

CONTENTS

5.1	Introduction	102
5.2	Preparation and Characterization of Unsaturated Polyester Resin/Natural Zeolite Composites	103
	5.2.1 Materials	103
	5.2.2 Sample Preparation	103
	5.2.3 Fabrication of Composites	104
	5.2.4 Characterization	104
5.3	Morphological Properties, Component Characterization and Crystallinity of Natural Zeolite Filler	106
	5.3.1 Morphological Properties and Component Characterization of Natural Zeolite Filler with Scanning Electron Microscope-Energy Dispersive X-ray (SEM-EDX)	106
	5.3.2 Crystallinity of Natural Zeolite Filler with X-ray Diffraction (XRD)	109
5.4	Mechanical Properties and Morphological Behavior of Unsaturated Polyester/Natural Zeolite Composite	110
	5.4.1 Tensile Strength	110
	5.4.2 Flexural Strength	111
	5.4.3 Impact Strength	112
	5.4.4 Density	113
	5.4.5 Water Absorption	114
	5.4.6 Morphological Properties	116
5.5	Conclusions	117
Acknowledgment		118
References		118

DOI: 10.1201/9781003221012-5

5.1 INTRODUCTION

Polymer matrix composite (PMC) is a composite material that contains polymeric materials embedded in a reinforcing phase such as fiber or powder. Today, PMC can be made/designed with superior properties so that the material is very attractive to industries, such as aviation, construction, automobile, sports equipment, furniture, and so on. The advantages of PMC include its impact strength and high thermal resistance.

Unsaturated polyester is a thermoset polymer that has a relatively low viscosity, cheap price, fast curing time and good dimensional resistance (Berthelot, 1999). In addition, unsaturated polyester is also strong (not easily torn), resistant to high temperatures, insoluble in organic acids and has low water absorption and minimal shrinkage when compared with other types of thermoset plastics (Cowd, 1982). However, the mechanical properties of polyester are not very good, and for this reason, components such as fillers are needed to improve its mechanical properties (Deswita and dan Sudirman, 2002).

The filler material used in the composite matrix can be either organic or inorganic. Several studies on unsaturated polyester composites using organic fillers have been widely reported, including the utilization of bagasse fiber (Rianto, 2011), wood and bamboo powder (Aprilia et al., 2013) and rice husk ash (Sufian Suri, 2009). Consideration of using organic fillers in unsaturated polyester is partly because organic fillers are easily obtained and have good biodegradability. But in terms of mechanical properties, especially impact strength and resistance to heat and water absorption, organic fillers still have unsatisfactory results. Therefore, the selection of inorganic material such as zeolite is worth considering as filler in an unsaturated polyester.

Zeolite is a crystalline aluminosilicate mineral with a microporous structure, is crystalline porous, has large surface areas, a high thermal stability and is non-toxic (Yuliusman, 2016). The incorporation of modified zeolite particles into a polymer matrix will improve the mechanical properties of the composite and maintain thermal stability and durability (Visakh et al., 2016). It also has good absorption behavior because it is a porous material. This porous material is chosen because it has a surface area in the cavity that is much larger than the surface area of the outer zeolite crystals. For porous material to have a large absorption capacity, the material must have a large specific area that shows the porous structure in the presence of micropores (Kurniasari, 2010). This ability of zeolite has been widely applied, such as in the research of Kajtar et al. (2017) and in the interaction of composite and filler interfaces on zeolite thermoplastics, which combines zeolites as fillers to absorb water, thereby preventing contact with moisture. Barbosa et al. (2015) researched the design and characterization of chitosan/zeolites as composite films; zeolites have a good ion exchange capacity, which makes composite films better (Deswita and dan Sudirman, 2002).

Zeolites can be modified by activation to improve the quality of the formation of empty cavities so that the absorbance of the matrix is optimal. Activation can be accomplished physically and chemically. The process of physical activation can be done by calcining natural zeolite at 600°C. Chemical modification of natural zeolite is done with acidic compounds (hydrochloric acid [HCl]) and bases (sodium hydroxide [NaOH]) at various concentrations (Ngapa, 2017). The advantage of using zeolite as a filler in the supply of composite materials is that the matrix will be absorbed by the zeolite through the surface absorption process and be trapped in the tunnel in the zeolite structure. The use of zeolite as filler is expected to increase the mechanical strength of composites because zeolite has the ability to absorb water and act as a hardener.

The manufacturing of composites, which have mechanical and physical properties, will be affected by the initial conditions. Some parameters that need to be considered are the volume and pressure fraction that will affect the characteristics of the composite. The research of Belibi et al. (2003) and Indra et al. (2016) showed that mechanical and physical properties depend on the operating conditions at the printing stage. The research of Prihandoko et al. (2010) showed that the effect of compression molding pressure variations on the composite will decrease porosity, whereas the density and flexural strength increases.

These studies show that it is necessary to conduct research to determine the characteristics of composites with natural zeolite-filled polyester matrix with the influence of filler composition and the amount of pressure during compression molding.

5.2 PREPARATION AND CHARACTERIZATION OF UNSATURATED POLYESTER RESIN/NATURAL ZEOLITE COMPOSITES

5.2.1 MATERIALS

Unsaturated polyester used as the matrix of composites with a density of 1.215 g/mL was purchased from Chemical Store Rudang Jaya (Medan). Natural zeolite, which acted as the filler, was supplied from Sukabumi, West Java, Indonesia. Methyl ethyl ketone peroxide (MEKPO) used as the catalyst that accelerates the curing process was obtained from PT. Indah Sari Windu (Medan). MEKPO is a colorless, oily liquid with the density of 1.11 g/mL. The MEKPO used was 1% by resin weight. HCl as a filler activator was also purchased from Chemical Store Rudang Jaya (Medan). The molecular weight and the density of HCl are 36.5 g/mol and 1.0455 g/mL. HCl is colorless, with a freezing point and boiling point of –85°C and –114°C g/cm^3, respectively. Glycerin used as the mold lubricant and Aquadest (H$_2$O) used as the washer were obtained from Chemical Store Rudang Jaya (Medan).

5.2.2 SAMPLE PREPARATION

Matrix preparation was done by mixing the unsaturated polyester resin and MEKPO (1% resin weight) with a stirring bar till homogenous. For the filler activation, natural zeolite was mixed with HCl 2 M solution with a 1:10 ratio of natural zeolites to HCl. The mixture was stirred with a stirrer for 2 hours at 50 rpm. Then the HCl solution was separated from the natural zeolite with filter paper. The residue of filtration was washed with Aquadest till the pH was neutral. It was then dried under the sun for 2 hours and then heated with the furnace at 600°C for 1 hour.

FIGURE 5.1 Compression molding machine.

5.2.3 Fabrication of Composites

The matrix was mixed with the filler in the container using various ratios: 100:0, 90:10, 80:20, 70:30 and 60:40. Glycerin lubricant was applied on the base of the specimen mold. The mixture was poured into the mold and the surface was flattened. The mixture was then compression-molded (Figure 5.1) at pressures of 75, 100 and 125 psi. The composites were left to dry at room temperature. The composites were then released from the mold and smoothed with a file.

5.2.4 Characterization

The composites were subjected to tensile tests using a universal testing machine (model 3366, Instron, United States) and the composites were selected and cut to form a specimen for tensile strength testing (tensile test) according to the ASTM D638 standard. Tensile strength testing was carried out with a tensiometer on each specimen. The tensiometer (Figure 5.2) was first conditioned at a load of 100 kgf at a speed of 500 mm/min, then it was clamped firmly with an existing clamp. The engine was turned on and the specimen was attracted to the top and observed until it broke; the maximum stress and strain was then noted.

Scanning electron micrographs (SEMs) of natural zeolite and tensile fracture surfaces of composites were obtained by using a field emission SEM (model Supra 35VP, Zeiss, Jena, Germany) operating at 5 kV. The samples were sputter coated with a layer of carbon (on a sputter coater SC515, Polaron, United States) to avoid

FIGURE 5.2 Tensiometer.

electrostatic charging during the examination. The image results were analyzed to investigate the distribution of natural fibers in the polymer matrix and their interaction.

Density measurement was carried out according to ASTM D792-91. Composites were cut to a size of 5 × 5 cm and a 2.5 mm thickness. The volume was then calculated and the composites were weighed. The density was calculated as follows:

$$\text{Density} = \frac{M}{V}$$

where M and V were the weight and volume of the composite, respectively.

The water absorption measurement was carried out according to ASTM D570. Composites were cut to a diameter of 50.8 mm and a thickness of ±0.18 mm. The composites were weighed and then dipped in a container filled with distilled water at a temperature of 23 ± 1°C for 24 hours. The composite was then removed from the water, gently wiped dry with a clean cloth and weighed. The percentage of water absorption was calculated as follows:

$$\text{Water absorption } (\%) = \frac{M_1 - M_0}{M_0} \times 100$$

where M_0 and M_1 were the dried weight and final weight of the composite, respectively.

5.3 MORPHOLOGICAL PROPERTIES, COMPONENT CHARACTERIZATION AND CRYSTALLINITY OF NATURAL ZEOLITE FILLER

5.3.1 Morphological Properties and Component Characterization of Natural Zeolite Filler with Scanning Electron Microscope-Energy Dispersive X-ray (SEM-EDX)

The activation of filler is important to increase the mechanical properties of the composite. The morphological properties of non-activated and activated natural zeolite with SEM-energy dispersive X-ray (EDX) are depicted in Figure 5.3.

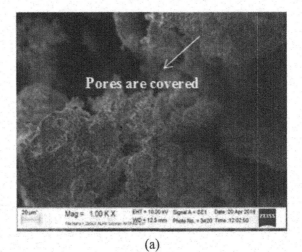

(a)

(b)

FIGURE 5.3 The morphological properties of natural zeolite with SEM-EDX: (a) Non-activated. (b) Activated.

Figure 5.3a shows that the surface of the zeolite that was non-activated was still covered with impurities that covered the pores of the zeolite. Zeolite is a porous tetrahedral alumina silica crystal mineral that has a three-dimensional structure. It is often used as an adsorbent because it has cavities filled with metal ions. Non-activating zeolites tend to be low because they have many impurities, and for this reason modification is necessary (Las et al., 2011). The activation process can be carried out by chemical and physical methods. Physical activation can be done by reducing the size and heating at high temperatures, whereas chemically activation is done with the addition of acids (Aidha, 2013).

Figure 5.3b illustrates that the zeolite morphology that had been activated has a clearer surface with cavities that were previously covered with impurities. Zeolites can be multifunctional if they have been modified both physically and chemically. Activation is a modifying step that aims to cleanse the pore surface and get rid of impurities (Atikah, 2017). Figure 5.3b shows that zeolite had formed empty cavities that were previously occupied by impurities. The absorption ability of these zeolite cavities will be utilized as a better binder with the matrix so that a strong composite can be produced.

The loss of metals and other impurities was also proven by the results of SEM-EDX. The component characterization of non-activated and activated natural zeolite with SEM-EDX is depicted in Figure 5.4.

Figure 5.4a demonstrates the composition of zeolites, namely elements O, Si, Al, Fe, Mg, K and C, with a content of 38.26, 30.95, 6.89, 10.0, 5.5, 1.44 and 1.36 (wt%), respectively. Si and O content is the most dominant because they are the main constituents of zeolites. Electron beam energy in the form of X-rays will be detected and calculated by an EDX and an output will be produced in the form of a graph of the peaks representing the elements contained.

Figure 5.4a indicates that the highest peak was the element Si followed by Fe and the metals Al and K. It further indicates that the impurity metal elements (Fe, Mg and K) are still bound to the zeolite structure so that the nature of the zeolites was not maximized, thus modification was needed.

Figure 5.5b shows that the composition of impurities was reduced and lost. This was caused by the existence of an activation treatment on zeolites that causes decationization (namely the cations will be released in the zeolite pores). The compositions of the remaining elements O, Si, Al and C were 31.27, 21.86, 15.18 and 2.26 wt%, respectively, The figure further shows that the composition of zeolite had decreased the amount of composition after activation with HCl. This was due to the process of dealumination with 2 M hydrochloric acid. This activation process caused the metal content in zeolites to decrease, as evidenced by Figure 5.4b, where the metal elements had been lost, whereas the main elements of zeolites, namely Si, O and Al, remain and even increase. This activated zeolite will increase the abilities of zeolite.

One factor that can determine the ability of zeolites is the ratio of Si/Al in the zeolite structure. Figure 5.4b demonstrates that the impurity content of zeolites that have been activated by using HCl has been lost and the elements O and S have decreased composition. This is inversely proportional to Al and C, which have increased composition after activation. According to Svehla (1979), HCl with dilute or concentrated

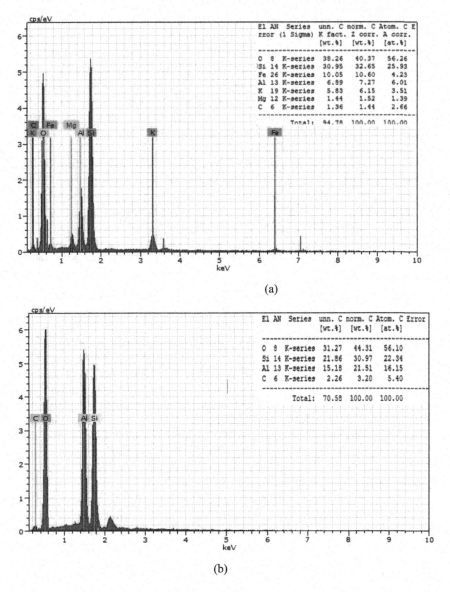

FIGURE 5.4 The components characterization of natural zeolite with SEM-EDX (a) non-activated (b) activated.

concentrations can dissolve metals such as Fe, Zn, Mn and Mg, resulting in the total percentage of impurities present in the zeolite after the activation process changes including the Si/Al ratio (Prasetyo et al., 2012).

From Figure 5.4a and b, we can calculate the non-activated and activated zeolite Si/Al ratio. The ratio can be calculated by comparing the composition of silicate with aluminum. The non-activated zeolite Si/Al ratio is 4.4, whereas the activated

Si/Al ratio has de creased to 1.44. The smaller ratio of Si/Al will make zeolite absorb more water. According to Prasetyo et al (2012), the inability of the Si element can substitute for the lost Al content. Changes in the Si/Al ratio of a material will affect the nature of the material (Prasetyo et al., 2012), and the higher the Si/Al ratio of a material is, the more hydrophobic the material (Lestari, 2010)

Therefore, the ability of activated zeolite to absorb more water will later help improve the mechanical properties of composites by utilizing these empty voids.

5.3.2 Crystallinity of Natural Zeolite Filler with X-ray Diffraction (XRD)

The purpose of zeolite X-Ray diffraction (XRD) characterization is to analyze the crystallinity index obtained using X-rays. The results of testing for crystallinity using XRD can be seen in Figure 5.5.

Based on the graph in Figure 5.5, the results of diffraction using XRD in its operation involved Cu radiation at 40 kV 30 mA. Determination of the crystallinity index of a material can be done using the Segal method.

Non-activated zeolites have high tendencies in the diffraction angle range (2) between 25.6° and 28°, whereas activated zeolite tendencies in the angular range are between 25.7° and 27.7°. This can be seen from the sharp peaks in activated and non-activated zeolites. Based on the peak at angle 2 19°–27° between zeolite non-activation and activation with HCl 2 M, there is a shift in angle 2 that is not too far between the zeolite non-activation and activation. According to Aidha (2013), shifts occurred because of phase changes after activation with HCl. This shows that the metal had disappeared from the zeolite pores that caused angular changes 2.

By modifying the zeolite with HCl activation, there was no structural change and only a slight change in the crystallinity of the zeolite. This was indicated by the appearance of a typical peak of activated zeolite at 2 of 20°–30°, which is relatively the same between non-activated zeolites. The crystallinity value for non-activated zeolite was 50.6%, whereas the modified zeolite had a crystallinity of 66%. The crystallinity value of non-activated and activated zeolites did not differ greatly (namely 53.14% and 63.42%) from the research of Siregar (2014) and Subariyah (2011). This

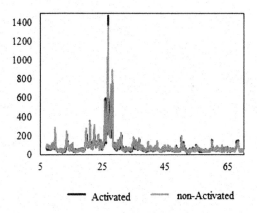

FIGURE 5.5 The crystallinity of non-activated and activated natural zeolite with XRD.

increase in crystallinity was caused by the presence of acid treatment, which results in the loss of impurities in zeolites (Pardoyo et al., 2009). Therefore, the process of modifying zeolites by activation is a way to increase crystallinity.

5.4 MECHANICAL PROPERTIES AND MORPHOLOGICAL BEHAVIOR OF UNSATURATED POLYESTER/NATURAL ZEOLITE COMPOSITE

5.4.1 Tensile Strength

The purpose of tensile strength testing is to find out how much force is needed to pull the material until it breaks. The greater the tensile strength value of a material is, the greater the force is needed to attract the material. The effects of comparing activated zeolite composition and hot press pressure on the tensile strength (composite strength) of polyester composites is illustrated in Figure 5.6.

Figure 5.6 shows that added activated zeolite fillers had higher tensile strength compared with unsaturated polyester because zeolite-filled composites were able to withstand the stronger force exerted on composites. The tensile strength value of polyester composites increased to reach 38.51 MPa with a 70:30 ratio of activated polyester:zeolite and a pressure of 125 psi, but the tensile strength decreased at a ratio of 60:40 with a value of 32.13 MPa.

Figure 5.6 also demonstrates that with the addition of zeolite fillers, the value of the composite tensile strength also increased because the structure of the zeolite, which has cavities and a large surface contact area that allows wetting, binds strongly with the matrix and exerts an effect on the increase in tensile strength

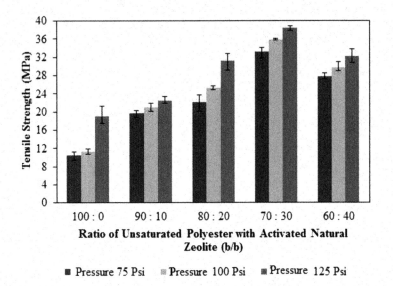

FIGURE 5.6 The effect of comparing activated zeolite composition and pressure on hot press with the tensile strength of polyester composites.

(Gultom et al., 2015). However, there was a decrease in the tensile strength value in the ratio of composition of activated polyester:zeolite of 60:40. This is because when the filler composition has been saturated (saturated), the filler particles are no longer able to accommodate unsaturated polyester in the cavities of activated zeolite, causing imperfect wetting. This is in accordance with the study of Gultom et al. (2015) in which the ability of nano-zeolites increased with the addition of compositions by 20 wt% (i.e., 2.9 MPa), and then it decreased to 2.5 MPa at a composition of 25 wt%. This occurs because of the decrease in the interaction of fillers with the matrix due to the addition of fillers.

The tensile strength of the composite increased with increasing pressure on the hot press because when the pressure was applied to the composite, it was easier for the matrix to enter the activated zeolite cavities. When a large addition of activated zeolite pressure increases the density of the composite, the resulting composite becomes stronger. This is in accordance with the research of Lykidis and Grigoriou (2011) who reviewed variations in hot press pressure and reported increasing pressure exerted influence on mechanical strength.

5.4.2 FLEXURAL STRENGTH

The purpose of flexural strength testing is to demonstrate the ability of a material to withstand the load applied transversally above it. The effect of comparing activated zeolite composition and hot press pressure with the flexural strength of polyester composites is illustrated in Figure 5.7.

Figure 5.7 shows that the addition of activated zeolite fillers increased flexural strength, where the highest flexural strength of zeolite-filled composites in the polyester:zeolite 80:20 ratio at 125 psi pressure is 96.22 MPa, whereas for the

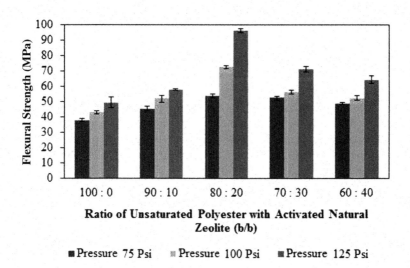

FIGURE 5.7 Effect of comparing the activated zeolite composition and hot press pressure with the flexural strength of polyester composites.

lowest flexural strength values (i.e., at a ratio of 100:0) the pressure is 75 psi, which is 37.57 MPa.

The increasing filler of the composite showed an increase in the flexural strength of a zeolite-filled composite because the addition of fillers will increase the interaction of zeolite fillers, which have a hollow structure with matrix. This was in accordance with research by Embu et al. (2000), who reported that the addition of fillers from polypropylene composites can increase the flexural strength value of composites. The addition of fillers increases the interaction of the fillers and the matrix, but if the interaction between the fillers and the matrix is low there will be a decrease in the value of the flexural strength of the composite. At the same pressure in the ratio of fillers with a matrix of 70:30, with the decrease from 96, 22 MPa becomes 71.10 MPa, and then the filler is added again so it decreases again to 64.24 MPa. This happened because there was good wetting of the composite, which causes the polyester not to bind well to the filler, causing the transfer of stress from the filler and the matrix to be inefficient (Uygunoglu et al., 2015). Thus the zeolite filler cannot withstand any load, so the mechanical strength of the composite decreases. The decrease occurs because the filler is at its optimum point, which is triggered because the structure of the zeolite itself has cavities that should be the entry point of unsaturated polyester. High volume fraction will increase the composite cavity, and the cavity will affect the decrease in bending stress on the composite. The existence of the cavity is a place of stress concentration and the place of initiation/initial cracking so that the composite experiences a low bending value (Oza, 2010).

Figure 5.7 demonstrates that a large increase in hot press pressure can increase the flexural strength of a composite. This was in accordance with the research of Younesi and Bahrololoom (2009), who reported that an increase in pressure will result in increasingly strong mechanical properties (i.e., increased flexural strength with increasing pressure from 300 to 450 kg/cm^2). By increasing the pressure, the interface interaction between the filler and the matrix will be better, thereby increasing mechanical strength.

5.4.3 Impact Strength

The purpose of testing the impact strength is to find out how much energy is produced to destroy material through impact on a surface. The impact strength is a parameter of whether a material is strong or brittle. Strong material has a high impact strength value, whereas fragile material has a low impact strength value. The effect of comparing activated zeolite composition and hot press pressure with impact strength of polyester composites can be seen in Figure 5.8.

Figure 5.8 demonstrates that with the addition of zeolite fillers, the value of the impact strength of zeolite-filled polyester composites was higher than that of unsaturated polyester impact strength. The value of the impact strength of polyester composites increased to 8.89 J/m^2 at a polyester:zeolite ratio of 70:30 and hot press pressure of 125 psi, but decreased at a ratio of 60:40 and hot press pressure of 125 psi with a value of 7.19 J/m^2.

Also, Figure 5.8 demonstrates that with an increase in the addition of zeolite fillers, the value of the impact strength also increases because of the role of the

Utilization of Natural Zeolite as Filler

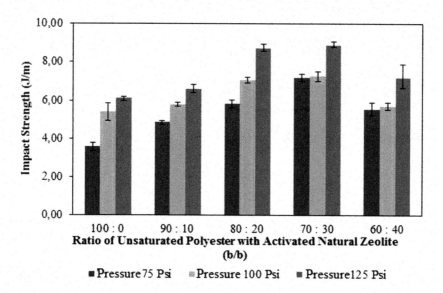

FIGURE 5.8 Effect of comparing activated zeolite composition and hot press pressure with impact strength of polyester composites.

filler in increasing the impact resistance of the composite. In this case the filler interacted with the crack formation and the stress transferring medium (Sain and Suhara, 2007). The addition of fillers is also influenced by the size and dispersion of particles in the fillers. Small well-dispersed particles generally give better results. Particles that have good dispersion will certainly form a good interphase network between the filler and the matrix so that the presence of composite fillers will absorb higher impact energy. However, there was a decrease in the value of the impact strength in the polyester:zeolite ratio of 60:40 because the more fillers are added the less they are well distributed. The composition of activated zeolite fillers that exceed the optimum limit will cause wetting, which does not work well in certain areas, thus the impact strength of the composite decreases. Based on research from Silva et al. (2013), one of the decreases in the value of impact strength was by the addition of a filler, which makes the area around the filler decrease.

The composite impact strength increases with increasing hot press pressure. Based on research by Cunha et al. (2003), the effect of compression molding produced good composites due to strong bonding interfaces, and can increase the rigidity of composites. Thus, with the increase in hot press pressure makes the number of filling cavities that blend with unsaturated polyester so that the composite was denser and requires more energy to destroy the material.

5.4.4 Density

The effect of comparing activated zeolite composition and hot press pressure with density of polyester composites is illustrated in Figure 5.9. This figure shows that the

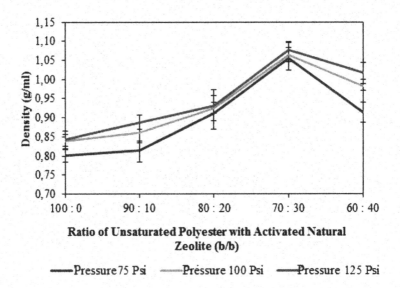

FIGURE 5.9 Effect of comparing the activated zeolite composition and hot press pressure with the density of polyester composites.

addition of zeolite and hot press pressure to the density of the composite obtained the highest density of 1.077 g/cm^3 at a ratio of 70:30 and a pressure of 125 psi, whereas the lowest density value obtained at a ratio of 100:0 at a pressure of 75 psi is 0.802 g/cm^3.

Figure 5.9 shows that with the increasing zeolite added, the density value obtained is also increasing. The highest density value was obtained by adding 70:30 zeolite fillers at 125 psi pressure. However, the subsequent addition of fillers at the same pressure revealed a decrease in density value of 1017 g/cm^3. This is caused by the addition of fillers, which causes no wetting between the filler and the matrix on the composite and thus reduces the interaction between the filler and the composite. When the addition of fillers is reached, an optimum point will be reached, which decreases the mechanical properties of the composite. This has been proven by research from Silva et al. (2013) that reported the density decrease is due to the addition of fillers, which reduces the concentration of the area around the fillers.

Figure 5.9 further shows that a large increase in hot press pressure will increase the density value. The higher the pressure used in making zeolite-filled composites is, the higher the density of composites is produced. This is in accordance with the research of Lee et al. (2007), who reported that the increased pressure had an effect on producing denser composites.

5.4.5 Water Absorption

The purpose of the analysis of water absorption properties is to show whether a composite can suffer damage if it is submerged. When the composite is immersed

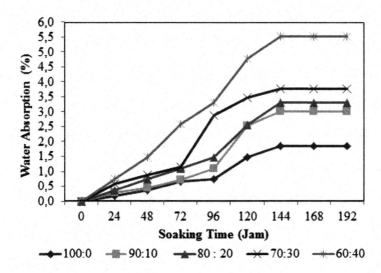

FIGURE 5.10 Effect of soaking time on water absorption (water absorption) polyester.

in water, water will diffuse into the composite. This is avoided because water can damage the composite structure from the inside, thereby reducing the mechanical properties of the composite. The effect of comparing activated zeolite composition and hot press pressure with water absorption of zeolite composites can be seen in Figure 5.10.

Figure 5.10 shows that the water absorption of the composite material increased with the addition of the filler material. The graph also shows that water absorption reached the saturation point (where the composite did not absorb more water) and the water content in the composite remained constant.

The addition of the zeolite composition caused an increase in the percentage of polyester composite water at a ratio of 100:0 by 1.53% to reach a value of 5.51% at a ratio of 60:40. This was caused by the zeolite filler absorbing water. Zeolite is one of the most used absorbents because the structure of the zeolite has empty cavities. The nature of zeolites as absorbents and molecular filters is possible due to the hollow structure of zeolites; thus, zeolites are able to absorb large numbers of molecules that are smaller or in accordance with the size of their sockets (Rini and dan Fendy, 2010). Adding a filler to the composite will result in an increase in the percentage of water absorption, but if too much is added the filler will not be able to wet the matrix properly. This will weaken the interface adhesion between the filler and the matrix, thereby causing variations in the formation of gaps in the interface area. An increase in the gap at the interface can increase the number of water molecules to be able to penetrate the composite and get stuck in the gap. This had been researched by Kaymakci et al. (2017), who found that more fill content from zeolites will make the percentage of absorption water rise from fill conditions of 0–55 wt%. Based on the results obtained, this research is in accordance with the theory that greater zeolite composition causes an increase in the percentage of water absorption.

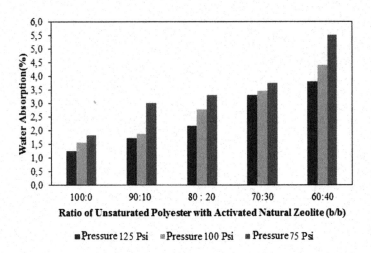

FIGURE 5.11 Effect of comparing activated zeolite composition and hot press pressure with water absorption of polyester composites.

The effect of comparing the composition of polyester-zeolite and the pressure on the hot press with the water absorption properties of polyester composites can be seen in Figure 5.11. The figure shows that the water absorption of the composite material increases with the addition of the filler material.

Figure 5.11 demonstrates that the increase in pressure on the hot press causes a decrease in the percentage of absorption of polyester composite water at a ratio of 100:0 at 75 psi pressure of 1.83% to decrease 1.26% at 125 psi pressure. Increasing the pressure when printing a composite can reduce voids and increase the interface bond between the matrix and the filler, thereby increasing the composite density. Then the percentage of water absorption of the composite decreases with increasing hot press pressure (Younesi and Bahrololoom, 2009).

The results obtained are in accordance with the research that greater pressure on the hot press when printing composites causes a decrease in the percentage of composite water absorption.

5.4.6 Morphological Properties

Figure 5.12a illustrates a polyester composite with a composition of polyester:zeolite activated at a ratio of 60:40 and 75 psi. The filler composition had been saturated, and the filler particles no longer are able accommodate unsaturated polyester in the cavities of activated zeolite, which caused imperfect wetting. The filler was not dispersed and did not get inside the zeolite.

Figure 5.12b shows a polyester composite with a composition ratio of 70:30 and a 125 psi hot press pressure, indicating that the fillers are well dispersed where unsaturated polyester occupies cavities of activated zeolites; thus, wetting between the filler and the matrix went well.

Utilization of Natural Zeolite as Filler 117

(a)

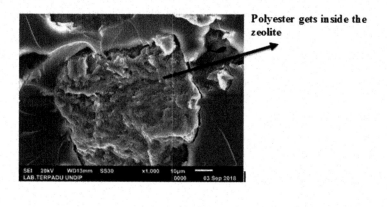

(b)

FIGURE 5.12 SEM characterization of (a) zeolite polyester composite activated at a ratio of 60:40 and 75 psi pressure with 1000× magnification and (b) zeolite polyester composite activated at a ratio of 70:30 pressure and 125 psi.

5.5 CONCLUSIONS

In this chapter, research demonstrated that the natural zeolite effectively enhanced the mechanical and physical properties of polymer composites. The study revealed that the best properties of tensile and impact strength were found in the polyester composition:activated zeolite ratio of 70:30 zeolite (w/w) at 125 psi with a tensile strength of 38.51 MPa and impact strength of 8.89 J/m^2. The best properties of flexural strength of composites were found in the polyester:zeolite ratio of 80:20 at 125 psi, which is 96.22 MPa. SEM showed that at the polyester:zeolite ratio of

60:40 (w/w) at 75 psi pressure the breaking surface was rougher because there was no good wetting between the matrix and activated zeolite filler. The study also showed that the composite water density and absorption tended to increase with the addition of fillers.

ACKNOWLEDGMENT

The authors wish to acknowledge the Directorate of Research and Community Service Director, General Strengthening Research and Development Ministry of Research and Technology and the Higher Education Republic of Indonesia for a grant from 2018 to 2019.

REFERENCES

Aidha, Novi Nur. 2013. "Activation of Zeolite by Physical and Chemical Methods to Reduce the Hardness (Ca And Mg) of Groundwater." *Jurnal Kimia Kemasan* 35 (1): 58–64.

Aprilia, Wiwi, Yenni Darvina, and Ratna Wulan. 2013. "Sifat Mekanis Komposit Berpenguat Bilah Bambu dengan Matriks Polyester akibat Variasi Susunan." *Jurnal Pillar of Physics* 2: 51–58.

Atikah, Wulan Safrihatini. 2017. "The Potentiality of Activated Natural Zeolite from Gunung Kidul as Adsorben to Textile Dyes." *Arena Tekstil* 32 (1): 17–24.

Barbosa, Gustavi P., Henrique S. Debone, Patricia Severino, Eliana B. Souto, and Classius F. Da Silva. 2015. "Design and Characterization of Chitosan/Zeolite Composite Films – Effect of Zeolite Type and Zeolite Dose on the Film Properties." *Materials Science & Engineering C* S0928-4931 (15): 30565–30568. https://doi.org/10.1016/j.msec.2015.11.034

Belibi, Pierre Celestin, T. Jean Daou, and Jean-Marie B. Ndjaka. 2003. "Tensile and Water Barrier Properties of Cassava Starch Composite Films Reinforced by Synthetic Zeolite and Beidellite." *Journal of Food Engineering* 115: 339–346. https://doi.org/10.1016/j.jfoodeng.2012.10.027

Berthelot, J.M. 1999. *Composite Materials Teknosia Vol. III, No. 1,. Mechanical Behavior Structural Analysis*. New York: Springer-Verlag.

Cowd, M.A. 1982. *Polymer Chemistry*. London: John Murray.

Cunha, Antonio M., Rui A.S., Rui L.R., and Michael J.B. 2003. "Processing and Properties of Bobe-Analogue Biodegradable and Bioinert Polymeric Composite." *Composite Science and Technology* 63: 389–402.

Deswita, Aloma Karo, and Grace Tj. Sulungbudi dan Sudirman. 2002. "Pengaruh Penambahan Filler Jerami Terhadap Sifat Mekanik dan Termal Komposit Berbasis Polipropilena." *Jurnal Sains Materi Indonesia*, 12 (1): 24–29.

Embu, Y. E., C. C. Briggs, and R. J. Heath. 2000. "The Effect of Mica Reinforcement on The Mechanical Properties of Polypropylene." *Nigerian Journal of Polymer Science* 1 (1): 40–45.

Gilang R., D., Alfian W. S., Hery S., Nur F. F., and Nanik D. N. 2017. "Synthesis of Natural Ni/Zeolite Activated by Acid as Catalyst for Synthesis Biodiesel from Ketapang Seeds Oil." *JPKP* 2 (1): 72–79.

Gultom, Fransiskus, Basuki Wirjosentono, Hamongan Nainggolan, and Eddiyanto. 2015. "Preparation and Characterization from Natural Zeolite Sarulla of North Sumatera Polyurethane Nanocomposite Foams." *Chemistry and Materials Research* 2 (10): 20–28.

Indra, Kurniawan P., Wijang Wisnu Raharjo, and Teguh Triyono. 2016. "Pengaruh Variasi Temperatur *Hotpress* terhadap Kekuatan *Bending* Komposit RHDPE/*Cantula*." *Prosiding SNST* 1 (1): 26–29.

Kajtar, Dora Andrea, Csaba Kenyo, Karoly Renner, Janos Moczo, Erika Fekete, Christoph Krohnke, and Bela Pukanszky. 2017. "Interfacial Interactions and Reinforcement in Thermoplastic/Zeolite Composites." *Composites part B: Engineering* 114: 386–394. https://doi.org/10.1016/j.compositesb.2016.12.015

Kaymakci, Alperen, Turker Gulec, Seyyed Khalil Hosseinihashemi, and Nadir Ayrilmis. 2017. "Physical, Mechanical and Thermal Properties of Wood/Zeolite/Plastic Hybrid Composite." *Maderas Ciencia y Tecologia* 19(3): 339–348. https://doi.org/10.4067/S0718-221X2017005000029

Kurniasari, L. 2010. "Potensi Zeolit Alam Sebagai Adsorben Air Pada Alat Pengering." *Jurnal Teknik Kimia* 6 (1): 15–17.

Las, T., F. Firdiyono, and A. Hendrawan. 2011. "Adsoprsi Unsur Pengotor Larutan Natrium Silikat menggunakan Zeolits Alam Karangnunggal." *Valensi* 2 (2): 368–378.

Lee, H.S., H.J. Kim, S.G. Kim, S.H. Ahn. 2007. "Evaluation of Graphite Composite Bipolar Plate For PEM (Proton Exchange Membrane) Fuel Cell: Electrical, Mechanical, and Molding Temperature." *Journal of Materials Processing Technology* 187–188: 425–428. https://doi.org/10.1016/j.jmatprotec.2006.11.213

Lestari D.Y. 2010. "Kajian Modifikasi dan Karakterisasi Zeolit Alam dari Berbagai Negara." *Prosiding Seminar Nasional Kimia dan Pendidikan Kimia*, 30: 1–6.

Lykidis, C., and Grigoriou, A. 2011. "Quality Characteristics of Hydrothermally Recycled Particleboards Using Various Wood Recovery Parameter." *The Wood Technology Society of the Institute of Materials* 2 (1): 38–43. https://doi.org/10.1179/2042645311Y.0000000002

Ngapa, Yulius Dala. 2017. "Kajian Pengaruh Asam-Basa pada Aktivasi Zeolit dan Karakterisasinya Sebagai Adsorben Pewarna Biru Metilena." *Jurnal Kimia dan Pendidikan Kimia* 2 (2): 90–96.

Oza, S. 2010. "Thermal and Mechanical Properties of Recycled High Density Polyethylene/hemp Fiber Composites." PhD dissertation, University City Blvd Charlotte.

Pardoyo, P., L. Listiana, and A. Darmawan. 2009. "Pengaruh Perlakuan HCl pada Kristalinitas dan Kemampuan Adsorpsi Zeolit terhadap Ion Ca^{2+}." *Jurnal Sains dan Matematika* 17 (2): 100–104.

Prasetyo, Anton, Rini Nafsiati, Susi Nurul Kholifahm, and Agie Botioanovi. (2012) "Analisa Permukaan Zeolit Alam Malang yang Mengalami Modifikasi Pori Dengan Uji SEM-EDS." *Saintis* 1 (2): 39–46.

Prihandoko, B., Yunita San Desto Wahu Novianto. 2010. "Pengaruh Tekanan Hot Press Terhadap Karakter Pelat Bipolar PEMFC." *Jurnal Ilmu Pengetahuan dan Teknologi TELAAH* 27, 28–32.

Rianto, Yanu. 2011. "Pengaruh Komposisi Campuran Filler terhadap Kekuatan Bending Komposit Ampas Tebu – Serbuk Kayu dalam Matrik Polyester." PhD dissertation, Universitas Sebelas Maret, Surakarta.

Rini, Dian Kusuma, and Anthonius L. dan Fendy. 2010. "Optimasi Aktivasi Zeolit Alam Untuk Dehumidifikasi." PhD dissertation, Universitas Diponegoro.

Sain, Mohini, and Suhara Panthapulakkal. 2007. "Injection – Molded Short Hemp Fiber/Glass Fiber – Reinforced Polypropylene Hybrid Composites – Mechanical, Water Absorption And Thermal Properties." *Journal of Applied Polymer Science* 103: 2432–2441.

Silva, F., James Njuguna, Sophia Sachse, Krzysztof Pielichowski, Agnieszka Leszczynska, and Marco Giacomelli. 2013. "The Influence of Multiscale Fillers Reinforcement Into Impact Resistance and Energy Absorption Properties of Polyamide 6 and Polypropylene Nanocomposite Structures." *Material & Design* 50: 244–252. https://doi.org/10.1016/j.matdes.2013.02.041

Siregar, T. 2014. "Penggunaan Zeolit Alam Sentani Sebagai Pengisi Bahan Komposit Polietilen." *Journal Teknologi Mineral dan Batubara* 10 (1): 22–31.

Subariyah, I. 2011. "Adosrpsi Pb (II) Menggunakan Zeolit Alam Termodifikasi Asam Fosfat." PhD dissertation, Institut Pertanian Bogor.

Sufian Suri, Rahmatunnisa. 2009. "Komposit Poliester Tak Tepu – Sekam Padi: Kesan Pencuacaan Terhadap Sifat Mekanikal Komposit." PhD dissertation, Universitas Terbuka.

Svehla. G. 1979. *Vogel's Textbook of Macro and Semi-Micro Qualitative Inorganic Analysis*, 5th Edition. Oxford, UK: The Chaucer Press.

Uygunoglu, Tayfun, Ibrahim Gunes, and Witold Brostov. 2015. "Physical and Mechanical Properties of Polymer Composites with High Content of Wasters Including Boron." *Material Research* 18(6): 1188–1196. http://dx.doi.org/10.1590/1516-1439.009815

Visakh, P. M., Olga B. Nazarenko, Yulia A. Amelkovich, and Tatyana V. Melnikova. 2016. "Effect of Zeolite and Boric Acid on Epoxy-Based Composites." *Polymer Advance Technology* 27 (8): 1098–1101. https://doi.org/10.1002/pat.3776

Younesi, Mousa, and Mohammad Erbrahim Bahrololoom. 2009. "Effect of Temperature and Pressure of Hot Pressing on The Mechanical Properties of PP–HA Bio-Composites." *Materials and Design* 30: 3482–3488. https://doi.org/10.1016/j.matdes.2009.03.011

Yuliusman, Y. 2016. "Aktivasi Zeolit Alam Lampung Sebagai Adsorben Karbon Monoksida Asap Kebakaran." *Prosiding Seminar Nasional Teknik Kimia* 4: 1–6.

6 Effect of Glut Palmitate Coupling Agent on Vulcanized Silica-Filled Natural Rubber

Dalina Samsudin, Faiezah Hashim, and Noor Aishatun Majid
Universiti Teknologi MARA
Arau, Malaysia

Hanafi Ismail
Universiti Sains Malaysia
Nibong Tebal, Malaysia

CONTENTS

6.1 Introduction 121
6.2 Methodology 123
    6.2.1 Materials 123
    6.2.2 Preparation of Rubber Composite 123
    6.2.3 Characterization 123
6.3 Results and Discussion 125
    6.3.1 Cure Characteristic 125
    6.3.2 Mechanical Properties 126
    6.3.3 Rubber Filler Interaction Study 129
    6.3.4 Scanning Electron Microscopy (SEM) Study 129
    6.3.5 Fourier Transform Infrared Spectroscopy (FTIR) 131
6.4 Conclusion 133
Acknowledgment 133
References 133

6.1 INTRODUCTION

Silica, also known as silicon dioxide (SiO_2), is rapidly gaining acceptance as a filler in the polymer composites industry. Commercial silica is available in ground, precipitated, fumed and gel forms. Silica may be crystalline or amorphous (Jesionowski et al. 2002) and its surface has silanol (Si-OH) and siloxane (Si-O-Si) groups

(Kingsley Iler 1979). There are approximately 3–4.5 hydrophilic silanol groups per square nanometer of the silica's surface; therefore, it exhibits hydrophilic characteristics. The hydrogen bonds between the OH groups of silanol molecules are formed as the OH groups get closer together. The hydrogen bonding between active silanol groups enables the silica molecules to aggregate and agglomerate (Jesionowski et al. 2002). Also, the excessive amount of amino silane coupling agent creates an additional hydrogen bond among neighboring silica, thus making silica molecules agglomerate (Jesionowski and Krysztafkiewicz 2001).

The use of silica as a reinforcing filler or an extended filler in the composites mostly depends on the specific industry (Rodgers and Waddell 2005). Silica's stiffness causes high moduli of compounded polymers, which can be employed in various applications, such as an ingredient in the food, cosmetics, microelectronics, structural and packaging materials and in the automotive industry.

Natural rubber (NR) is a natural polymer derived from the *Hevea brasiliensis* tree. It is an amorphous non-polar rubber that can induce strain crystallization, which results properties such as tensile strength, abrasion and tear resistance (Jansomboon et al. 2020). These properties make it one of the important materials used in manufacturing industries, household products, transportation and engineering (Zheng et al. 2018; Phaneendra et al. 2020). NR has a branching and network structure consisting of terminal cross-linking and entanglements. The entanglement acts as crosslinking points to increase network density during vulcanization. In that case, the entanglement cannot be loosened by segmental movement in which it becomes a permanent entanglement (Huang et al. 2018). In current studies, the curing temperature for vulcanization usually is in the range of 140°C–160°C (Jong 2019).

Presently, silica filler is widely used with NR for various rubber applications. Silica can reinforce NR by increasing the mechanical properties of the composites. However, the factors responsible for significant property enhancement in polymer composites are the properties of the polymer matrices, the fillers and the filler/matrix interfaces (Goda et al. 2013). Numerous studies have found that adequate adhesion between filler/matrix interfaces resulted in enhanced polymer composites property (Ten Brinke et al. 2003; Pattanawanidchai et al. 2014). Unfortunately, the hydrophilic character of silica results in incompatibility with the hydrophobic NR. Hence, it makes an ineffective stress and energy transfer, thus reducing the mechanical properties of the composites.

Coupling agents have gained recognition among researchers and today they are employed as the solution to these incompatibility issues. They have been used in rubber composite formulations to improve the interfacing polarity, forming a bonding between matrices and fillers in the composites. Bonds occurring at the interface may enhance the mechanical properties of rubber composites (Ramli et al. 2012; El-Sabbagh 2014; Kakou et al. 2014). The study of using glut palmitate (GP) as a coupling agent was first carried out by Samsudin et al. (2018) in which they synthesized the GP from palmitic acid and glutamine precursor. The use of GP is then reported in several papers (Samsudin et al. 2016, 2018; Zaini et al. 2019). Samsudin et al. (2016) investigated the effectiveness of GP as a coupling agent at various loadings, and its effectiveness was compared with a maleated coupling agent. In their study, adding GP showed an effect similar to the maleated coupling agent in a silica-filled high-density polyethylene (HDPE) composite in which both coupling agents enhanced the composite's mechanical property. The study indicated that the coupling agents effectively improved interfacial bonding, thus reducing the incompatibility between the silica and the HDPE. In a different matrix system, Zaini et al. (2019) reported the effect of GP in a sepiolite-filled ethylene propylene diene monomer (EPDM) composite. In an investigation of 9-phr GP in various sepiolite loadings in EPDM, the GP showed improvement in tensile strength and elongation at break, and the morphology exhibited the greatest matrix tearing line and surface roughness, which correlate to a high tensile strength. However, there is no report on the application of GP in silica-filled NR composite. Therefore, in this study, the effect of GP on rubber composites may broaden the function of GP as a coupling agent.

In this chapter, various GP loadings were investigated to determine its effect on silica-filled NR composites in terms of cure characteristics, cross-link density, rubber-filler interaction, tensile and hardness properties, chemical interaction and tensile fracture morphology.

6.2 METHODOLOGY

6.2.1 Materials

The GP synthesized from our lab (Samsudin et al. 2018) with a density of 1.2423 ± 0.0026 g/cm^3 was used. The GP was added in the rubber composite in a range of 1–11 phr. The NR, SMR-L grade with a density of 0.92 g/cm^3, was purchased from Guthrie (M) Sdn. Bhd. White amorphous powder of reinforced precipitated silica (Vulkasil S) 2–35 μm in size with a density of 2.0 g/cm^3 and toluene with a density of 0.8669 g/cm^3 was purchased from Bayer. The silica was dried in a vacuum oven at 80°C for 24 hours before use. Zinc oxide (ZnO), stearic acid, N-isopropyl-N′-phenyl-p-phenylenediamine (IPPD), dibenzothiazyl disulfide (MBTS) and sulfur were supplied by Bayer Co. (M) Sdn. and used as compounding ingredients in rubber composites.

6.2.2 Preparation of Rubber Composite

The silica-filled rubber composite was compounded for 20 minutes using a lab-scaled two-roll mill (model XK-160). The compounded composite was then orderly added into the masticated 100-phr SMR-L, followed by 5-phr ZnO, 2-phr stearic acid, 30-phr silica, range of 0- to 11-phr GP, 2-phr IPPD, 1.5-phr MBTS and 1.5-phr sulfur. The compound was then press-molded into a sheet at 150°C based on the curing time (t_{90}) from the curing test characteristics.

6.2.3 Characterization

Curing characteristics were determined at temperature 150°C according to ISO 3417 by a moving die rheometer (model MDR 2000). The scorch time (t_{S2}) and t_{90} were recorded from the torque versus time rheograph.

The cross-link density and rubber filler interaction study of the composite was characterized using the molded composite 30 × 5 × 2-mm sheet. The composites were initially weighed, immersed in toluene and kept at room temperature in a dark place for 24 hours. The weight of the swollen composites after 24 hours was recorded. The constant weights of the composites were obtained with a repeated drying process in an oven at 70°C for 15 minutes.

The cross-link density $[X]_{phy}$ quantitatively expressed in Equation 6.1 is based on the Flory Rehner equilibrium swelling equation, where χ is the NR-toluene interaction parameter (0.39), ρ_r is the density of rubber (NR = 0.92 g/cm³), V_0 is the molar volume of the toluene (106.3 mL/mol) and v_r is the volume fraction of the swollen rubber

$$-\ln(1-v_r) - v_r - \chi v_r^2 = 2\rho_r V_0 [X]_{phy} v_r^{\frac{1}{3}} \quad (6.1)$$

The v_r was calculated based on Equation 6.2, where w_s is swollen weight, w_d is the dried weight, and ρ_s is the density of the solvent (toluene = 0.8669 g/cm³)

$$v_r = \frac{(w_d/\rho_r)}{\dfrac{(w_d)}{\rho_r} + \left(\dfrac{w_s - w_d}{\rho_s}\right)} \quad (6.2)$$

The interaction of rubber filler was measured by the filler-rubber interaction index (Qf/Qg), where Qf is the weight of toluene uptake per gram of composite and Qg refers to the weight of toluene uptake per gram of vulcanized NR. The Qf/Qg value indicates the interaction between rubber and filler. The Qf/Qg ratio represented by the Lorez Park model and the value of Q can be determined according to the following equation:

$$Q = \frac{\text{Swollen weight} - \text{dried weight}}{\text{Initial weight} \times 100/(\text{Formula weight})} \quad (6.3)$$

Mechanical properties of the composite were investigated by tensile and hardness tests. The composites for the tensile test were shaped like a dumbbell. The tensile testing was performed according to ISO 37 using an Instron, model 3366, with a crosshead speed of 500 mm/min. Data for tensile strength, elongation at break, modulus at 100% elongation (M100) and modulus at 300% elongation (M300) were recorded. The composites for the hardness test were prepared using a 0.4-cm thick and 4.4-cm diameter mold. The sample was indented with a Shore A type manual durometer according to ISO 769-I. The applied force during the indentation was consistently set without any shock. The average values of indentation depth from three samples were then recorded.

The morphological observations of the composite with and without GP were made on the cross-section of the tensile fracture surface. The morphology was observed using scanning electron microscope (SEM) at 1000× magnification. The composites were coated with a thin layer of gold before being observed to keep them from becoming electron charged.

The interaction of GP between the silica and the rubber was investigated by the Fourier transform infrared (FTIR) model Perkin Elmer System 2000. A spectrum of composites with and without GP was scanned within the frequency range of 4000–550 cm^{-1}.

6.3 RESULTS AND DISCUSSION

6.3.1 Cure Characteristic

The effects of GP loadings on the t_{90} and t_{S2} of the silica-filled NR were presented in Figure 6.1. The figure shows the t_{S2} was increased up to 5 phr and then reduced when the GP content was further increased. Meanwhile, the addition of GP had decreased t_{90} with the increased GP content. The carboxylic group of GP structure reduces the sulfuring activity as the carboxylic group generates carboxylic chalates between the Zn ion and the accelerators. Meanwhile, the amine group of the GP acts as an accelerator to the rubber composites because the amine becomes a base during vulcanization. In a study on palm oil as additives in carbon black-filled SMR-L, it was reported that the presence of palmitic acid in palm oil could increase the scorch time of the rubber composites (Ismail et al. 1997). According to Coran (1964), increasing the amount of stearic acid reduced the vulcanization of activation energy because of the formation of chelates between the zinc ion and the accelerator or cross-link precursors.

The mobility of the hydocarbon chain in a cross-linked rubber is a function of its cross-link density (Fei et al. 2011). The cross-link density of the composite, with the addition of GP, is presented in Figure 6.2. The incorporation of the GP in the composites has led to increased cross-link densities compared with that of the composite without GP. The coupling reaction between the GP and the silica has prevented the silanol group from absorbing the curatives. Thus, the curatives could effectively participate in the cross-linking process and more compact cross-linking structures were

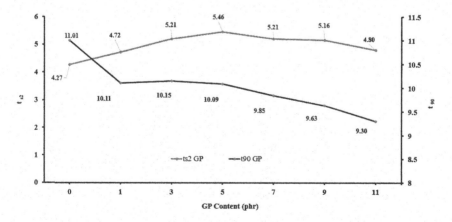

FIGURE 6.1 The effects of GP contents on scorch times (t_{S2}) and cure times (t_{90}) of the composites.

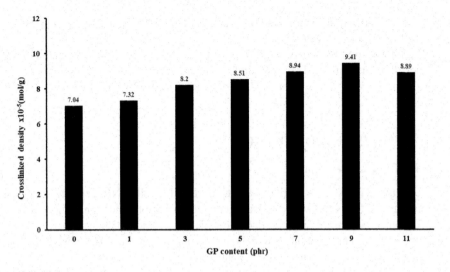

FIGURE 6.2 The effects of GP contents on the cross-link density of composites.

created by the compatible interfaces between the silica and the NR. These compact structures lessened the ability of the NR chains to extend because the toluene was diffused into the NR (Park and Cho 2003). The GPs tend to form a layer within themselves when in excess, and then ineffectively coupling with silica. Consequently, the silica would absorb the curatives, which would reduce the compactness of the NR chain, thus lowering the composites' cross-link density.

6.3.2 Mechanical Properties

Figure 6.3 presents the results obtained from tensile testing on silica-filled NR composites. The column bar shows a clear trend of increasing tensile strength of the composites, with the incorporation of up to 9 phr in GP. However, a decreasing

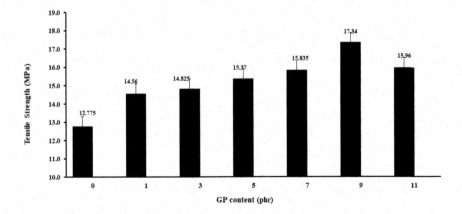

FIGURE 6.3 The effects of GP contents on the tensile strength of the composites.

trend began to appear with a further increase in the GP contents. The main reason for the observed enhancement in tensile strength could be attributed to the ability of the GP to improve the interfacial adhesion between silica and NR. This improvement is responsible for effective transfer of stresses across the interface. Similar results were reported by Indra et al. (2014), where the addition of a coupling agent, known as aminopropyltriethoxysilane (APES), had increased tensile strength. The ethoxy (CH_3OH) groups of APES had condensed with the silica, while the amino groups had covalently bonded with the NR (Ansarifar et al. 2004; Hidehiko and Horiuchi 2007). In this study, the interfacial adhesion within the silica and the NR had improved with the addition of GP via the covalent bond and hydrogen bonding. This observation was supported by IR spectra. However, excessive GP contents may increase the tendency of silica's particles to agglomerate by forming hydrogen bonds with neighboring modified silica. Consequently, filler-filler interaction could become more prominent than filler-matrix interaction (Jesionowski et al. 2002). The agglomeration of the silica particles may act as a stress concentration point to initiate fracture. Furthermore, an excessive layer may be formed, with the excess of GP, in which this layer may cause slippage to occur between the filler and the matrix. This slippage could be due to the presence of the palmitate constituent in GP. The improvement in tensile strength could also be explained by the plasticization and coupling action of the GP at the silica-rubber interfaces. The proper plasticization and dispersion of silica could reduce void formation and eliminate the propagation of microcracks. In a study on vegetable oil as a coupling agent in carbon black-reinforced rubber, the proper plasticization and coupling action of vegetable oil had improved the mechanical properties of the rubber compound (Kundu 2000).

As presented in Figure 6.4, the elongation at break for composites with GP showed a higher value than a composite without GP. The addition of GP in up to 5 phr enhanced the elongation at break, which was then decreased with increasing GP content. This can be attributed to the palmitic acid constituent in GP, which provides mobility to the rubber chain.

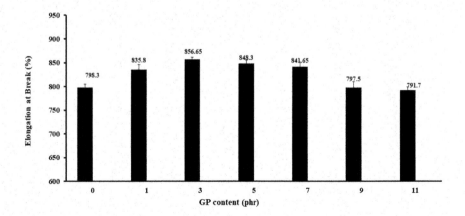

FIGURE 6.4 The effects of GP contents on the elongation at break of the composites.

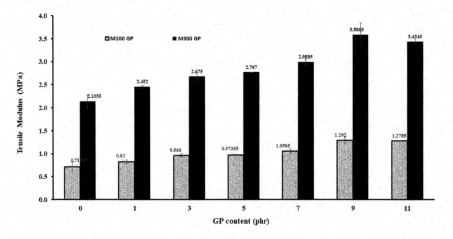

FIGURE 6.5 The effects of GP contents on M100 and M300 of the composites.

The effects of GP contents on the tensile modulus (M100 and M300) of the composites are demonstrated in Figure 6.5. These results showed an increment of the modulus, with the addition of GP up to 9 phr. This modulus trend is in agreement with the hardness results in Figure 6.6, where the tensile modulus is the measure of hardness of a rubber composite. Incorporating coupling agent in the composites had increased the cross-link density, whereby the chains became more compact. Thus, this condition restricted the orientation of the stretched inter-cross-link chains during applied stress and, consequently, the modulus and hardness of the composites were increased. It was reported that the hardness and M300 of NR vulcanizates were dependent on the cross-link density (Fei et al., 2011).

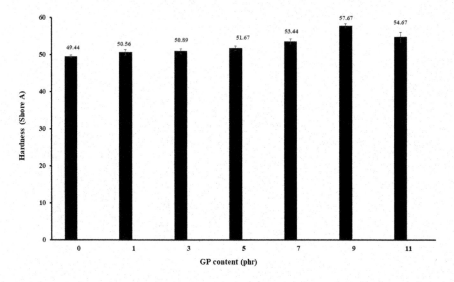

FIGURE 6.6 The effects of GP contents on the hardness of the composites.

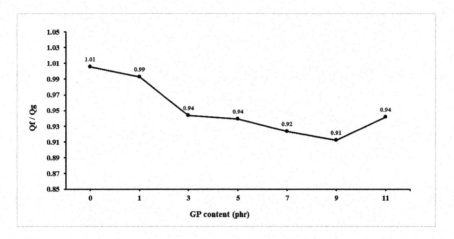

FIGURE 6.7 The effects of GP contents on Qf/Qg composite values.

6.3.3 RUBBER FILLER INTERACTION STUDY

The interaction between the silica and the rubber can be described by the Qf/Qg value. A low Qf/Qg value indicates good interaction between the filler and the rubber (Haseena et al. 2004). Figure 6.7 shows the Qf/Qg value when incorporating of GP in the composites. The Qf/Qg of these composites decreased with increased GP contents (up to 9 phr). This result indicated that the coupling agents had improved the interaction between the silica and the NR.

However, the Qf/Qg values increased when GP contents were increased to higher than 9 phr. This could be due to the content of the excessive coupling agents, which could have formed a layer when they form hydrogen bonds among themselves (Jesionowski and Krysztafkiewicz 2001). The formation of this layer could absorb, coat and trap the silica. Consequently, the tendency of silica to agglomerate could be high, which could form a silica-silica network and reduce the rubber-filler interaction (Indra et al., 2014).

6.3.4 SCANNING ELECTRON MICROSCOPY (SEM) STUDY

SEM was used to corroborate the results of the tensile strength. Figure 6.8 shows SEM micrographs of the silica-filled NR composites without GP. These micrographs show tensile fractures at 1000× magnification. As clearly seen from the figure, the existence of the void between the silica filler and the rubber showed that the silica could not adhere to the rubber phase. This result indicated the incompatibility between the filler and the rubber matrix phase. These micrographs support the previous discussion on tensile strength.

Figure 6.9 shows the fractured surface of silica-filled NR composites with the addition of GP at 9 phr. Furthermore, the silica filler showed strong adhesion with the rubber matrix, as shown in the figure. This observation supported the high tensile strength of the silica-filled NR composites with the addition of 9-phr GP.

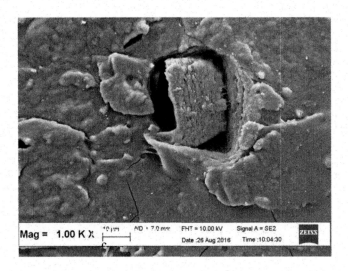

FIGURE 6.8 SEM micrographs of the composite without GP.

However, when 11-phr GP was used, numerous voids and loose silica particles were observed on the matrix surface (Figure 6.10). The constituents of the palmitic acid in GP were mostly responsible for the loose silica from the matrix host. Silica particles were easily detached from the matrix due to plasticizing effect of the GP. It was also observed that the silica particles tend to agglomerate when GP content was 11 phr. This result undoubtedly provided supporting evidence of the poor tensile strength at 11 phr of GP.

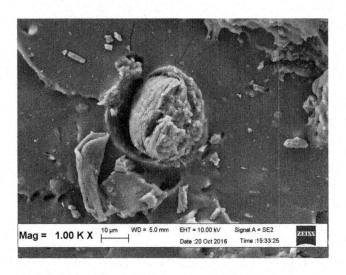

FIGURE 6.9 SEM micrographs of the composite with the addition of 9-phr GP.

Vulcanized Silica-Filled Natural Rubber

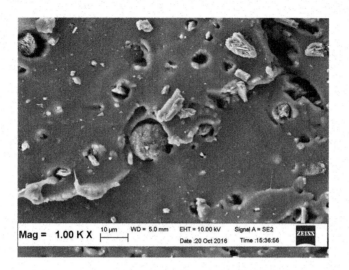

FIGURE 6.10 SEM micrographs of the composite with the addition of 11-phr GP.

6.3.5 Fourier Transform Infrared Spectroscopy (FTIR)

Figures 6.11 and 6.12 illustrate the IR spectrum of the composites without GP and with 9-phr GP, respectively. From the spectrum in Figure 6.11, the characteristic peaks of NR can be observed at 2954, 1397, 2915, 2847 and 1456 cm^{-1} corresponding to the asy-CH$_3$, scissor modes of CH$_3$, asy-CH$_2$, sy-CH$_2$ and scissor modes of CH$_2$ in

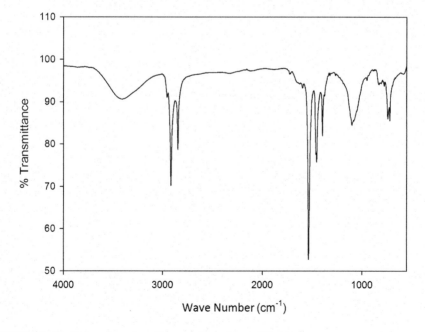

FIGURE 6.11 Infrared spectra of composites without GP.

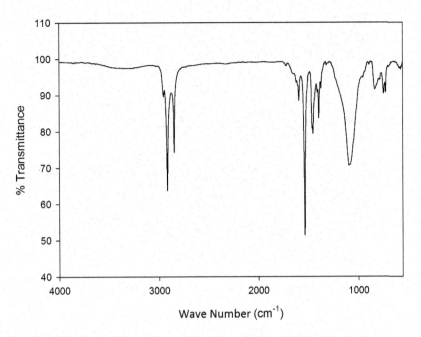

FIGURE 6.12 Infrared spectra of composites with the addition of 9 phr GP.

the vinyl chains, respectively, and at 1594 and 1535 cm^{-1} represent the peptide bond of the NR protein (Rolero et al. 2015). Meanwhile, the IR characteristic peaks of silica can be observed at the broad peak of 3405 cm^{-1} and at 1667 cm^{-1}, which can be assigned to the OH stretching and OH bending, respectively. The OH group was hydrogen-bonded to the silica surface. The peak at 1099 cm^{-1} was from asy-Si-O stretching, and the peak at 779 cm^{-1} was from sy-Si-O stretching (Kralevich and Koenig 1998). The bands at 946 cm and 832 cm^{-1} can be assigned to silanol groups and Si-O-Si stretching, respectively (Musić et al. 2011).

Figure 6.12 demonstrates the spectrum of silica-filled NR with 9-phr GP added. The similar peak of NR and silica characteristics were observable in the spectrum. A broadening of OH stretching region at 3405 cm^{-1} indicated an interaction between the hydrogen bonding of the OH silica surface and the GP. The shifted wave number and increasing intensity at the 1095-cm^{-1} region corresponded to the interaction between Si-O from silica and the GP (Kralevich and Koenig 1998). Based on a comparison between the spectra of the composites without GP and composites with GP, new feature peaks can be observed at approximately 1413 and 1621 cm^{-1}, indicating the C-N stretching and COO^{-} stretching. These new peaks could be due to the interaction with Si-O from silica, which shifted the wave number and increased the intensity of the Si-O peak region at 1095 cm^{-1}. This result indicated the interaction of the GP with silica. The intensity of the ethylene chain from the rubber part was increased with the addition of GP, and the GP has interacted with NR. The possible interactions between GP, NR and silica are illustrated in Figure 6.13.

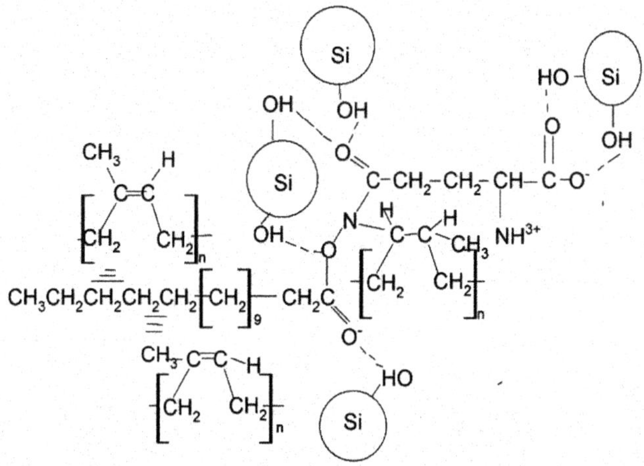

FIGURE 6.13 Possible interaction between GP with NR and Silica.

6.4 CONCLUSION

In this study, the effect of GP as a coupling agent on the properties of NR composites was investigated. The presence of GP clearly demonstrated an improvement in interfacial interaction resulting in improved cross-link density and mechanical properties. This finding reveals that the highest tensile strength and modulus was achieved by adding 9-phr GP. The tensile strength is increased by 36%, whereas M100 and M300 exhibit an 82% and 68% increase, respectively. However, elongation at break reduced 0.1% with the addition of the 9-phr GP. It can be concluded that the composite has good strength and rigidity without compromising the flexibility with the addition of GP.

ACKNOWLEDGMENT

The authors would like to thank Universiti Teknologi MARA (UiTM) for the funding and Universiti Sains Malaysia (USM) for providing the instruments to run the research.

REFERENCES

Ansarifar, A., H.P. Lim, and R. Nijhawan. 2004. "Assessment of the Effect of a Bifunctional Organosilane on the Bound Rubber and Properties of Some Natural Rubber Compounds." *International Journal of Adhesion and Adhesives* 24 (1): 9–22. https://doi.org/10.1016/S0143-7496(03)00095-2

Coran, A.Y. 1964. "Vulcanization. Part V. The Formation of Crosslinks in the System: Natural Rubber-Sulfur-MBT-Zinc Ion." *Rubber Chemistry and Technology* 37(3): 679–688. https://doi.org/10.5254/1.3540360

El-Sabbagh, A. 2014. "Effect of Coupling Agent on Natural Fibre in Natural Fibre/Polypropylene Composites on Mechanical and Thermal Behaviour." *Composites Part B: Engineering* 57: 126–135. https://doi.org/10.1016/j.compositesb.2013.09.047

Fei Zhao, Weina Bi, and Shugao Zhao. 2011. "Influence of Crosslink Density on Mechanical Properties of Natural Rubber Vulcanizates." *Journal of Macromolecular Science, Part B* 50(7): 1460–1469. https://doi.org/10.1080/00222348.2010.507453

Goda, Koichi, Meyyarappallil Sadasivan Sreekala, Sant Kumar Malhotra, Kuruvilla Joseph, and Sabu Thomas. 2013. "Advances in Polymer Composites: Biocomposites–State of the Art, New Challenges, and Opportunities." *Polymer Composites*. Weinheim, Germany: Wiley-VCH, 1–10. https://doi.org/10.1002/9783527674220.ch1

Haseena, A.P., K. Priya Dasan, R. Namitha, G. Unnikrishnan, and Sabu Thomas. 2004. "Investigation on Interfacial Adhesion of Short Sisal/Coir Hybrid Fibre Reinforced Natural Rubber Composites by Restricted Equilibrium Swelling Technique." *Composite Interfaces* 11(7): 489–513. https://doi.org/10.1163/1568554042722955

Hidehiko Dohi, and Shin Horiuchi. 2007. "Locating a Silane Coupling Agent in Silica-Filled Rubber Composites by EFTEM." *Langmuir* 23(24): 12344–12349. https://doi: 10.1021/la701537k

Huang, Cheng, Guangsu Huang, Shiqi Li, Mingchao Luo, Han Liu, Xuan Fu, Wei Qu, Zhengtian Xie, and Jinrong Wu. 2018. "Research on Architecture and Composition of Natural Network in Natural Rubber." *Polymer* 154: 90–100. https://doi.org/10.1016/j.polymer.2018.08.057

Indra Surya, H. Ismail, and A.R. Azura. 2014. "The Comparison of Alkanolamide and Silane Coupling Agent on the Properties of Silica-Filled Natural Rubber (SMR-L) Compounds." *Polymer Testing* 40: 24–32. https://doi.org/10.1016/j.polymertesting.2014.08.007

Ismail, H., I. Salmiah, and Y. Tsukahara. 1997. "Palm Oil Fatty Acid as an Activator in Carbon Black Filled Natural Rubber Compounds: Effect of Vulcanization System." *Polymer International* 44: 523–529. https://doi.org/10.1002/(SICI)1097-0126(199712)44:4<523::AID-PI887>3.0.CO;2-M

Jansomboon, Worawat, Paweena Prapainainar, Surapich Loykulnant, Paisan Kongkachuichay, Peerapan Dittanet, Pisist Kumnorkaew, Zheling Li, Ian Kinloch, and Robert J. Young. 2020. "Raman Spectroscopic Study of Reinforcement Mechanisms of Electron Beam Radiation Crosslinking of Natural Rubber Composites Filled with Graphene and Silica/Graphene Mixture Prepared by Latex Mixing." *Composites Part C: Open Access* 3: 100049. https://doi.org/10.1016/j.jcomc.2020.100049

Jesionowski, T., J. Żurawska, and A. Krysztafkiewicz 2002. "Surface Properties and Dispersion Behaviour of Precipitated Silicas." *Journal of Materials Science* 37: 1621–1633. https://doi.org/10.1023/A:1014936428636

Jesionowski, Teofil, and Andrzej Krysztafkiewicz. 2001. "Influence of Silane Coupling Agents on Surface Properties of Precipitated Silicas." *Applied Surface Science* 172 (1–2): 18–32. https://doi.org/10.1016/S0169-4332(00)00828-X

Jong, L. 2019. "Improved mechanical properties of silica reinforced rubber with natural polymer." *Polymer Testing* 79: 106009. https://doi.org/10.1016/j.polymertesting.2019.106009

Kakou, C.A., F.Z. Arrakhiz, A. Trokourey, R. Bouhfid, A. Qaiss, and D. Rodrigue. 2014. "Influence of Coupling Agent Content on the Properties of High Density Polyethylene Composites Reinforced with Oil Palm Fibers." *Materials & Design* 63: 641–649. https://doi.org/10.1016/j.matdes.2014.06.044

Kingsley Iler, Ralph. 1979. *The Chemistry of Silica: Solubility, Polymerization, Colloid and Surface Properties, and Biochemistry.* New York: John Wiley & Sons. https://doi.org/10.1002/ange.19800920433

Kralevich, Mark L., and Jack L. Koenig. 1998. "FTIR Analysis of Silica-Filled Natural Rubber." *Rubber Chemistry and Technology* 71(2): 300–309. https://doi.org/10.5254/1.3538486

Kundu, P.P. 2000. "Improvement of Filler–Rubber Interaction by the Coupling Action of Vegetable Oil in Carbon Black Reinforced Rubber." *Journal of Applied Polymer Science* 75: 735–739. https://doi.org/10.1002/(SICI)1097-4628(20000207)75:6<735::AID-APP1>3.0.CO;2-T

Musić, Svetozar, Nada Filipović-Vinceković, and Lavoslav Sekovanić. 2011. "Precipitation of Amorphous SiO$_2$ Particles and their Properties." *Brazilian Journal of Chemical Engineering* 28(1): 89–94. https://doi.org/10.1590/S0104-66322011000100011

Park, Soo-Jin, and Ki-Sook Cho. 2003. "Filler–Elastomer Interactions: Influence of Silane Coupling Agent on Crosslink Density and Thermal Stability of Silica/Rubber Composites." *Journal of Colloid and Interface Science* 267(1): 86–91. https://doi.org/10.1016/S0021-9797(03)00132-2

Pattanawanidchai, Sirichai, Surapich Loykulnant, Pongdhorn Sae-oui, Naruewan Maneevas, and Chakrit Sirisinha. 2014. "Development of Eco-Friendly Coupling Agent for Precipitated Silica Filled Natural Rubber Compounds." *Polymer Testing* 34: 58–63. https://doi.org/10.1016/j.polymertesting.2014.01.002

Phaneendra Kulkarni, Burney Jose, Sreedha Sambhudevan, and Balakrishnan Shankar. 2020. "Influence of SiC and TiO$_2$ on the Cure Characteristics and Mechanical Properties of Natural Rubber Composites." *Materials Today: Proceedings*. https://doi.org/10.1016/j.matpr.2020.09.678

Ramli, R., R.M. Yunus, M.D.H. Beg, and D.M.R. Prasad. 2012. "Oil Palm Fiber Reinforced Polypropylene Composites: Effects of Fiber Loading and Coupling Agents on Mechanical, Thermal, and Interfacial Properties." *Journal of Composite Materials* 46(11): 1275–1284. https://doi.org/10.1177/0021998311417647

Rodgers, Brendan, and Walter Waddell. 2005. "9 – The Science of Rubber Compounding." *Science and Technology of Rubber* (Third Edition). Academic Press, 401–454. https://doi.org/10.1016/B978-012464786-2/50012-2

Rolero, Sébastien, Siriluck Liengprayoon, Laurent Vaysse, Jérôme Sainte-Beuve, and Frédéric Bonfils. 2015. "Investigating Natural Rubber Composition with Fourier Transform Infrared (FT-IR) Spectroscopy: A Rapid and Non-Destructive Method to Determine Both Protein and Lipid Contents Simultaneously." *Polymer Testing* 43:83–93. https://doi.org/10.1016/j.polymertesting.2015.02.011

Samsudin, D., Hanafi Ismail, Nadras Othman, and Zuratul Ain Abdul Hamid. 2016. "Comparative Study of Glut Palmitate Salt and Polyethylene Grafted Maleic Anhydride Compatibilizer on the Properties of Silica Filled High-Density Polyethylene Composites." *Polymer Testing* 52: 104–110. https://doi.org/10.1016/j.polymertesting.2016.03.017

Samsudin, D., Hanafi Ismail, Nadras Othman, and Zuratul Ain Abdul Hamid. 2018. "The Effects of Glutamine Palmitic Acid Content on Properties of High Density Polyethylene/ Silica Composites." *Journal of Vinyl Additive Technology* 24: 217–223. https://doi.org/10.1002/vnl.21553

Ten Brinke, J. W., S. C. Debnath, Louis A.E.M. Reuvekamp, and Jacobus W.M. Noordermeer. 2003. "Mechanistic Aspects of the Role of Coupling Agents in Silica–Rubber Composites." *Composites Science and Technology* 63(8): 1165–1174 https://doi.org/10.1016/S0266-3538(03)00077-0

Zaini, Nurul Aizan Mohd, Hanafi Ismail, and Arjulizan Rusli. 2019. "Effect of Glut Palmitate (GP) Salt on the Properties of Sepiolite Filled Ethylene Propylene Diene Monomer (EPDM) Composites." *AIP Conference Proceedings* 2068: 020085. https://doi.org/10.1063/1.5089384

Zheng, Junchi, Dongli Han, Xin Ye, Xiaohui Wu, Youping Wu, Yiqing Wang, and Liqun Zhang. 2018. "Chemical and Physical Interaction Between Silane Coupling Agent with Long Arms and Silica and its Effect on Silica/Natural Rubber Composites." *Polymer* 135: 200–210. https://doi.org/10.1016/j.polymer.2017.12.010

7 Effect of Gamma Irradiation on the Properties of Sepiolite-Filled Ethylene Propylene Diene Monomer Composites

N.A. Mohd Zaini
Universiti Teknologi MARA
Arau, Malaysia

Hanafi Ismail, A. Rusli
Universiti Sains Malaysia
Nibong Tebal, Malaysia

Sofian Ibrahim
RAYMINTEX Plant
Kajang, Malaysia

CONTENTS

7.1 Introduction 138
7.2 Preparation of Sepiolite-Filled EPDM Composites 140
    7.2.1 Materials 140
    7.2.2 Preparation of Sample 140
    7.2.3 Characterization of Sepiolite-Filled EPDM
         Composites.. 141
7.3 Tensile Properties, and Cross-Link Density of Non-Irradiated
    and Irradiated EPDM/Sepiolite Composites 141
    7.3.1 Tensile Properties of Non-Irradiated and Irradiated
         EPDM/Sepiolite Composites 141
    7.3.2 Cross-Link Density of Non-Irradiated and Irradiated
         EPDM/Sepiolite Composites 144

DOI: 10.1201/9781003221012-7

7.4 Thermal and Morphological Properties of Non-Irradiated
     and Irradiated of EPDM/Sepiolite Composites 145
     7.4.1 Thermogravimetric (TGA) Analysis 145
     7.4.2 Field Emission Scanning Electron Microscopy Analysis
            (FESEM) of the Tensile Fractured Surface of Non-Irradiated
            and Irradiated EDPM/Sepiolite Composites 147
7.5 Conclusions 149
Acknowledgments 149
References 149

7.1 INTRODUCTION

In the rubber industry, clay minerals are also classified as non-black additives. For applications with extremely significant costs, a material such as clay or calcium carbonate may be used due to its relative abundance. Sepiolite is among the minerals of clay classified in the 2:1 family and has a chemical half-unit cell chemical formula of $Mg_8Si_{12}O_{30}(OH)_4 \cdot 12H_2O$, also known as hydrated magnesium silicate (Guggenheim 2015). Sepiolite morphology consists of several loosely adhered blocks and tunnels that are aligned along the fiber axis. Each sepiolite nanofiber structural unit contains $Mg(OH)_6$, an octahedral layer of magnesium that is sandwiched by two tetrahedron silicate sheets (SiO_4) (Masood et al. 2018). Silanol groups (Si-OH) that formed on the outer surface edges of the sepiolite particles led to the development of hydrogen bonds and van der Waals interactions, thereby promoting improved chemical interactions between the sepiolite and polymer (Bilotti et al. 2014; Sarossy et al. 2012). The sizes of the sepiolite fibrous structure ranged from 2 to 4 μm long, 10 to 30 nm wide and 5 to 10 nm thick (Abbasi et al. 2017).

Vulcanization is a chemical process of cross-linking that is required to shape a three-dimensional molecular network structure. The curing agent interacts with rubber chains and creates cross-links with the functional groups of rubber chains. In the rubber industry, cross-linking is a common term in reference to vulcanization, where various types of curing agents, such as sulfur and peroxides, metal oxides and phenolic resins have been applied, thereby influencing the structure and efficiency of cross-linking (Kruželák et al. 2018). In contrast to the cross-linking of sulfur and peroxide, cross-linking by irradiation is a more recent cross-linking method with promise for the future. Meanwhile, irradiation refers to the exposure of polymers to a source of high radiation for improving its properties. X-rays and gamma rays (γ-rays) are forms of electromagnetic radiation that contain energy and have the speed of light. Some of the main sources of radiation are γ-rays of radioactive isotopes, such as Co-60 (60Co); electron beams of electron accelerators and X-rays from electron beams (Makuuchi and Cheng 2012). Both wavelengths are short and have a very high frequencies and energy levels (Kalkornsurapranee et al. 2021). Wavelength and source are different, whereas the X-rays and γ-rays are identical in many ways.

γ-Rays have a slightly higher frequency and lower wavelength relative to X-rays. Radioactive atoms emit γ-rays that decay and release energy during the atomic rearrangement of electron emissions. The material molecule reacts with the radioactive decay created by the γ-rays, in which they are radiated via secondary electrons generated by ionization with an elevated energy electromagnetic radiation (Tarawneh et al. 2021). Gamma irradiation is a continuous operation at room temperature cross-linking, minimal atmospheric emissions and increased process control versatility. The practical thickness range of the material is much smaller because of the disadvantages in electron beam radiation, such as lower penetration into materials (Hassan et al. 2014).

Polymers may be affected in two ways by exposure to irradiation sources: they undergo cross-linking or chain cleavage. Both reactions are two opposing mechanisms that occur concurrently during irradiation (Chai et al. 2016). When a cross-linking reaction develops a three-dimensional network, this improves the polymer properties while breaking the chains and the polymer backbone chains, thereby causing the degradation of the polymer properties. Although chain scission reaction is undesirable, the reaction cannot be prevented and a cross-linking reaction would normally ensue. The major impact is subject to these two variables, which prevail at a given time and have a substantial effect on the resulting properties (Bandzierz et al. 2018; Javad et al. 2009). In contrast, radiation cross-linking provides faster and more efficient vulcanization, creating uniform cross-links, using less energy, and occupying less space (El-Nemr 2011). Several studies have reported on a variety of rubbers types, such nitrile butadiene rubber (NBR) (Khankishiyeva et al. 2020), ethylene propylene diene monomer (EPDM) rubber (Deepalaxmi and Rajini 2014; Madani 2004), epoxidized natural rubber (Chai et al. 2016), silicone rubber (Montoya-Villegas et al. 2020) and natural rubber composites (Ibrahim et al. 2018; Kalkornsurapranee et al. 2021). The gamma irradiation caused cross-linking and chain scission, which led to the restructuring of the network structure. In contrast, Planes et al. (2010) proposed that radicals can also be trapped by the additives with large interfaces due to their ability to interact with the intermediate chemical species responsible for the degradation of the matrix. A previous study by Eyssa et al. (2018) utilized nano-silica-filled nitrile butadiene composites for irradiation between 25 and 300 kGy. The authors believe that accelerated radiation treatments can boost a composite's properties. Increased tensile strength was described by both the reduction in dose and the reduction in the cross-link density. Elshereafy et al. (2016) conducted a similar study, portraying the adoption of different levels of gamma irradiation for vulcanizing the composites of EPDM/styrene-butadiene rubber (SBR)/waste polyethylene (PE)/montmorillonite (MMT) clay. From the results obtained in this work, it was concluded that there has been a considerable achievement in the physical and mechanical properties of all composites irradiated, therefore, indicating the occurrence of cross-linking. The effect of gamma radiation on EPDM/Sep composites was studied in this research. Different loadings of sepiolite ranging between 0 and 70 phr underwent irradiation at a gamma irradiation dose of 50 kGy, in which it was performed subsequent to the samples undergoing compression molding. In addition, analyses were done on the tensile properties, cross-link density, thermal stability analysis and SEM analysis on the irradiated EPDM/Sep, which were compared with the non-irradiated EPDM/Sep composites.

7.2 PREPARATION OF SEPIOLITE-FILLED EPDM COMPOSITES

7.2.1 Materials

EPDM (grade Vistalon 2504N) procured from Exxon Mobil Chemical was employed in this work. It is composed of 54% ethylene and 3.6% ethylidene norbornene (ENB), with Mooney viscosity [ML (1 + 4) at 125°C] of 26.8 (Mooney Unit). The density of the EPDM was 0.818 g/cm^3, as assessed via an analytical weighing balance (XB220A, Precisa Gravimetrics Ag, Dietikon, Switzerland). The sepiolite clay originated from Hebei DFL Minmet Refractories Corp., Hebei, China. Before the density measurement is conducted via a gas pycnometer (AccuPyc II 1330, Micromeritics Instrument Corp., USA), the sepiolite was dried at 80°C for 24 hours, in which the density of sepiolite was established at 2.94 g/cm^3.

7.2.2 Preparation of Sample

To remove moisture, the sepiolite was dried in an oven for 24 hours at 80°C prior to the mixing process. A laboratory two-roll mill (XK-160, Shanghai Rubber Machine Works, Shanghai, China) in compliance with ASTM D3568 was employed for a total mixing period of 21 minutes in preparation of the EPDM/Sep composites. Table 7.1 shows the compounding formulations for EPDM/sepiolite composites. Different loadings of sepiolite ranging between 0 and 70 phr were utilized for preparing the composites. All composite formulations were performed via the semi-efficient vulcanization system. Furthermore, the rubber composites had undergone compression molding within their respective curing time (tc$_{90}$) into two sheets with dimensions of 150 × 122 × 2 mm and 145 × 110 × 3 mm. This process was conducted at 160°C and a force of 10 MPa via a compression molding machine (GT-7014-A30C, GoTech Testing Machine Inc., Taichung City, Taiwan). The composite sheets were then kept in desiccant that was left in place for at least 24 hours prior to testing.

TABLE 7.1
Compounding Formulations for the Sepiolite-Filled EPDM Composites

Material	ES0	ES4	ES10	ES20	ES30	ES60	ES70
EPDM	100	100	100	100	100	100	100
Zinc oxide	5	5	5	5	5	5	5
Stearic acid	1.5	1.5	1.5	1.5	1.5	1.5	1.5
TMTD	1.5	1.5	1.5	1.5	1.5	1.5	1.5
MBT	0.8	0.8	0.8	0.8	0.8	0.8	0.8
Sulfur	1.5	1.5	1.5	1.5	1.5	1.5	1.5
Sepiolite	0	4	10	20	30	60	70

Composition (phr)

Abbreviations: TMTD, tetramethylthiuram disulphide.

7.2.3 CHARACTERIZATION OF SEPIOLITE-FILLED EPDM COMPOSITES

At 160°C, the moving die rheometer (MDR 2000, Alpha Technologies, Ohio, USA) was used to test the curing characteristics of EPDM/Sep. From the 2-mm compression-molded sheets originally formed in a desiccator, the dumbbell-shaped specimens were then cut. A universal tensile testing machine (Instron 3366, Instron, Singapore) in compliance with ASTM D412 was used to measure tensile properties, such as tensile strength, elongation at break (EB) and tensile modulus at 100% elongation (M100). The crosshead speed was set at 500 mm/min and the load cell at 10 kN. For each compound, five specimens were used. Cross-link density for the EPDM/sepiolite composites is calculated using Equation 7.1 by applying the Flory-Rehner (Hergenrother and Hilton 2003) equation:

$$\upsilon = -\frac{\ln(1-V_r) + V_r + \chi V_r^2}{V_l \left(V_r^{1/3} - V_r/2\right)} \tag{7.1}$$

where, V_l denotes the molar volume of the solvent (107.0 mL/mol for toluene), and V_r refers to the toluene balanced volume fraction of the swollen rubber in a polymer network. Three samples were analyzed for each compound, and the average values were determined. Cross-link density is typically expressed in mol/cm³, and in a polymer network there is a calculated number of cross-linked points per unit volume (Mok and Eng 2018). The 10-mg samples were taken for thermogravimetric analyzer (TGA) analysis purposes, with heating temperatures between 30°C and 600°C and a rise of 20°C/min under a 20 mL/min nitrogen flow using the TGA (PyrisMT 6 TGA, PerkinElmer, USA). The study included weight loss calculation in relation to the temperature of the TGA curve. The TGA curve then demonstrates temperatures at 5%, 25% and 50% of mass degradation (T5%, T25% and T50%) and the temperature at the maximum rate of mass loss (T_{max}). When establishing the morphology of the EPDM/Sep composite tensile fracture surfaces via a field emission scanning electron microscope (FESEM), a 10-kV accelerating voltage electron microscope with energy dispersion X-ray spectrometers (EDX) was employed. The test specimens were observed to have been covered with a thin film of gold palladium. Throughout the test, the coating was a requirement for the removal of electrostatic charges. The morphological properties of the EPDM/Sep composites were researched with respect to the degree of filler dispersion and its interaction with the rubber matrix.

7.3 TENSILE PROPERTIES, AND CROSS-LINK DENSITY OF NON-IRRADIATED AND IRRADIATED EPDM/SEPIOLITE COMPOSITES

7.3.1 TENSILE PROPERTIES OF NON-IRRADIATED AND IRRADIATED EPDM/SEPIOLITE COMPOSITES

Figure 7.1 illustrates a comparison of the tensile strength of non-irradiated and gamma-irradiated EPDM/Sep composites at varying sepiolite loadings. The sepiolite loadings increased and subsequently peaked at 60 phr, and there was

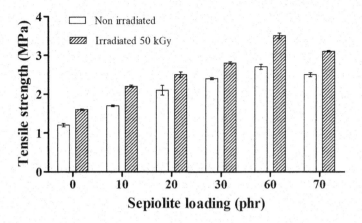

FIGURE 7.1 Comparison of the tensile strength at different sepiolite loadings for non-irradiated and irradiated EPDM/Sep composites.

improvement in the tensile strength of both non-irradiated and irradiated samples of EPDM/Sep composites. Then, tensile strength decreased at sepiolite loadings of 70 phr. The increased tensile strength of both EPDM/Sep composites may be attributable to the small particle size of the sepiolites, which offers a broad contact area for interaction with the rubber and decreases the spacing between the particles. As such, it is deemed to be capable of transferring stress efficiently from EPDM to sepiolite on the application of stress. In addition, the fibrous sepiolite structure also leads to better sepiolite dispersion in the EPDM matrix, resulting in high tensile strength. However, at 70 phr of sepiolite loading, slight reduction of tensile strength could be due to the agglomeration of sepiolite that results from the high filler-filler interaction.

EPDM/Sep composites demonstrate greater tensile strength than non-irradiated samples at all sepiolite loadings relative to non-irradiated and irradiated composites. In the irradiation vulcanization process, two reactions take place simultaneously, namely cross-linking and chain scission (Javad et al. 2009). Based on work by Wang et al. (2009), there is a close relation between the cross-link density and energy dissipation to the tensile strength of the polymer composites. The increased tensile strength of the irradiated samples could be due to the formation of cross-linking on the irradiated EPDM/Sep composites caused by gamma irradiation. Gamma irradiation appears to form active sites on the EPDM matrix, initiating cross-links between the EPDM chains via free radical combination, thus, leading to the creation of more cross-link structures. Consequently, this enhances the tensile strength of the irradiated EPDM/Sep composites. Meanwhile, increasing sepiolite loadings further up to 70 phr resulted in a slight decrease of tensile strength. Apart from the sepiolite agglomerating, the chain scission of rubber molecules could also lead to lowering the tensile strength of irradiated EPDM/Sep composites.

Figure 7.2 portrays the comparison of EB of non-irradiated and irradiated EPDM/Sep composites with varying sepiolite loadings. An analogous finding was found, in

Sepiolite-Filled EPDM Composites

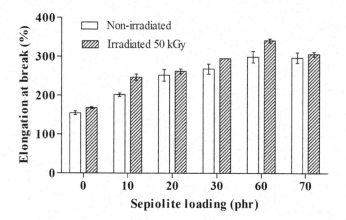

FIGURE 7.2 Comparison of the elongation at break at different sepiolite loadings for non-irradiated and irradiated EPDM/Sep composites.

which both composites increase their EB with an increase in sepiolite loadings. This may be associated with good interfacial adhesion of sepiolite and EPDM matrix, thus contributing to the capability of the composite to sustain greater elongation on rupture occurrence. Moreover, as shown later in Figure 7.6, uniform sepiolite dispersion in the composites and stress were transferred effectively from the matrix to the sepiolite. The agglomeration of sepiolite particles, however, had limited the EPDM chains' mobility to move stress from the EPDM chains to the sepiolite. The restriction of the movement of the chains resulted in less ability of the composites to elongate during the applied stress, resulting in decreased EB. Compared with non-irradiated composites, the EB of the irradiated composites was higher than the non-irradiated EPDM/Sep composites. These results may be exhibited due to an increase in cross-links between the chains of the EPDM that could accommodate more tension, thus, displaying greater elongation. However, after reaching the optimum at 60 phr, the EB slightly decreased with increased sepiolite loadings. Similar observations can be seen in the non-irradiated EPDM/Sep composites. The reduction of EB at 70 phr of sepiolite may be attributed to the excessive number of cross-links in the composites. The EB increased to a particular optimum cross-link density depending on the type of rubber matrix, as stated by Youssef et al. (2017); whereas the reduced Eb could be due to the high cross-links that limit the movement of the rubber chains.

Figure 7.3 demonstrates the tensile modulus (M100) of the non-irradiated and irradiated EPDM/Sep composites. The M100 of the non-irradiated and irradiated composites of EPDM/Sep are shown in Figure 7.3. The M100 of both composites was increased by the presence of sepiolite in the EPDM/Sep composites. As the sepiolite loadings increased for non-irradiated and irradiated composites, the enhancement of M100 of EPDM/Sep composites is expected. The increasing concentration of sepiolite into the EPDM caused the reduction of elasticity of EPDM and led to stiffer and harder EPDM vulcanizates. In the case of non-irradiated composites, M100 increased until the optimum value reached at 60 phr

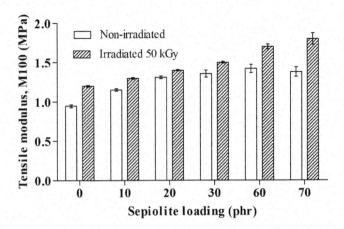

FIGURE 7.3 Comparison of the M100 at different sepiolite loadings for non-irradiated and irradiated EPDM/Sep composites.

and decreased when the sepiolite loadings were further increased. As frequently reported by other researchers (Hwang, Wei, and Wu 2004; Rooj, Das, and Heinrich 2011; Hayeemasae and Ismail 2018), the incorporation of high clay loadings into the composites can develop high stiffness of the composites. Nevertheless, when comparing the M100 of the non-irradiated EPDM/Sep composites, the M100 of irradiated EPDM/Sep composites exhibited a higher M100 value. This finding could be associated with the formation of a higher number of cross-links between the EPDM chains induced by the gamma irradiation, as shown subsequently in the swelling study. because the modulus also indicates the degree of cross-linking, the increment of M100 of EPDM/Sep composites may, therefore, be linked to the increase in cross-link density related to the development of stiffer EPDM composites.

7.3.2 Cross-Link Density of Non-Irradiated and Irradiated EPDM/Sepiolite Composites

Figure 7.4 shows the cross-link density of the non-irradiated and irradiated EPDM/Sep composites. The figure, illustrates that with increased sepiolite contents, the cross-link density of both composites also increased up to the maximum value at 60 phr and decreased gradually at 70 phr. Moreover, the cross-link density of irradiated composites was found higher than non-irradiated composites. Due to the formation of cross-links caused by the process of gamma irradiation, this result is predicted. The enhancement of the cross-link density of non-irradiated and irradiated EPDM/Sep composites also supports the M100, as previously discussed. The increase in cross-link density in MMT clay of SBR/EPDM composites cured by gamma irradiation was also reported by Shoushtari Zadeh Naseri and Jalali-Arani (2016), and they associated the increase with the formation of a higher number of cross-links, which led to better interaction between the clay and rubber blend.

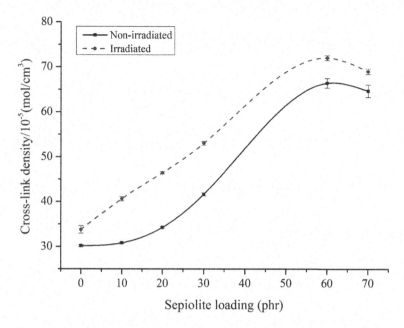

FIGURE 7.4 Comparison of cross-link density for non-irradiated and irradiated EPDM/Sep composites at various sepiolite loadings.

7.4 THERMAL AND MORPHOLOGICAL PROPERTIES OF NON-IRRADIATED AND IRRADIATED OF EPDM/SEPIOLITE COMPOSITES

7.4.1 Thermogravimetric (TGA) Analysis

Figure 7.5a and b demonstrates the characteristics of thermal decomposition and derivative weight thermograms of non-irradiated and irradiated EPDM/Sep, respectively, at various sepiolite contents. Table 7.2 summarizes the decomposition temperature at various weight losses and char residues both for non-irradiated and irradiated EPDM/Sep composites. Based on Figure 7.5 and Table 7.2, the thermal stability of non-irradiated and irradiated EPDM/Sep composites increased with the increasing amount of sepiolite loadings, and the char yield increased with the addition of the sepiolite. These findings could be due to the role of the sepiolite, which acts as a mass transport barrier toward the decomposition products, as previously discussed. Previous researchers (Abbasi et al. 2017; Bidsorkhi et al. 2014; Mohd Zaini, Ismail, and Rusli 2018) also found similar finding in which the addition of sepiolite serves as a heat shield for the degradation products of molecular chains and results in higher thermal stability of polymer composites.

The thermal stability of the non-irradiated EPDM/Sep composites showed no major changes compared with the irradiated composites in a close comparison of the two composites. As clearly summarized in Table 7.2, T5%, T_{max} and percentage char residues of irradiated composites is lower than that of non-irradiated composites.

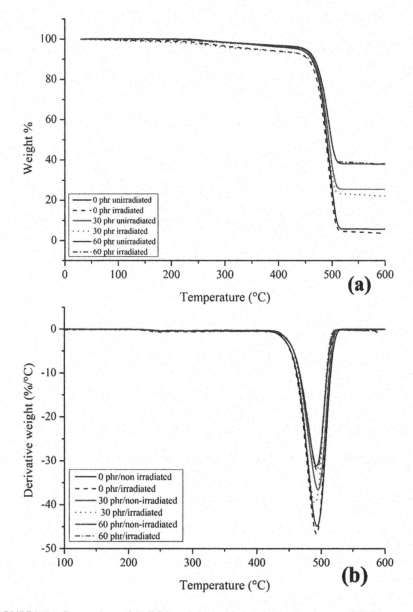

FIGURE 7.5 Comparison of (a) TGA and (b) derivative thermogravimetry (DTG) curves of non-irradiated and irradiated of EPDM/Sep composites at various sepiolite loadings.

The obtained results are unexpected because the EPDM/Sep had been exposed to gamma irradiation, thereby initiating cross-linking. In addition, because of the formation of cross-link density, the thermal stability of the composites could be improved, therefore, improving the rigidity of the composite system (Eyssa et al. 2018). During the thermal degradation process, the decrease in thermal stability of the composites caused by gamma irradiation is probably due to predominant chain

TABLE 7.2
Decomposition Temperature of Non-Irradiated and Irradiated EPDM/Sep Composites at Different Weight Losses and Char Residues

Composites	Sepiolite Loading (phr)	Temperature at 5 wt% Loss (°C)	Temperature at % Max. Loss (°C)	Char Residue (%)
Non-irradiated	0	432	493	5.7
Irradiated		359	488	3.7
Non-irradiated	30	446	490	25.4
Irradiated		391	490	22.0
Non-irradiated	60	449	492	37.9
Irradiated		450	493	38.1

splits over the cross-linking. As reported by Pasbakhsh et al. (2012), cross-linking and chain scissions are two competing reactions that occur during the irradiation process of the polymer. In the case of irradiated EPDM/Sep composites, it may be due to the presence of some parts of the free radicals that are prone to degradation, which, in turn, lowers thermal stability compared with that of non-irradiated composites. A similar finding was also reported previously by Bandzierz et al. (2018) in their study on the structure and properties of SBR cured by radiation. It was noted that a substantial decrease in the thermo-oxidative stability of the radiated sample was primarily due to the low number of cross-links and, at the same time, some chain-scission reactions occurred.

7.4.2 Field Emission Scanning Electron Microscopy Analysis (FESEM) of the Tensile Fractured Surface of Non-Irradiated and Irradiated EDPM/Sepiolite Composites

Figure 7.6a–f illustrates the SEM micrographs of various sepiolite loadings of non-irradiated and irradiated EPDM/Sep composites at 500× magnifications. The micrographs of tensile fragmented EPDM/Sep composites pre- and post-gamma irradiation were compared in Figure 7.6a and b. The effect of irradiation in morphology is apparent as the roughness increased with increased sepiolite loading. In Figure 7.6a, a smooth surface can be clearly observed with the presence of some detachment on the fractured surface of non-irradiated EPDM/20Sep composites. This indicates poor interaction between the sepiolite and EPDM. In contrast, rough surface and matrix tearing lines are observed in Figure 7.6b, which indicates more energy was required to break the sample. This finding could be related to lower tensile strength of non-irradiated EPDM/20Sep composites than irradiated composites at the same number of loadings. Similarly, for comparison purposes, Figure 7.6c and d demonstrates the non-irradiated and irradiated EPDM/Sep composites at 60-phr sepiolite loadings. Both micrographs clearly showed more

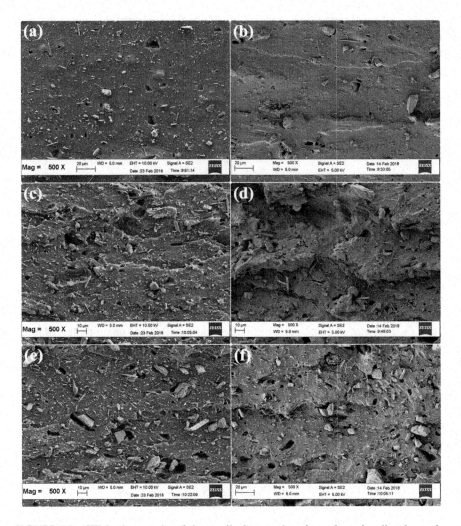

FIGURE 7.6 SEM micrographs of the tensile fractured surface of non-irradiated samples at (a) 20 phr, (c) 60 phr and (e) 70 phr, and irradiated samples at (b) 20 phr, (d) 60 phr and (f) 70 phr of EPDM/Sep composites at 500× magnification.

surface roughness compared with that in 20-phr sepiolite, whereas Figure 7.6d displays more apparent surface roughness. Moreover, the sample exhibited a tortuous path, which required more resistance toward crack propagation, resulting in higher tensile strength. The radiation-induced cross-links of the sepiolite in the EPDM matrix may be due to such changes in morphology. These observations are in accordance with the enhanced tensile strength, tensile modulus and cross-link density of EPDM/Sep irradiated composites at 60-phr loading. Furthermore, the surface roughness of irradiated composites shown in Figure 7.6f increased compared with Figure 7.6e. Furthermore, closely comparing Figure 7.6b, d, and f shows that the surface roughness enhanced with increasing sepiolite loadings. However, surface roughness in Figure 7.6f decreased compared with Figure 7.6d, and numerous voids were also observed due to the detachment of sepiolites. The presence of many voids on the tensile fracture surface indicates a weak rubber-filler interaction. The obtained results provide supporting evidence for the low tensile strength of irradiated EPDM/Sep composites at 70 phr with that at 60 phr loading. The micrographs of the tensile fracture surfaces of EPDM/halloysite composites were in agreement with the findings obtained by Pasbakhsh et al. (2012), which stated that by increasing halloysite clay loading and confirmed by the emergence of some cavities in the SEM micrographs.

7.5 CONCLUSIONS

Studies on tensile properties, cross-link density, thermal stability and the morphology of sepiolite/EPDM composites have been conducted on gamma irradiation at 50 kGy doses. Gamma irradiation can enhance the tensile strength, EB and tensile modulus, and up to 60 phr of sepiolite loadings is sufficient to achieve optimum strength. The tensile strength and tensile modulus results were in good agreement with the cross-link density determined by the swelling method. This proves that a higher cross-link density was obtained when gamma radiation was applied. The gamma irradiation of sepiolite-filled EPDM caused a changed in the thermo-oxidative stability of the rubber composites.

ACKNOWLEDGMENTS

The authors would like to thank all the staff at the Department of Materials and Mineral Resources Engineering, Universiti Sains Malaysia (USM), and at the Malaysian Nuclear Agency. They unconditionally provided a wide range of facilities to make this research a success. One of the writers is also profoundly indebted to the Ministry of Higher Education of Malaysia and Universiti Teknologi Mara (UiTM) for providing support for this study.

REFERENCES

Abbasi, Farideh, Shahram Mehdipour-Ataei, Zahra Tabatabaei-Yazdi, Samal Babanzadeh, and Ebrahim Abouzari-Lotf. 2017. "Effect of Sepiolite Nanoparticles on the Properties of Novel Poly(Sulfone Ether Imide)." *Polymers for Advanced Technologies* 28 (3): 404–10. https://doi.org/10.1002/pat.3903

Bandzierz, Katarzyna S., Louis A.E.M. Reuvekamp, Grażyna Przybytniak, Wilma K. Dierkes, Anke Blume, and Dariusz M. Bieliński. 2018. "Effect of Electron Beam Irradiation on Structure and Properties of Styrene-Butadiene Rubber." *Radiation Physics and Chemistry* 149: 14–25. https://doi.org/10.1016/j.radphyschem.2017.12.011

Bidsorkhi, Hossein Cheraghi, Mohammad Soheilmoghaddam, Raheleh Heidar Pour, Hossein Adelnia, and Zurina Mohamad. 2014. "Mechanical, Thermal and Flammability Properties of Ethylene-Vinyl Acetate (EVA)/Sepiolite Nanocomposites." *Polymer Testing* 37: 117–22. https://doi.org/10.1016/j.polymertesting.2014.05.007

Bilotti, Emiliano, Emmanuel Duquesne, Hua Deng, Rui Zhang, Franck Quero, Savvas N. Georgiades, Hartmut R. Fischer, Philippe Dubois, and Ton Peijs. 2014. "In Situ Polymerised Polyamide 6/Sepiolite Nanocomposites: Effect of Different Interphases." *European Polymer Journal* 56 (1): 131–39. https://doi.org/10.1016/j.eurpolymj.2014.04.004

Chai, C.K., C.T. Ratnam, L.C. Abdullah, and H.M. Yusoff. 2016. "Tensile Properties and Thermal Stability of Gamma Irradiated Epoxidized Natural Rubber Latex with the Presence of Sensitizer." *Journal of Polymer Materials* 33 (1): 223–32.

Deepalaxmi, R., and V. Rajini. 2014. "Gamma and Electron Beam Irradiation Effects on SiR-EPDM Blends." *Journal of Radiation Research and Applied Sciences* 7 (3): 363–70. https://doi.org/10.1016/j.jrras.2014.05.005

El-Nemr, Khaled F. 2011. "Effect of Different Curing Systems on the Mechanical and Physico-Chemical Properties of Acrylonitrile Butadiene Rubber Vulcanizates." *Materials and Design* 32 (6): 3361–69. https://doi.org/10.1016/j.matdes.2011.02.010

Elshereafy, E., M.M. El-Zayat, Nawal A. Shaltout, Magda M. Abou Zeid, and A.A. El-Miligy. 2016. "Effect of Gamma Radiation on the Properties of Ethylene Propylene Diene Monomer/Styrene Butadiene Rubber/Waste Polyethylene/Clay Nanocomposites." *Journal of Radioanalytical and Nuclear Chemistry* 307 (2): 1325–33. https://doi.org/10.1007/s10967-015-4320-1

Eyssa, H.M., D.E. Abulyazied, M. Abdulrahman, and H.A. Youssef. 2018. "Mechanical and Physical Properties of Nanosilica/Nitrile Butadiene Rubber Composites Cured by Gamma Irradiation." *Egyptian Journal of Petroleum* 27 (3): 383–92. https://doi.org/10.1016/j.ejpe.2017.06.004

Flory, Paul J., and John Rehner. 1943. "Statistical Mechanics of Cross-Linked Polymer Networks I. Rubberlike Elasticity." *The Journal of Chemical Physics* 11 (11): 512. https://doi.org/10.1063/1.1723791

Guggenheim, Stephen. 2015. "Phyllosilicates Used as Nanotube Substrates in Engineered Materials: Structures, Chemistries and Textures." In *Natural Mineral Nanotubes*. New York: Apple Academic Press, 3–48. https://doi.org/doi:10.1201/b18107-3

Hassan, Mehdat M., Nagwa A. Badway, Mona Y. Elnaggar, and El Sayed A. Hegazy. 2014. "Synergistic Effect of Gamma Radiation and Peroxide on Dynamic Vulcanization of Thermoplastics Vulcanizes Based on (Devulcanized Rubber)/Polypropylene." *Journal of Vinyl and Additive Technology* 20 (3): 168–76. https://doi.org/10.1002/vnl

Hayeemasae, Nabil, and Hanafi Ismail. 2018. "Reinforcement of Epoxidised Natural Rubber Through the Addition of Sepiolite." *Polymers Composites* 40(3): 924–31. https://doi.org/10.1002/pc.24762

Hergenrother, William L., and Ashley S. Hilton. 2003. "Use of χ as a function of volume fraction of rubber to determine crosslink density by swelling." *Rubber Chemistry and Technology* 76 (4):832–45. https://doi.org/10.5254/1.3547775

Hwang, Wei Gwo, Kung Hwa Wei, and Chang Mou Wu. 2004. "Mechanical, Thermal, and Barrier Properties of NBR/Organosilicate Nanocomposites." *Polymer Engineering and Science* 44 (11): 2117–24. https://doi.org/10.1002/pen.20217

Ibrahim, Sofian, Khairiah Badri, Chantara Thevy Ratnam, and Noor Hasni M. Ali. 2018. "Enhancing Mechanical Properties of Prevulcanized Natural Rubber Latex via Hybrid Radiation and Peroxidation Vulcanizations at Various Irradiation Doses." *Radiation Effects and Defects in Solids* 173 (5–6): 427–34. https://doi.org/10.1080/10420150.2018.1462366

Javad, Seyed, Yu-dong Huang, Nanqi Ren, and Ahmad Mohaddespour. 2009. "The Comparison of EPDM/Clay Nanocomposites and Conventional Composites in Exposure of Gamma Irradiation." *Composites Science and Technology* 69 (7–8): 997–1003. https://doi.org/10.1016/j.compscitech.2009.01.006

Kalkornsurapranee, Ekwipoo, Suchart Kothan, Sirilak Intom, Jobish Johns, Siriprapa Kaewjaeng, Chittra Kedkaew, Wuttichai Chaiphaksa, Thanapong Sareein, and Jakrapong Kaewkhao. 2021. "Wearable and Flexible Radiation Shielding Natural Rubber Composites: Effect of Different Radiation Shielding Fillers." *Radiation Physics and Chemistry* 179 (April): 109261. https://doi.org/10.1016/j.radphyschem.2020.109261

Khankishiyeva, R.F., S.M. Mammadov, H.N. Akhundzada, J.S. Mammadov, A.I. Azadaliyev, P.I. Ismayilova, and G.A. Mammadova. 2020. "Comparative Study of the Effect of Gamma-Radiation on the Structural and Thermophysical Properties of Nitrile-Butadiene Rubber Filled with Different Nanometal Oxides." *Problems of Atomic Science and Technology* 126 (2): 39–46.

Kruželák, Ján, Ivan Chodák, Daniela Jochec Mošková, Rastislav Dosoudil, and Ivan Hudec. 2018. "Cross-Linking and Properties of Rubber Magnetic Composites Cured with Different Curing Systems." *Polymers for Advanced Technologies* 29 (1): 216–25. https://doi.org/10.1002/pat.4106

Madani, M. 2004. "Effect of γ-Irradiation on the Properties of Rubber-Based Conductive Blend Composites." *Polymers and Polymer Composites* 12 (6): 525–34.

Makuuchi, Kenzo, and Song Cheng. 2012. *Radiation Processing of Polymer Materials and Its Industrial Applications*. First Edition. New Jersey: John Wiley & Sons, Inc.

Masood, Farha, Maryam Aziz, Hasnain Haider, Omer Shakil, Tariq Yasin, and Abdul Hameed. 2018. "Biodegradation of Gamma Irradiated Poly-3-Hydroxybutyrate/Sepiolite Nanocomposites." *International Biodeterioration and Biodegradation* 126: 1–9. https://doi.org/10.1016/j.ibiod.2017.09.012

Mohd Zaini, Nurul Aizan, Hanafi Ismail, and Arjulizan Rusli. 2018. "Tensile, Thermal, Flammability and Morphological Properties of Sepiolite Filled Ethylene Propylene Diene Monomer (EDPM) Rubber Composites." *Iranian Polymer Journal (English Edition)* 27 (5): 287–96. https://doi.org/10.1007/s13726-018-0609-6

Mok, K.L., and K.H. Eng. 2018. "Characterisation of Crosslinks in Vulcanised Rubbers: From Simple to Advanced Techniques." *Malaysian Journal of Chemistry* 20 (1): 118–27.

Montoya-Villegas, Kathleen A., Alejandro Ramírez-Jiménez, Arturo Zizumbo-López, Sergio Pérez-Sicairos, Benjamín Leal-Acevedo, Emilio Bucio, and Angel Licea-Claverie. 2020. "Controlled Surface Modification of Silicone Rubber by Gamma-Irradiation Followed by RAFT Grafting Polymerization." *European Polymer Journal* 134 (April): 109817. https://doi.org/10.1016/j.eurpolymj.2020.109817

Pasbakhsh, P., H. Ismail, A.F. Mohd Nor, A. Abu Bakar, P. Pasbakhsh, H. Ismail, A.F. Mohd Nor, and A. Abu Bakar. 2012. "Electron Beam Irradiation of Sulphur Vulcanised Ethylene Propylene Diene Monomer (EPDM) Nanocomposites Reinforced by Halloysite Nanotubes." *Plastics, Rubber and Composites* 41 (10): 430–40. https://doi.org/10.1179/1743289811Y.0000000058

Planes, Emilie, Laurent Chazeau, Gérard Vigier, and Thomas Stuhldreier. 2010. "Influence of Silica Fillers on the Ageing by Gamma Radiation of EPDM Nanocomposites." *Composites Science and Technology* 70 (10): 1530–36. https://doi.org/10.1016/j.compscitech.2010.05.010

Rooj, Sandip, Amit Das, and Gert Heinrich. 2011. "Tube-like Natural Halloysite/Fluoroelastomer Nanocomposites with Simultaneous Enhanced Mechanical, Dynamic Mechanical and Thermal Properties." *European Polymer Journal* 47 (9): 1746–55. https://doi.org/10.1016/j.eurpolymj.2011.06.007

Sarossy, Zsuzsa, Thomas O.J. Blomfeldt, Mikael S. Hedenqvist, Christian Bender Koch, Suprakas Sinha Ray, and David Plackett. 2012. "Composite Films of Arabinoxylan and Fibrous Sepiolite: Morphological, Mechanical, and Barrier Properties." *ACS Applied Materials and Interfaces* 4 (7): 3378–86. https://doi.org/10.1021/am3002956

Shoushtari Zadeh Naseri, Aida, and Azam Jalali-Arani. 2016. "Study on the Morphology, Static and Dynamic Mechanical Properties of (Styrene Butadiene Rubber/Ethylene Propylene Diene Monomer/Organoclay) Nanocomposites Vulcanized by the Gamma Radiation." *Journal of Applied Polymer Science* 133 (25): 1–9. https://doi.org/10.1002/app.43581

Tarawneh, Mou'ad A., Sherin A. Saraireh, Ruey Shan Chen, Sahrim Hj Ahmad, Musab A.M. Al-Tarawni, and Lih Jiun Yu. 2021. "Gamma Irradiation Influence on Mechanical, Thermal and Conductivity Properties of Hybrid Carbon Nanotubes/Montmorillonite Nanocomposites." *Radiation Physics and Chemistry* 179 (May): 109168. https://doi.org/10.1016/j.radphyschem.2020.109168

Wang, Qingguo, Fenlan Wang, and Kuo Cheng. 2009. "Effect of Crosslink Density on Some Properties of Electron Beam-Irradiated Styrene-Butadiene Rubber." *Radiation Physics and Chemistry* 78 (11): 1001–5. https://doi.org/10.1016/j.radphyschem.2009.06.001

Youssef, Hussein A., Yasser K. Abdel-monem, and Walaa W. Diab. 2017. "Effect of Gamma Irradiation on the Properties of Natural Rubber Latex and Styrene-Butadiene Rubber Latex Nanocomposites." *Polymer Composites* 38: E189–98. https://doi.org/10.1002/pc

8 Properties of Sepiolite-Reinforced Irradiated Linear Low-Density Polyethylene Nanocomposites

*Siti Nadia Aini Ghazali and
Zurina Mohamad*
Universiti Teknologi Malaysia
Johor Bahru, Malaysia

CONTENTS

8.1 Introduction 153
8.2 Materials and Method 155
    8.2.1 Properties Determination and Preparation of Irradiated LDPE/Sepiolite Nanocomposite 155
8.3 Properties and Characterization of Irradiated LDPE/Sepiolite Nanocomposites 157
    8.3.1 X-Ray Diffraction Analysis 157
    8.3.2 Gel Content 157
    8.3.3 Tensile Properties 159
    8.3.4 Thermal Properties 161
    8.3.5 Morphology Analysis 164
    8.3.6 Flammability Properties 164
8.4 Conclusions 166
Acknowledgments 166
References 166

8.1 INTRODUCTION

Recently, thermoplastics have been subject to demand in the polymer industry due to their wide range of applications in various industries, such as the automotive, packaging, construction and electrical fields. One thermoplastic that is widely used and commercialized is polyethylene (PE). In one study, PE was in the great global demand, monopolizing more than 70% of the plastics market (Tamboli et al., 2004). PE can be categorized into three different grades based on density and degree of branching: low-density polyethylene (LDPE), high-density polyethylene (HDPE), and linear low-density polyethylene (LLDPE) (Malpass, 2010). In this work, LDPE will be used as a polymer matrix due to its excellent electrical insulating properties (Ju et al., 2014). LDPE is a semi-crystalline polymer produced by the polymerization of ethylene. It is lightweight and formable and has good chemical resistance, toughness, flexibility, high impact strength at low temperature and relatively low cost compared with other polymers. It has many possible uses in the electrical field; for instance, it can be used in the application of insulation of wire and cables. However, LDPE has to overcome certain limitations, such as low tensile strength, soft surface, high flammability and high thermal expansion (Gao et al., 2019).

The development of nanocomposites based on sepiolite nanofiller is the subject of a great deal of attention due to a unique physicochemical characteristic of sepiolite: it improves processing, dimensional stability, mechanical strength and thermal resistance. Sepiolite nanofiller also has gained attention due to its unique, needle-like clay species that can be easily dispersed in polymeric matrices, in contrast to the platelet-like clay of the same aspect ratio (Bilotti et al., 2008). Beyond this, sepiolite can perform strongly because of the mechanical properties, thermal stability, flame retardancy and barrier properties derived from its special structure (Mejía et al., 2014; Singh et al., 2016; Wu et al., 2015; Li et al., 2019).

Generally, polymer nanocomposites are made by the homogenous dispersion of nanometer-sized filler into either a thermoplastic or a thermoset. The radiation cross-linking technologies are widely used in various products, such as wire and cable, rubber tires, vulcanization of rubber latex, composites used in automotive and aerospace industry, medical devices and molded parts. According to Basfar (2002), the radiation cross-linking process is a well-known method used to improve the flammability and the thermal, mechanical and electrical properties of polymers in wire and cable applications. Electron beam (EB) irradiation has received tremendous attention in the last few years, primarily because of its ability to produce cross-linked networks with various polymers. The EB processing of cross-linked polymeric material has yielded materials with better dimensional stability, reduced stress cracking and reduced permeability of water and solvent. In addition, it has provided some significant improvement in mechanical, physical and thermal properties (Bhattacharya, 2000; Chmieleweski et al., 2005). Furthermore, an EB has a short wavelength and a high frequency that produces greater penetrating power than other types of radiation sources, such as ultraviolet (UV) rays, X-rays and gamma rays (Bhattacharya, 2000). However, a superior irradiation dosage is needed because excessive cross-linking can cause polymer materials to become brittle (Bee et al., 2013; Entezam et al., 2017).

LDPE's low flammability properties have restricted its usage in the electrical engineering field, especially in the insulation of wire and cable applications. Reinforcing a flame-retardant filler such as sepiolite into the LDPE matrix is expected to enhance LDPE's flammability properties. However, this could lead to weaker mechanical properties of the polymer composite, such as tensile properties. This problem can be improved by adding sepiolite nanofiller into the polymer matrix because the nanofiller particle can disperse better than microfiller. Beyond this, a polymer filled with micrometric-sized particles reduces its mechanical and thermal properties (Nohales et al., 2011).

8.2 MATERIALS AND METHOD

8.2.1 PROPERTIES DETERMINATION AND PREPARATION OF IRRADIATED LDPE/SEPIOLITE NANOCOMPOSITE

The LDPE resin (LDF260GG) used in this study was obtained from Lotte Chemical Titan (M) Sdn Bhd. It has a density of 0.922 g/cm^3 and a melt flow rate (MFR) of 5 g/10 min. The natural, needle-like sepiolite clay (Pangel S9) was supplied by Tolsa (Spain) and was used as received. The LDPE/sepiolite nanocomposites were prepared by melt compounding using a twin-screw extruder at 160°C under a constant screw speed of 50 rpm. The palletized materials were then dried at 65°C for 24 hours and injected using an injection molding machine to produce the testing samples. The formulation for the nanocomposites is depicted in Table 8.1. Before testing, EB irradiation was performed in air at room temperature using a 3.0 Cockroft Walton type EB accelerator (model NHV EPS-3000). The samples were subjected to radiation doses of 50, 100, 150 and 200 kGy at a dose rate of 50 kGy per pass. The tensile test of LDPE/sepiolite nanocomposites was carried out at room temperature using a universal tensile testing machine (Lloyd Instrument Tensile Tester model EZ) according to ASTM D638. The crosshead speed used was 5 mm/min with a 20-kN load cell. All of the results were taken as the average values of at least five samples for each formulation. A thermogravimetric analysis (TGA) of LDPE/sepiolite nanocomposites was performed on 10- to 15-mg samples using a thermal gravimetric analyzer (TGA 4000, Perkin-Elmer, USA), by heating from ambient temperature to 900°C with a heating ramp of 20°C/min under a nitrogen atmosphere.

The melting and crystallization behavior testing of polymer composites was carried out using a differential scanning calorimeter (DSC 7, Perkin-Elmer, USA), according to ASTM D3418. The 5- to 12-mg samples were heated under nitrogen flow at 50 mL/min. The samples were first heated at a rate of 10°C/min from 30°C to 250°C and then cooled from 200°C to 30°C. The melting point temperature (T_m) and

TABLE 8.1
Formulation of LDPE/Sepiolite Nanocomposite

Samples	LDPE (wt%)	Sepiolite (phr)	Irradiation Dose (kGy)
Pure LDPE	100	0	0, 50, 100, 150, 200
LDPE/SEP2		2	
LDPE/SEP4		4	
LDPE/SEP6		6	
LDPE/SEP8		8	
LDPE/SEP10		10	

heat of fusion were taken as those corresponding to the melting endotherms' peak values from the DSC thermogram.

The crystallinity percentage, X_c, of the LDPE component was calculated using the following relationship (Equation 8.1):

$$X_c\left(\% \text{ crystallinity}\right) = \frac{\Delta H_f}{\Delta H_f^\circ (w)} \times 100 \tag{8.1}$$

where ΔH_f is the heat of fusion of the sample, ΔH_f° is the heat of fusion for 100% crystalline LDPE equal to 293 J/g (Mirabella and Bafna, 2002) and w is the weight fraction of LDPE in the composites.

The limiting oxygen index (LOI) is widely used to quantify polymeric and composite materials' flammability and to investigate fire retardants' effectiveness in those materials. Higher LOI represents better flame retardancy for a material. An LOI test is conducted according to ASTM D2863 using an LOI analyzer (Dynisco Plastics, Germany) at room temperature. The result of oxygen concentration, expressed in volume percentage, was taken from the average of three specimens per formulation, as illustrated in Equation 8.2:

$$\text{LOI }(\%) = \frac{[O_{2,\text{cr}}]}{[O_{2,\text{cr}}] + [N_2]} \times 100 \tag{8.2}$$

where $[O_{2,\text{cr}}]$ is minimum oxygen concentration in the inflow gases required to support flaming combustion of the material and $[N_2]$ is nitrogen concentration in the inflow gases.

The horizontal burning mode (HB) of the UL94 test was carried out according to ASTM D635. In addition, UL testing is a method of classifying a material's tendency to either extinguish or spread a flame once it has ignited and determine the relative rate of burning self-supporting plastics. The standard bar sample dimensions are 125 mm long × 13 mm wide × 3 mm thick. The things observed in this test are time until the flame extinguishes itself, the distance that the flame propagates, the linear burning rate in millimeters per minute, and whether the flame burns through the test sample, sending drops from the test sample to ignite cotton below. The specimen that burns slowly or self-extinguishes and does not drip flaming is highest in the UL classification scheme. The linear burning rate (mm/min) for each formulation was calculated using Equation 8.3:

$$V = 60\, L/t \tag{8.3}$$

where L is the burned length (mm) and t is the time (seconds).

The morphologies of the nanoparticle were characterized by transmission electron microscopy (TEM). A cryogenic ultramicrotomy sectioned the ultrathin samples with a diamond knife, and the samples were observed under a JEOL JEM-2000FX microscope. The thickness of the samples is approximately 70 μm.

The X-ray diffraction (XRD) patterns were recorded using a D500 X-ray diffractometer (Siemens, Germany) with Cu Kα radiation to determine the dispersion and structure of sepiolite in the LDPE matrix. The measurement conditions of XRD are 45 kV and 15 mA, respectively. The samples were scanned at a rate of 2°/min in the range of 7° to 90° at a wavelength of 0.154060 nm. The d-spacing of sepiolite was extracted from XRD data using Bragg's law (Equation 8.4), as follows:

$$d-\text{spacing} = \lambda/2 \sin\theta \qquad (8.4)$$

where λ is the wavelength of X-ray radiation and θ is the diffraction angle.

The gel content test was carried out to investigate the total formation of the cross-linked network in the polymer composite. It was measured according to ASTM D2765 by immersing the samples gravimetrically in xylene at a temperature of 110°C for 24 hours. The initial weights of the samples were weighed and recorded. After 24 hours of extraction, the remaining samples were washed with clean xylene several times to eliminate the mark of soluble materials on the extracted sample. The extracted samples were dried in an oven at 100°C for 24 hours, and the test was repeated until a constant weight was obtained. The gel content percentage was calculated using Equation 8.5:

$$\text{Gel content}(\%) = \frac{W}{W_0} \times 100 \qquad (8.5)$$

where W and W_0 are the dried sample's weight after extraction and the sample's initial weight, respectively.

8.3 PROPERTIES AND CHARACTERIZATION OF IRRADIATED LDPE/SEPIOLITE NANOCOMPOSITES

8.3.1 X-Ray Diffraction Analysis

The nanocomposites' XRD pattern at different sepiolite content is shown in Figure 8.1. In the XRD pattern, the characteristic diffraction peaks of sepiolite were found at $2\theta = 7.44°$, corresponding to a layer spacing of 1.188 nm and (110) plane of sepiolite. In addition, the same sepiolite characteristic was reported by Fitaroni et al. (2019). The sepiolite characteristic peak disappears in LDPE/SEP nanocomposite, indicating that the sepiolite bundles are generally exfoliated (or delaminated) to fiber stick and homogenously dispersed into the LDPE matrix.

8.3.2 Gel Content

The degree of cross-linking formed via EB irradiation in LDPE/sepiolite nanocomposite was determined by calculating the gel content as a function of different irradiation doses (0–200 kGy), as shown in Figure 8.2. Beyond this, gel content was used

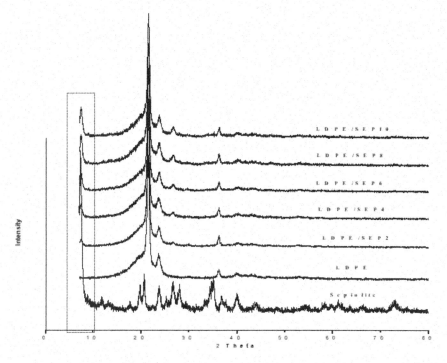

FIGURE 8.1 XRD pattern of sepiolite, pure LDPE and LDPE/sepiolite nanocomposites with 2θ value from 7° to 80°.

to evaluate the extent of cross-linking in the irradiated polymer and non-irradiated specimens (Satapathy et al., 2006). In general, the percentage of gel content slightly increased with increasing irradiation dose. The EB irradiation has rapidly increased LDPE/sepiolite nanocomposites' gel content, especially at 50 kGy. This indicates that nanocomposite exposure to a low irradiation dose could induce the cross-linking formation and become insoluble. In addition, the release of free radicals into the polymer

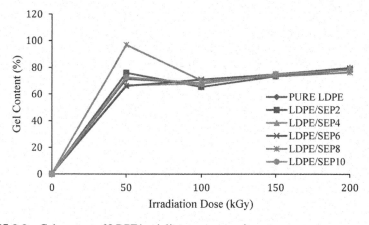

FIGURE 8.2 Gel content of LDPE/sepiolite nanocomposite.

matrix's amorphous region is evidence attributed to the cross-linking network's development. Next, the percentage of gel content slightly dropped at an irradiation dose of 100 kGy. The combination of free radicals to form cross-links becomes difficult, leading to a lower degree of cross-linking, and the chain scission or degradation of polymer chain might occur at this dose. Meanwhile, the percentage of gel content began to increase at 150 kGy until 200 kGy. This increment might be due to the existence of post-cross-linking at higher irradiation doses. Increasing, both irradiation doses and sepiolite loading up to 200 kGy and 10 phr, respectively, give marginal effect to gel content value. Similar results on the influence of irradiation dose on gel content values also have been reported by other scholars with different types of filler (Bee et al., 2012). The sepiolite loadings at 4 and 8 phr were chosen to undergo further investigation on characterization.

8.3.3 Tensile Properties

The tensile properties of LDPE/sepiolite nanocomposite before and after exposure to EB irradiation at various dosages are presented in Figure 8.3. Based on the figure, the trend of tensile strength showed an enhancement of about 4%–8% for all sepiolite loading after exposure to a 50-kGy irradiation dose. This increment indicates that the LDPE/sepiolite nanocomposite attributed to the radiation induces cross-linking, which had been proved by the gel content analysis, and, hence, improved the tensile strength. Moreover, the tensile strength of LDPE/sepiolite nanocomposite decreased at 100 and 200 kGy. This phenomenon might be true because degradation of the polymer chain is predominant over cross-linking reactions at a higher dosage (Satapathy et al., 2006), which led to the low-stress transfer.

Furthermore, the tensile strength at higher sepiolite loading (10 phr) showed some reduction, especially at an irradiation dose of 200 kGy, indicating the presence of agglomeration and poor distribution of sepiolite in the polymer matrix. However, unexpectedly, the tensile strength of LDPE/sepiolite showed its highest values at 150 kGy. Thus, the post-cross-linking reaction might occur in LDPE/sepiolite nanocomposites.

On the other hand, the Young's modulus of irradiated nanocomposites has marginally increased with increasing irradiation doses from 50 to 100 kGy compared with those of the non-irradiated sample. Young's modulus represents the material's stiffness; thus, a higher Young's modulus indicated that the nanocomposite stiffened. The cross-linking network formation might restrict LDPE chains' mobility and thus enhance the stiffness (Bee et al., 2013). Meanwhile, the increasing sepiolite loading from 0 to 10 phr under all irradiation dosages also increased Young's modulus. However, the further increments in irradiation doses from 150 to 200 kGy slightly decreased the Young's modulus. This could be attributed to the presence of chain scission of LDPE chains at higher irradiation doses.

The effect of sepiolite loading and irradiation dose on elongation at the breaking of the LDPE/sepiolite nanocomposite was investigated, as shown in Figure 8.3. The elongation at break of nanocomposites has steadily decreased, in line with the sepiolite loading level from 0 to 10 phr. This reduction might be due to the agglomeration of sepiolite at high loading, reducing the interfacial adhesion between the polymer

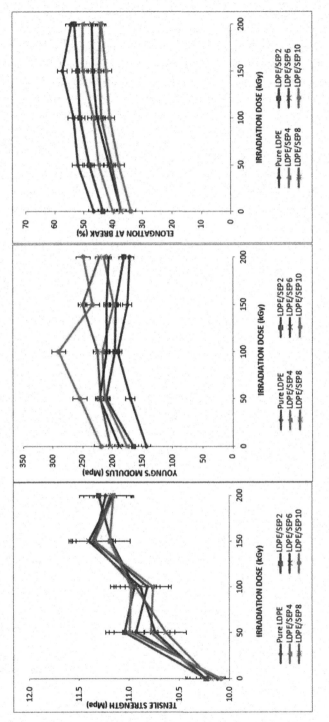

FIGURE 8.3 The tensile properties of non-irradiated and irradiated LDPE/sepiolite nanocomposites.

matrix and sepiolite particles (Yasin et al., 2013). In contrast, the irradiation dose effect on elongation at break was significantly increased after further exposure to irradiation doses from 50 to 200 kGy, compared with those of non-irradiated LDPE/sepiolite nanocomposites. This increment might be due to forming a cross-linking network that improves elongation at the breaking of the nanocomposite.

8.3.4 THERMAL PROPERTIES

Table 8.2 represents the data of melting temperature (T_m), the heat of fusion (ΔH_m) and percentage of crystallinity (X_c) of LDPE/sepiolite nanocomposites after irradiation, which were extracted from the DSC thermogram (Figure 8.4). The irradiation dose effect on LDPE was discussed only at 4 and 8 phr sepiolite content. From the DSC data obtained, the results revealed that the T_m, ΔH_m and X_c gradually decreased as the irradiation doses increased up to 150 kGy, with the addition of sepiolite loading. It began to decrease on increasing irradiation exposure at 50 kGy, which is about 2% of decrement for pure LDPE, LDPE/SEP4 and LDPE/SEP8. On this subject, Khonakdar et al. (2006) explained that radicals are formed in the crystalline region by irradiation and are frozen due to the chains' hindered mobility, causing no cross-linking within the crystalline region. These reductions also happen because of the concurring

TABLE 8.2
The DSC Data of LDPE/Sepiolite Nanocomposite at Different Irradiation Doses and Sepiolite Loading

Irradiation Dose (kGy)	T_m (°C)	ΔH_m (J/g)	X_c (%)
	Pure LDPE		
0	106.23	65.02	22.19
50	105.07	45.55	15.55
100	105.03	44.60	15.22
150	106.43	40.12	13.69
200	104.4	46.98	16.04
	LDPE/SEP4		
0	107.5	78.62	26.83
50	105.1	39.70	13.55
100	104.63	42.13	14.38
150	103.87	41.65	14.21
200	104.23	44.03	15.03
	LDPE/SEP8		
0	107.04	75.12	25.64
50	106.87	26.65	9.10
100	104.77	39.72	13.56
150	104.63	37.88	12.93
200	104.00	40.49	13.82

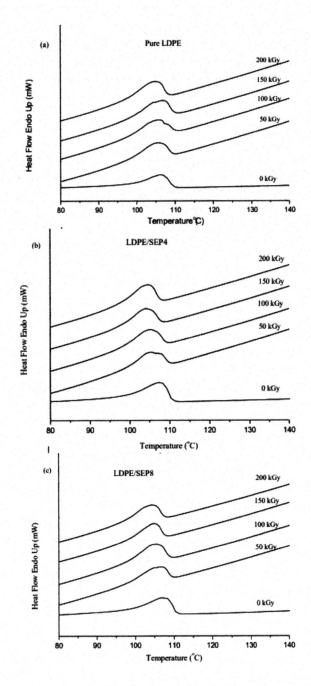

FIGURE 8.4 The DSC curve of (a) pure LDPE, (b) LDPE/SEP4 and (c) LDPE/SEP8 nanocomposites with different irradiation doses.

random chain scission reactions in the nanocomposite when exposed to irradiation. The chain scission reactions that cause polymer chains to become shorter lowered the nanocomposite's molecular weight so that it could not crystallize properly, reducing its melting temperature and crystallinity (Khonakdar et al., 2006). However, at a higher irradiation dose (200 kGy), the T_m and X_c values of LDPE/sepiolite nanocomposite slightly increased. In addition, the chain scission still occurred at this dose, but shorter polymer chains of LDPE/sepiolite nanocomposite could quickly crystallize into several small crystallites, thus increasing the X_c and T_m.

Table 8.3 shows the thermal stability behavior of LDPE/sepiolite nanocomposites at different irradiation doses, which recorded the decomposition temperature of nanocomposite at 10% and 90% weight loss. The maximum degradation temperature of nanocomposites taken from the derivative thermogravimetry (DTG) peak was also tabulated in Table 8.3. As the irradiation dose increased, the thermal stability was expected to gradually increase with the proper cross-linking. However, the result revealed that irradiated nanocomposite's thermal stability becomes lower than that of the non-irradiated nanocomposite with increasing irradiation doses. This could occur due to the degradation of the polymer chain when exposed to irradiation. The percentages of weight loss of non-irradiated and irradiated nanocomposites

TABLE 8.3
TGA Data for Irradiated LDPE-Filled Sepiolite Nanocomposite

Irradiation Dose (kGy)	Initial Degradation Temperature $T_{10\%}$ (°C)	Final Degradation Temperature $T_{90\%}$ (°C)	Maximum Degradation Temperature from DTG T_{max} (°C)
		Pure LDPE	
0	448.20	497.58	485.13
50	439.08	480.55	466.24
100	436.42	488.54	479.30
150	441.00	487.94	477.16
200	441.06	489.19	479.22
		LDPE/SEP4	
0	465.56	511.08	497.06
50	445.14	491.23	476.25
100	406.20	471.76	418.32
150	442.16	491.54	454.16
200	412.80	473.97	477.18
		LDPE/SEP8	
0	457.83	514.29	497.15
50	438.86	491.51	475.14
100	449.34	495.39	481.05
150	443.04	494.72	480.27
200	446.67	495.01	477.31

at 90% appeared approximately between 450°C and 520°C, indicating that irradiated pure LDPE, LDPE/SEP4 and LDPE/SEP8 decomposed at a lower temperature than non-irradiated samples. Although there are no significant changes in the values of $T_{10\%}$, $T_{90\%}$ and T_{max} with increasing irradiation doses, the final degradation temperature, $T_{90\%}$ of LDPE/SEP8, was higher than that of pure LDPE or LDPE/SEP4. This means that increases in sepiolite loading could improve the thermal stability of nanocomposites. To this end, Satapathy et al. (2006) proved in their study that thermal stability for all waste PE and its blends with LDPE and HDPE is not affected by radiation or remains constant.

8.3.5 Morphology Analysis

The morphology of the LDPE/sepiolite nanocomposites was further accessed by TEM. In this study, LDPE/sepiolite at 4- and 10-phr sepiolite content with both non-irradiated and irradiated samples under a dose of 150 kGy were evaluated. The sepiolite loading at 4 phr was selected because it showed excellent tensile strength compared with other loadings. In addition, the 10-phr sepiolite loading was selected to observe LDPE/sepiolite nanocomposites' morphology at a higher loading.

The TEM image reveals that sepiolite has a fibrous and needle-like morphology, exhibiting a high aspect ratio and large surface area. By comparing the non-irradiated samples of 4 and 10 phr, 10 phr of sepiolite tends to agglomerate with a larger size than 4-phr loading throughout the LDPE matrix. This sepiolite agglomeration at 10 phr gives poor interfacial adhesion between LDPE matrix and sepiolite particles, particularly hindering cross-linking formation, reducing the tensile strength of the nanocomposite. However, after the penetration of 150-kGy irradiation on both 4- and 10-phr sepiolite, the sepiolite filler's agglomeration in the LDPE matrix was reduced, as shown in Figure 8.5b and d. It can be seen that the sepiolite particles at 150 kGy are well separated and dispersed into a small aggregate in the LDPE matrix compared with non-irradiated samples. Therefore, the formation of the cross-linking network in nanocomposites could improve particle separation and reduce the agglomeration of sepiolite particles (Bee et al., 2014). Furthermore, the LDPE/sepiolite nanocomposite might contain the mixing of both exfoliated and intercalated structures.

8.3.6 Flammability Properties

In this section, the UL94 was discussed instead of LOI because LOI showed no variation changes throughout all irradiation doses. Figure 8.6 graphs the UL94 horizontal burning test for irradiated LDPE/sepiolite nanocomposites at various irradiation doses, from 50 to 200 kGy. In addition, UL94HB was carried out to determine the flammability behavior of the nanocomposite. Non-irradiated LDPE/SEP10 showed the highest value at the burning rate 49.67 mm/min compared with non-irradiated pure LDPE and other sepiolite loadings. This indicates that LDPE/SEP10 burned and dripped faster to reach the 100-mm reference mark. It is believed that 10 phr of sepiolite was not well dispersed in the polymer matrix. However, LDPE/SEP10 rapidly decreased to 35.05 mm/min after 50-kGy irradiation exposure and then slowly

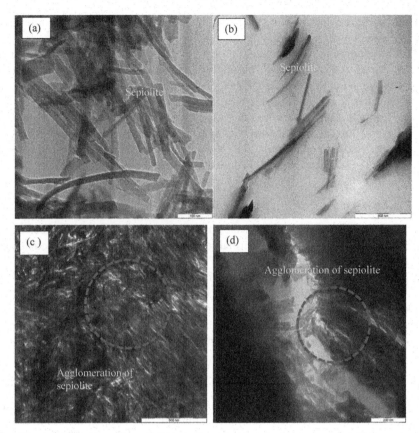

FIGURE 8.5 TEM micrographs of LDPE/sepiolite nanocomposite at (a) 4 phr, 0 kGy; (b) 4 phr, 150 kGy; (c) 10 phr, 0 kGy and (d) 10 phr, 150 kGy.

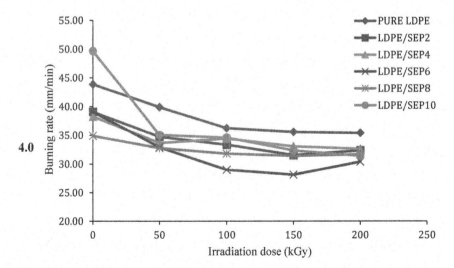

FIGURE 8.6 Burning rate of LDPE/sepiolite loading at different irradiation dosages.

reduced, meaning that the time taken for the flame to pass the 100-mm reference mark became slower with time.

Further increasing of irradiation doses up to 200 kGy also decreased the linear burning rate of nanocomposites. This might have been due to the irradiation-induced cross-linking in the LDPE/Sepiolite nanocomposite, which led to the formation of a protective char layer, hindering the burning of polymers (Bourbigot and Duquesne, 2007). The reduction of burning rate indicates good flame retardancy of sepiolite filler. Beyond this, the constant dripping of samples was observed during the experiment in the irradiated nanocomposites. Notably, sepiolite can be considered a flame retardant with increasing irradiation doses, thus exhibiting low flammability.

8.4 CONCLUSIONS

The tensile properties of nanocomposites have marginally improved with increasing irradiation doses. In addition, the thermal stability of nanocomposites showed no significant effect with increasing these doses. Furthermore, solid dispersion of sepiolite was found in the lower content of sepiolite in the PE matrix. Irradiation cross-linking may have changed the morphology of the composites because after the irradiation of 150 kGy, the agglomerations of the nanocomposite reduced and became more homogenous. The linear burning rate decreased with increasing irradiation doses and sepiolite loading, displaying better flammability properties of the PE/sepiolite nanocomposites.

ACKNOWLEDGMENTS

The authors would like to thank the Universiti Teknologi Malaysia (UTM) and Ministry of Education (MOE) Malaysia for funding this research under the UTM-TDR14.0 (05G85), UTM-TDR14.1 (05G86), CRG 37.0 (908G52), CRG 37.1 (08G50) and Fundamental Research Grant Scheme FRGS/1/2019/TK05/UTM/02/17 (5F185).

REFERENCES

Basfar, A. A. 2002. "Flammability of Radiation Cross-Linked Low Density Polyethylene as an Insulating Material for Wire and Cable." *Radiation Physics and Chemistry* 63(3–6): 505–508. https://doi.org/10.1016/S0969-806X(01)00545-X

Bee, S. T., Hassan, A., Ratnam, C. T., Tee, T. T., and Sin, L. T. 2012. "Effects of Montmorillonite on the Electron Beam Irradiated Alumina Trihydrate Added Polyethylene and Ethylene Vinyl Acetate Nanocomposite." *Polymer Composites* 33: 1883–1892. https://doi.org/10.1002/pc.22328

Bee, S. T., Hassan, A., Ratnam, C. T., Tee, T. T., and Sin, L. T. 2013. "Investigation of Nano-Size Montmorillonite on Electron Beam Irradiated Flame Retardant Polyethylene and Ethylene Vinyl Acetate Blends." *Nuclear Instruments and Methods in Physics Research Section B: Beam Interactions with Materials and Atoms* 299: 42–50. https://doi.org/10.1016/j.nimb.2013.01.040

Bee, S. T., Ratnam, C. T., Sin, L. T., Tee, T. T., Wong, W. K., Lee, J. X., and Rahmat, A. R. 2014. "Effects of Electron Beam Irradiation on the Structural Properties of Polylactic Acid/Polyethylene Blends." *Nuclear Instruments and Methods in Physics Research Section B: Beam Interactions with Materials and Atoms* 334: 18–27. https://doi.org/10.1016/j.nimb.2014.04.024

Bhattacharya, A. 2000. "Radiation and Industrial Polymers." *Progress in Polymer Science* 25(3): 371–401. https://doi.org/10.1016/S0079-6700(00)00009-5

Bilotti, E., Fischer, H. R., and Peijs, T. 2008. "Polymer Nanocomposites Based on Needle-like Sepiolite Clays: Effect of Functionalized Polymers on the Dispersion of Nanofiller, Crystallinity, and Mechanical Properties." *Journal of Applied Polymer Science* 107: 1116–1123. https://doi.org/10.1002/app.25395

Bourbigot, S., and Duquesne, S. 2007. "Fire Retardant Polymer: Recent Development and Opportunities." *Journal of Materials Chemistry* 22 (47): 2283–2300. https://doi.org/10.1039/B702511D

Chmieleweski, A. G., Haji-Saeid, M., and Ahmed S. 2005. "Progress in Radiation Processing of Polymers." *Nuclear Instruments and Methods in Physics Research B* 236: 44–45. https://doi.org/10.1016/j.nimb.2005.03.247

Entezam, M., M. K. R. Aghjeh, and Ghaffari, M. 2017. "Electron Beam Irradiation Induced Compatibilization of Immiscible Polyethylene/Ethylene Vinyl Acetate (PE/EVA) Blends: Mechanical Properties and Morphology Stability." *Radiation Physics and Chemistry* 131: 22–27. https://doi.org/10.1016/j.radphyschem.2016.10.016

Fitaroni, L. B., Venâncio, T., Tanaka, F. H., Gimenez, J. C. F., Costa, J. A. S., and Cruz, S. A. 2019. "Organically Modified Sepiolite: Thermal Treatment and Chemical and Morphological Properties." *Applied Clay Science* 179: 105149. https://doi.org/10.1016/j.clay.2019.105149

Gao, J., Cai, W., Hu, Y., and Chen, C. 2019. "Improving the Flame Retardancy of Polyethylenes Through the Palladium-Catalyzed Incorporation of Polar Comonomers." *Polymer Chemistry* 10 (12): 1416–1422. https://sci-hub.se/10.1039/c8py01772g

Ju, S., Zhang, H., Chen, M., Zhang, C., Chen, X., and Zhang, Z. 2014. "Improved Electrical Insulating Properties of LDPE Based Nanocomposite: Effect of Surface Modification of Magnesia Nanoparticles." *Composites Part A: Applied Science and Manufacturing* 66: 183–192. https://doi.org/10.1016/j.compositesa.2014.07.003

Khonakdar, H. A., Jafari, S. H., Wagenknecht, U., and Jehnichen, D. 2006. "Effect of Electron-Irradiation on Cross-Link Density and Crystalline Structure of Low and High-Density Polyethylene." *Radiation Physics and Chemistry* 75: 78–86. https://doi.org/10.1016/j.radphyschem.2005.05.014

Li, W., S. Li, Z. Cheng, X. Hu, W. Yang, and Yao, Y. 2019. "The Effect of Flame Retardant-Modified Sepiolite Nanofibers on Thermal Degradation and Fire Retardancy of Low-Density Polyethylene." *Journal of Thermal Analysis and Calorimetry* 138 (2): 1011–1019. https://doi.org/10.1007/s10973-019-08162-3

Malpass, D. B. 2010. *Introduction to Industrial Polyethylene: Properties, Catalysts, and Processes.* Vol. 45. Hoboken, NJ: Wiley-Scrivener.

Mejía, A., García, N., Guzmán, J., and Tiemblo, P. 2014. "Surface Modification of Sepiolite Nanofibers with PEG Based Compounds to Prepare Polymer Electrolytes." *Applied Clay Science* 95: 265–274. https://doi.org/10.1016/j.clay.2014.04.023

Mirabella, F. M., and Bafna, A. 2002. "Determination of the Crystallinity of Polyethylene/α-Olefin Copolymers by Thermal Analysis: Relationship of the Heat of Fusion of 100% Polyethylene Crystal and the Density." *Journal of Polymer Science, Part B: Polymer Physics* 40(15): 1637–1643. https://doi.org/10.1002/polb.10228

Nohales, A., Muñoz-Espí, R., Félix, P., and Gómez, C. M. 2011. "Sepiolitereinforced Epoxy Nanocomposites: Thermal, Mechanical, and Morphological Behavior." *Journal of Applied Polymer Science* 119: 539–547. https://doi.org/10.1002/app.32797

Satapathy, S., Chattopadhyay, S., Chakrabarty, K. K., Nag, A., Tiwari, K. N., Tikku, V. K., and Nando, G. B. 2006. "Studies on the Effect of Electron Beam Irradiation on Waste Polyethylene and its Blends With Virgin Polyethylene." *Journal of Applied Polymer Science* 101: 715–726. https://doi.org/10.1002/app.23970

Singh, V. P., Kapur, G. S., and Choudhary, V. 2016. "High-Density Polyethylene/Needle-Like Sepiolite Clay Nanocomposites: Effect of Functionalized Polymers on the Dispersion of Nanofiller, Melt Extensional and Mechanical Properties." *RSC Advances* 6 (64): 59762–59774. https://doi.org/10.1039/C6RA08124J

Tamboli, S. M., Mhaske, S. T., and Kale, D. D. 2004. "Crosslinked Polyethylene." *Indian Journal of Chemical Technology* 11: 853–864.

Wu, J., Xiaoxuan, Z., Bo, J., and Wenli, D. 2015. "Effect of Sepiolite on the Crystallization Behavior of Biodegradable Poly(Lactic Acid) as an Efficient Nucleating Agent." *Polymer Engineering and Science* 55: 1104–1112. https://doi.org/10.1002/pen.23981

Yasin, T., Nisar, M., Shafiq, M., Nho, Y. C. and Ahmad, R. 2013. "Influence of Sepiolite and Electron Beam Irradiation on the Structural and Physicochemical Properties of Polyethylene/Starch Nanocomposites." *Polymer Composites* 34: 408–416. https://doi.org/10.1002/pc.22431

9 Effects of Multiwalled Carbon Nanotube, Compatibilizers and Silane Coupling Agent on the Mechanical and Morphological Properties of Feldspar/Polypropylene Hybrid Composites

M.N.M. Ansari
Universiti Tenaga Nasional
Kajang, Malaysia

A. Atiqah
Universiti Kebangsaan Malaysia
Bangi, Malaysia

H. Ismail
Universiti Sains Malaysia
Nibong Tebal, Malaysia

CONTENTS

9.1	Introduction	170
9.2	Hybrid Polymer Matrix Composites (HPMCs)	170
9.3	Effects of MWCNT on Tensile Properties of Feldspar/PP Hybrid Nanocomposites	172
9.4	Effects of MWCNT on Morphological Properties of Feldspar/PP Hybrid Nanocomposites	174
9.5	Effects of MWCNT on Flexural Properties of Feldspar/PP Hybrid Nanocomposites	175

DOI: 10.1201/9781003221012-9

9.6 Effects of MWCNT on the Impact Strength of Feldspar/PP Hybrid Nanocomposites..................177
9.7 Effect of Compatibilizers on the Mechanical and Morphological Properties..................177
    9.7.1 Effects of Compatibilizers on Tensile Strength..................178
    9.7.2 Effects of Compatibilizers on the Morphological Properties..................181
    9.7.3 Effects of Compatibilizers on Tensile Modulus..................182
    9.7.4 Effects of Compatibilizers on Flexural Strength..................183
    9.7.5 Effects of Compatibilizers on Flexural Modulus..................183
    9.7.6 Effects of Compatibilizers on Impact Strength..................184
9.8 Effects of Silane Coupling Agent on Mechanical and Morphological Properties..................185
    9.8.1 Effects of Silane Coupling Agent on Tensile Strength..................186
    9.8.2 Effects of Silane Coupling Agent on Morphological Properties..................188
    9.8.3 Effects of Silane Coupling Agent on Tensile Modulus..................188
    9.8.4 Effects of Silane Coupling Agent on Flexural Strength..................190
    9.8.5 Effects of Silane Coupling Agent on Flexural Modulus..................190
    9.8.6 Effects of Silane Coupling Agent on Impact Strength..................191
9.9 Summary and Conclusions..................192
Acknowledgments..................193
References..................193

9.1 INTRODUCTION

Products made from polymers contribute enormously to the global economy in terms of performance, reliability, cost-effectiveness, and high added value. There are many reasons polymers are widely used. First, polymers can be operated in various environments and have useful ranges of deformability and durability, which can be exploited by careful design. Second, polymers can often be readily available, rapid, and low cost. Last, they can be transformed into usable products with complicated shapes and reproducible dimensions. This chapter mainly focuses on the effects of multiwalled carbon nanotubes (MWCNT), compatibilizers and silane coupling agent on the mechanical and morphological properties of Feldspar reinforced polypropylene hybrid composites. This chapter also introduces the polymer matrix composites, their importance, and current polymer products and further research objectives.

9.2 HYBRID POLYMER MATRIX COMPOSITES (HPMCs)

The hybrid organic-inorganic composites are promising materials because they synergistically integrate the advantages of both organic polymers and inorganic materials, for instance, the excellent process properties of polymers and good strength from inorganic material (Asim et al. 2017; El-Wazery 2017). However, the properties of the hybrid organic-inorganic composites are greatly influenced by the length scale of the component phase. The important changes in plastics' properties resulting from incorporating special additives permit their use in various fields where the polymer alone would have had little chance to meet specific performance specifications. Fillers and reinforcements are solid additives that differ from the plastic matrices with respect to their composition and structures. They are dispersed uniformly throughout the polymer matrix to obtain the required optimum properties, known as polymer matrix composites.

Inorganic fillers are usually used in the plastics industry to improve the mechanical properties of thermoplastics, commonly known as polymer composites. Polymer composites play an essential role in the engineering field due to their high strength to weight ratio and better corrosion resistance. These materials usually comprise an effective polymeric matrix in which fibers and/or small filler particles are thoroughly dispersed in composite systems. The filler must be well dispersed in the matrix to avoid weaker cohesion zones in which flaws and other defects will be initiated during stress (Hemath et al. 2020). Polypropylene (PP)-based composite material is one of the many composite systems that are successfully utilized in engineering applications. PP has been known for its good mechanical properties and processability, which allows it to accept numerous types of natural and synthetic fillers. Its versatility has also led to the possibility of producing particulate-filled composites (Kahramanov et al. 2017; Kaczmarek et al. 2019; Mittal et al. 2019).

The incorporation of fillers such as talc (Inácio, Nonato, and Bonse 2018; Świetlicki et al. 2020; Zhao et al. 2020), calcium carbonate ($CaCO_3$) (Essabir et al. 2017; Srivabut, Ratanawilai, and Hiziroglu 2018; Feng, Yang, and Qian 2020), mica (Kajiyama et al. 2018; Mohammadi and Moghbeli 2018; Mohammadi and Moghbeli 2019), kaolin (Yang et al. 2017; Yao et al. 2018; Akbari, Sharafi, and Goodarzi 2020), and wollastonite (Chaiwutthinan, Suwannachot, and Larpkasemsuk 2018; Ding et al. 2019; Fatt et al. 2020) into thermoplastics is a common practice in the plastics industry because it helps to reduce the production costs of the molded products. Fillers, which consists of three different entities (K, O, Al) are also used to improve the functional properties of thermoplastics, such as strength, rigidity, durability, and hardness (Sápi, Butler, and Rhead 2019; Chan et al. 2020). Thus, this chapter focuses on the investigation of the potential new filler, viz., feldspar reinforcement in the PP matrix, as this filler has not been used in the polyolefin groups before for any applications. Feldspars are a group of minerals with similar characteristics to other feldspar groups due to their similar structure. It is an aluminum silicate with exchangeable cations and reactive OH groups on the surface. All feldspars have low symmetry because they are only monoclinic to triclinic. They tend to twin easily, and one crystal can twin up multiple times on the same plane, producing parallel layers of twinned crystals. They are slightly hard, approximately 6 on the Mohs scale, and have an average density of 2.55–2.76 g/cc. They have a rather dull to rarely vitreous luster and the crystals tend to be blocky. Some feldspar may be triboluminescent. They have two directions of cleavage that are at nearly right angles. Feldspars also tend to crystallize in igneous environments but are also present in many metamorphic rocks (Amethyst Galleries 2011). Feldspar is the most important single group of rock forming silicate minerals. K-feldspar ($KAlSi_3O_{8\,22}O_3SiO_2$) can be described as an infinite network of tetrahedral SiO_4 and AlO_4, which is a stuffed derivative of the SiO_2 structures with the substitution of Al for some Si into the tetrahedral sites, and accommodation of K into the voids (Smith 2012; Ribbe 2018).

One way of compatibilizing PP with inorganic particles is by using functionalized polyolefin, e.g., PP grafted with maleic anhydride (PP-g-MAH). Unfortunately, there have only been limited achievements in polyolefin functionalization, especially in

PP, which have not succeeded either during its polymerization or post-polymerization processes. Also, the interfacial bonding between the hydrophilic fillers and the hydrophobic matrix (PP) has been an important issue in the research field because the interfacial adhesion between the filler and PP plays an essential role in determining the properties of the composites.

The other compatibilizing PP and inorganic filler methods are modifying the filler surface using coupling agents such as silane and titanate and grafting small molecules such as acrylic acid, maleic anhydride, and acrylic esters onto the polyolefin chain. The modified PP, such as PP-g-MAH, is successfully used as a compatibilizer in PP-based composites. This compatibilizer efficiently improves the fiber-matrix bonding due to the formation of covalent linkages and hydrogen bonds between the malleated anhydride and the fillers' hydroxyl groups (Cisneros-Rosado and Uribe-Calderon 2017; Kučera et al. 2019). Other than PP-g-MAH, much cheaper and nonreactive compatibilizers have also been successfully employed in polymers with a lack of reactive groups particularly, PP and polyethylene (PE).

9.3 EFFECTS OF MWCNT ON TENSILE PROPERTIES OF FELDSPAR/PP HYBRID NANOCOMPOSITES

The effects of multiwalled carbon nanotubes (MWCNTs) on the tensile properties of the feldspar-filled PP composites were studied. Figure 9.1 shows that the tensile strength of MWCNT/feldspar/PP hybrid composites increased as the MWCNT loading increased up to 0.1 wt% and then the tensile strength reduces as the loading of MWCNT increases from 0.1 to 0.5 wt%. A similar finding was also observed by Acierno et al. (2017) in their work on the thermal and mechanical properties of single-walled CNT–PE composites prepared by melt-spinning. Burmistrov et al. (2017) found that in addition to a good dispersion of CNTs in polymers, their orientation

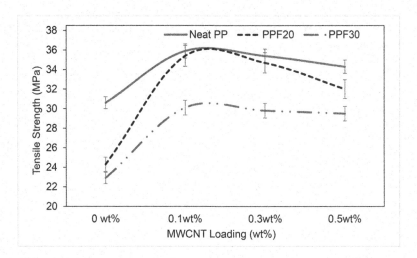

FIGURE 9.1 Effects of MWCNT loading on tensile strength of feldspar/PP composites. (From Ansari, Ismail, and Zein 2009.)

and the interface between the CNT and polymer also play a critical role in improving the composites' mechanical properties. Park et al. (2016) used a melt processing technique to prepare MWCNT/PP composite films and observed enhancement of the mechanical properties. Yetgin (2019) reported that the significant improvements in the nanocomposites' mechanical properties were due to the reinforcement of finely dispersed MWCNT nanofillers throughout the matrix and the strong interfacial interaction between the MWCNTs and PP matrix, thus being favorable to stress transfer from polymer to CNTs. The tensile strength decreases after 0.1wt% of MWCNT because of the entanglement and bundling effect of the MWCNTs on the feldspar/PP composite (Ansari, Ismail, and Zein 2009a).

Generally, adding a rigid particle into the PP matrix decreased the elongation at break. Table 9.1 shows that unfilled PP exhibits ductile failure with elongation at a break of 133%. The addition of feldspar into PP results in the immediate transition of the deformation characteristic, i.e., from ductile to brittle behavior typically at 20 wt% where the elongation at break of feldspar-filled PP has been reduced down to 26.8%, as observed from Table 9.1. However, with the incorporation of MWCNT into the feldspar-filled PP composite, the elongation at break has further reduced to 18.5%. Enhancement in the brittleness of the composites (i.e., reduction of elongation at break) could be due to the presence of MWCNT, which makes a strong bond with PP. Consequently, the ductility of feldspar-filled PP composites reduces as the MWCNT loading is increased from 0.1 to 0.3, and 0.5 wt%. This is confirmed by Mergen et al. (2020), who reported that when the amount of CNTs in composites exceeds 10 wt%, the mechanical properties of the composites decreases due to the residual stress in the poly(methyl methacrylate) (PMMA) matrix, and the composites become very brittle.

TABLE 9.1
Tensile Results of MWCNT-Reinforced Feldspar/PP Composites

Felspar Loading (wt%)	Tensile Strength (MPa)	Elongation at Break (%)	Tensile Modulus (MPa)
PP	30.6	133.3	1171
PPMWCNT0.1	35.9	21.3	1510
PPMWCNT0.3	35.4	14.1	1527
PPMWCNT0.5	34.5	6.2	1545
PPF20	24.3	26.8	1389
PP20MWCNT0.1	35.4	18.5	1626
PP20MWCNT0.3	34.7	12.8	1635
PP20MWCNT0.5	32.0	4.9	1643
PPF30	22.9	23.4	1547
PP20MWCNT0.1	30.1	5.32	1684
PP20MWCNT0.3	29.8	4.5	1695
PP20MWCNT0.5	29.5	4.4	1747

Source: Ansari and Ismail (2009a).

9.4 EFFECTS OF MWCNT ON MORPHOLOGICAL PROPERTIES OF FELDSPAR/PP HYBRID NANOCOMPOSITES

Figure 9.2 shows the proposed MWCNT dispersion and its interaction with the feldspar/PP composites. A microscopic examination across the tensile specimens' fractured surface would confer that the MWCNTs are well distributed and dispersed in the feldspar/PP composite, particularly at a low loading.

The scanning electron microscope (SEM) micrograph of feldspar (20 wt%)/PP composite with MWCNT (0.1 wt%) is shown in Figure 9.3a. With the addition of MWCNT, a good interfacial adhesion and less pull-out of feldspar from the PP matrix can be observed and as a result it provides better tensile strength. Figure 9.3b shows the SEM micrograph of feldspar (20 wt%)/PP composite with MWCNT (0.3 wt%), and Figure 9.3c presents the SEM micrograph of feldspar/PP (20 wt%) composite with MWCNT (0.5 wt%). Figure 9.3d shows the SEM micrograph of the control composite feldspar (20 wt%)/PP (without MWCNT). The presence of 0.1 wt% of MWCNT dispersion promotes both the feldspar/PP adhesions. Figure 9.3a shows that the feldspar is still embedded in the PP matrix at 0.1 wt% of MWCNT, which causes high tensile strength compared with Figure 9.3b and c where a large amount of pull-out of feldspar particles was seen. Reduction in strength was due to the bundling effect of the MWCNT at filler loading >0.1 wt%.

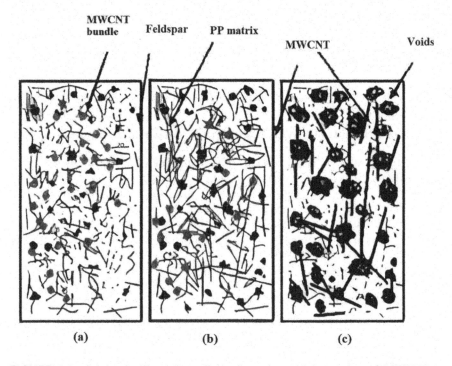

FIGURE 9.2 Schematic illustration of the dispersion and interaction of MWCNT in feldspar/PP composites: (a) 0.1 wt% of MWCNT, (b) 0.3 wt% of MWCNT, and (c) 0.5 wt% of MWCNT. (From Ansari, Ismail, and Zein 2009.)

Effects of Compatibilizers and Silane Coupling Agent

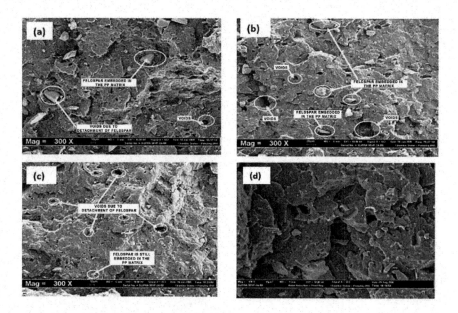

FIGURE 9.3 Tensile fractured surface of 20 wt% feldspar/PP composites at magnification 300×: (a) 0.1 wt% MWCNT, (b) 0.3 wt% MWCNT, (c) 0.5 wt% MWCNT, and (d) control composite. (From Ansari and Ismail 2009a).

Figure 9.4a–c presents the tensile fractured surface of MWCNT/PP of 0.1, 0.3, and 0.5 wt%, respectively, without the addition of feldspar. Figure 9.4a and b clearly shows that the stretching of the PP fiber was due to the strong interfacial adhesion between PP and MWCNT. Figure 9.4c and d shows the tensile fractured surface of PP/MWCNT (0.5 wt%) and pure PP did not exhibit any stretching of the PP matrix on their fractured surface. This indicates why their tensile strength is lower than the PP/MWCNT (0.3 wt%) and PP/MWCNT (0.1 wt%).

9.5 EFFECTS OF MWCNT ON FLEXURAL PROPERTIES OF FELDSPAR/PP HYBRID NANOCOMPOSITES

Figure 9.5 illustrates the effects of MWCNT on the flexural strength of feldspar/PP composites. The figure shows that there is an increase in the flexural strength of the composite as the MWCNT loading increases up to 0.1 wt% and then there was a decline in the flexural strength as the MWCNT loading increases up to 0.5 wt%.

The flexural strength increases up to 0.1 wt% of MWCNT and then reduces because the MWCNT entangles and forms as a bundle at higher loading (>0.1 wt%). This bundling of MWCNT causes reduction in the flexural strength, as seen in Figure 9.5. Similar results were also obtained by other researchers (Nguyen-Tran et al. 2018; Kumar, Jayanarayanan, and Balachandran 2020).

Figure 9.6 shows the effects of MWCNT on the flexural modulus of feldspar/PP composites. The flexural modulus of the feldspar/PP (20 and 30 wt%) composites increases as the MWCNT loading increased from 0 to 0.5 wt%. Compared with

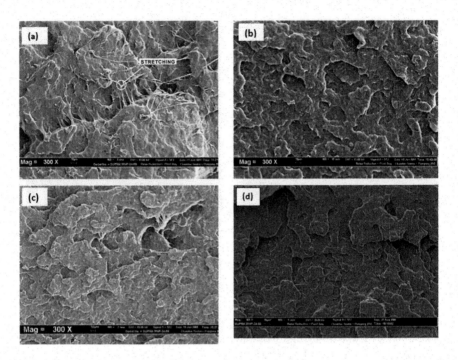

FIGURE 9.4 Tensile fractured surface of PP composite without feldspar and at different MWCNT loading (magnification 300×): (a) 0.1 wt% MWCNT (b) 0.3 wt% MWCNT, (c) 0.5 wt% MWCNT, and (d) neat PP. (From Ansari and Ismail 2009a.)

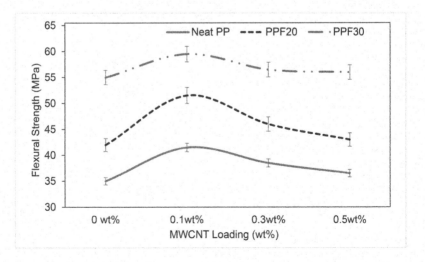

FIGURE 9.5 Effects of MWCNT loading on flexural strength feldspar/PP composites. (From Ansari and Ismail 2009a.)

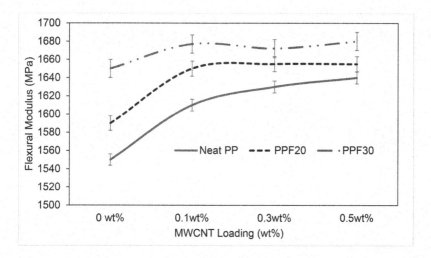

FIGURE 9.6 Effects of MWCNT loading on flexural modulus of feldspar/PP composites. (From Ansari and Ismail 2009a.)

the feldspar/PP control composites (without MWCNT), the presence of MWCNTs provides a better enhancement effect on the composite matrix, which indicates that the interfacial bonding enables an effective stress transfer between the feldspar/PP composites and the MWCNT's.

9.6 EFFECTS OF MWCNT ON THE IMPACT STRENGTH OF FELDSPAR/PP HYBRID NANOCOMPOSITES

Generally, the unnotched impact strength is a measure of crack initiation. The fillers, which are not bonded with the polymer, can act as a crack initiation source, whereas a good interfacial bonding reduces this effect (Rothon and DeArmitt 2017; Wang et al. 2020). Figure 9.7 shows the effects of MWCNT on the impact strength of feldspar/PP composites compared with the control composites (feldspar/PP composite without MWCNT). The figure also illustrates the impact strength increases as the MWCNT loading increased up to 0.1 wt% and then decreases with the increase in MWCNT loading from 0.1 to 0.5 wt%. The reduction of impact strength beyond 0.1 wt% MWCNT loading can be attributed to the immobilization of the macromolecular chains due to the bundling effect of MWCNTs, which limits their ability to deform freely, making the materials less ductile (Banerjee and Dutta 2019; Rasana et al. 2019).

9.7 EFFECT OF COMPATIBILIZERS ON THE MECHANICAL AND MORPHOLOGICAL PROPERTIES

This section discusses the experimental results of feldspar/PP composites with PP-g-MAH and PE co-acrylic acid (PEAA) as the compatibilizers. Feldspar/PP composites' mechanical properties depend on the type of compatibilizers used, i.e., PEAA

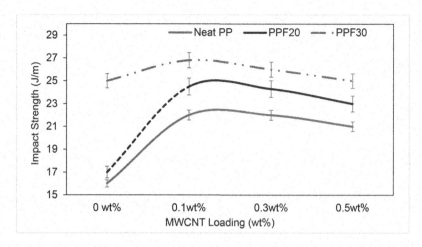

FIGURE 9.7 Effects of MWCNT loading on impact strength of feldspar/PP composites. (From Ansari and Ismail 2009a.)

or PP-g-MAH. The effect of the compatibilizers with the feldspar/PP composites on the mechanical and morphological properties is presented.

9.7.1 Effects of Compatibilizers on Tensile Strength

Figure 9.8 shows the effects of adding compatibilizers, viz., PP-g-MAH and PEAA, on the tensile properties of the feldspar/PP composites. The figure also demonstrates that at similar filler loading, the tensile strength of feldspar/PP composites has improved with the addition of PP-g-MAH or PEAA. For example, at 20 wt%

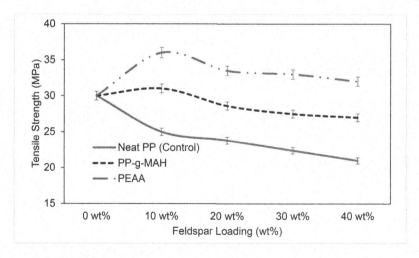

FIGURE 9.8 Effects of compatibilizers on tensile strength of feldspar/PP composites. (From Ansari and Ismail 2009a.)

TABLE 9.2
Tensile Results of Feldspar/PP Composites with Compatibilizers

Feldspar Loading (wt %)	Tensile Strength (MPa)	Elongation at Break (%)	Tensile Modulus (MPa)
PP	30.6	133	1171
PPF10	25.6	72	1243
PPF20	24.3	27	1389
PPF30	22.9	23	1547
PPF40	21.9	21	1590
PPF10M	35.7	98	1280
PPF20M	34.5	31	1422
PPF30M	33.8	29	1589
PPF40M	32.3	26	1622
PPF10E	31.2	96	1189
PPF20E	29.1	29	1250
PPF30E	27.5	26	1367
PPF40E	26.3	25	1520

Source: Ansari and Ismail (2009a).

of feldspar loading, the control composite's tensile strength was determined to be 24.3 MPa. After the addition of PP-g-MAH and PEAA, the tensile strength was improved to 34.5 and 29.1 MPa, respectively. This indicates that PP-g-MAH enhances the interaction between the feldspar and PP, causing the stresses transferred from PP to feldspar to become more effective, thus increasing the composites' tensile strength. The tensile test results are summarized in Table 9.2.

Yang (2010) found that PP-g-MAH improved the interfacial adhesion between PP and wollastonite and increased the composites' tensile strength. Chuayjuljit and Ketthongmongkol (2013) also observed similar findings in their research on PP/wollastonite composites. Pavlidou et al. (2005) reported that i-PP/SiO_2 nanocomposites show better mechanical properties than pure i-PP. The addition of PP-g-MAH as a compatibilizer in i-PP/SiO_2 nanocomposites resulted in further enhancement of the mechanical properties due to the reduction of nanoparticle agglomeration. The reduction in agglomerate size and dispersing them into individual SiO_2 nanoparticles were attributed to the silica hydroxyl group's reaction with the maleic anhydride group of PP-g-MAH.

In most cases, hydrophobic PP is functionalized with the polar molecules and becomes more hydrophilic and interacts with the polar functional group of the mineral fillers. The application of PEAA as the compatibilizer in feldspar/PP composites has shown a significant improvement in the tensile strength. For instance, 10 wt% of feldspar loading in PP matrix with PEAA as the compatibilizers have improved the tensile strength from 25.6 to 31.2 MPa. The formation of a bridge between the PEAA and the hydroxyl group from feldspar occurs due to the physical interaction, which improves the compatibility between the feldspar and PP matrix, thus increasing

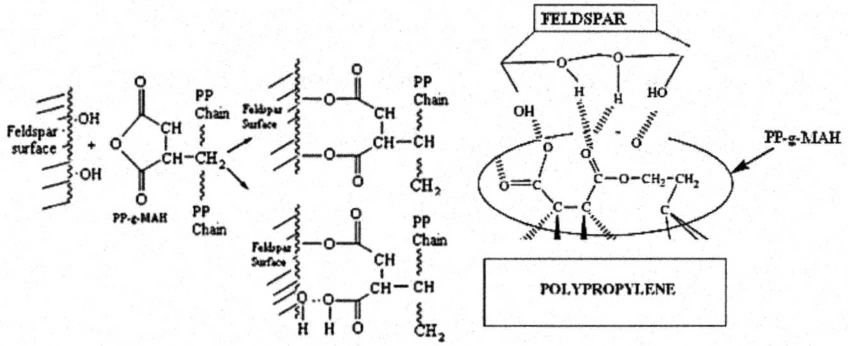

FIGURE 9.9 Schematic illustration of the physical interaction involved in feldspar/PP composites with PP-g-MAH as a compatibilizer. (From Ansari and Ismail 2009a.)

the tensile strength of the composites. The schematic illustration of the proposed reactions involved in feldspar/PP composites with PP-g-MAH as a compatibilizer is shown in Figure 9.9. The –C=O group in maleic anhydride physically interacts with the –OH group forming an O–H (hydrogen bonding) between the feldspar and PP-g-MAH, thus, making a composite with a good interfacial adhesion between the PP and feldspar particles.

Figure 9.10 demonstrates the effects of compatibilizers on the percentage of elongation at the break of the composites. The figure shows that the unfilled PP exhibits ductile failure with the elongation at break of 133%. The addition of feldspar into PP results in the immediate transition of the deformation characteristic, i.e., from ductile to brittle behavior typically at 10 wt% where the elongation at break of feldspar/PP has been reduced down to 72% (as shown in Figure 9.10). However, with the incorporation of PP-g-MAH into feldspar/PP, the elongation at break has slightly

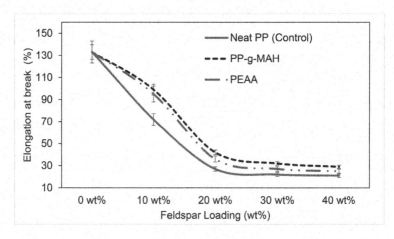

FIGURE 9.10 Effects of compatibilizers on elongation at break of feldspar/PP composites. (From Ansari and Ismail 2009a.)

Effects of Compatibilizers and Silane Coupling Agent   181

improved compared with the feldspar/PP without compatibilizers (control). For example, incorporating PP-g-MAH and PEAA into the same composition increased the elongation at break value from 72% to 98% and 96%, respectively.

From the graph in Figure 9.10, we can see that the elongation at break of the composites with the presence of PEAA shows the higher values than the composites with the presence of PP-g-MAH and control. Enhancement in ductility (i.e., elongation at break) could be due to the carboxylic group (–COOH) in PEAA and C=O group in PP-g-MAH. Consequently, the ductility of the feldspar/PP composite has improved.

9.7.2 Effects of Compatibilizers on the Morphological Properties

Figure 9.11a is an SEM micrograph of feldspar (20 wt%)-filled PP composite with PP-g-MAH. With the addition of PP-g-MAH, good interfacial adhesion and less pull-out of feldspar from the PP matrix can be observed and, as a result, it provides

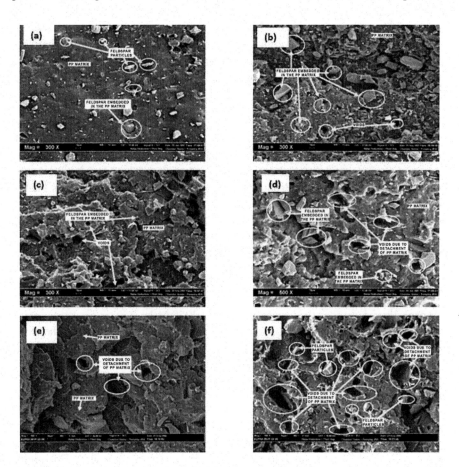

FIGURE 9.11 Tensile fractured surface of 20 wt% feldspar/PP composites: (a) PP-g-MAH, (b) PEAA, (c) control, (d) tensile fractured surface of 40 wt% feldspar/PP composites, (e) PP-g-MAH, and (f) PEAA. (From Ansari and Ismail 2009a.)

better tensile strength. Figure 9.11b shows a portion of feldspar detached from the PP and that voids occurred in the PP composite with PEAA compatibilizers. Therefore, the composite with PEAA has a lower tensile strength compared with the composite with PP-g-MAH.

Figure 9.11c shows that many voids were formed due to the pull-out of feldspar from the PP matrix because of poor interfacial adhesion, which was explained earlier in Section 9.4. Consequently, compatibilizers lowered the tensile strength of the control composites compared with the composites with PP-g-MAH and PEAA.

In Figure 9.11d, the SEM micrograph reveals that with the presence of PP-g-MAH at higher feldspar loading (40 wt%), the feldspar particles are still embedded in the PP. However, feldspar particles tend to agglomerate and, consequently, reduce the tensile strength of the composites. Figure 9.11e shows the tensile fractured surface of 40 wt% feldspar/PP with the addition of PEAA. It could be explained that feldspar had formed an agglomeration and voids on the PP matrix, which indicates a poor interaction between the feldspar and PP compared with Figure 10.11a. The existence of feldspar agglomerates is believed to reduce the tensile strength of feldspar/PP composites because the agglomeration of the feldspar can act as a stress concentration point and increase the composites' ability to initiate cracks.

9.7.3 Effects of Compatibilizers on Tensile Modulus

Tensile modulus is also known as Young's modulus of a material, which provides information about a composite's stiffness. Table 9.2 shows the effects of compatibilizers on the tensile modulus of the feldspar/PP composites. The table also illustrates that the tensile modulus of feldspar/PP composites with the compatibilizers PEAA and PP-g-MAH increased with an increase in filler loading compared with uncompatibilized control composites. However, at similar filler loading, the feldspar/PP composites with the presence of PP-g-MAH show the highest tensile modulus followed by the control composites and the feldspar/PP composites with PEAA. For example, at 20 wt% feldspar loading, the tensile modulus of the control composites was determined to be 1389 MPa. After the addition of the PP-g-MAH compatibilizer, the tensile modulus increased to 1422 MPa, whereas the addition of the PEAA compatibilizer decreased the tensile modulus to 1250 MPa.

George and Ishida (2018) reported that the three main factors affecting the composite's modulus were filler modulus, filler loading, and filler aspect ratio. High stiffness in composites requires filler particles of high modulus and high aspect ratio and preferably higher filler loading. The presence of PP-g-MAH has led to a significant improvement of tensile modulus in the feldspar/PP composites compared with the control composites and composites with PEAA as the compatibilizer. This result was due to an increase in the efficiency of the perfect bonding between PP and feldspar, which consequently gives rise to a higher modulus. However, the addition of PEAA reduced the tensile modulus compared with control composites. This might be attributed to the presence of a –COOH group in PEAA, which reduced the composites' elasticity (Zaaba, Ismail, and Jaafar 2017; Luthra, Singh, and Kapur 2019; Wang et al. 2019).

9.7.4 Effects of Compatibilizers on Flexural Strength

Figure 9.12 shows the effects of compatibilizers (PEAA and PP-g-MAH) on the flexural strength of feldspar/PP composites compared with control composites. The figure further shows that the flexural strength of feldspar/PP composites compatibilized by PEAA and PP-g-MAH had higher flexural strength than the uncompatibilized control composites. For example, at 20 wt% feldspar loading, the flexural strength of feldspar/PP composites was determined to be 42.5 MPa. After the addition of PP-g-MAH and PEAA compatibilizers, the flexural strength increased to 49.5 and 46.3 MPa, respectively. This enhancement is a good indication of the improvement in the filler-matrix interaction in the presence of compatibilizers. The improvement in the flexural strength of PEAA and PP-g-MAH compatibilized feldspar/PP composites is probably due to the improvement in the dispersion of the feldspar particles' reduction of agglomeration that could impart more resistance to bending.

Figure 9.12 demonstrated that the addition of PEAA and PP-g-MAH compatibilizers increased the flexural strength of the feldspar/PP composites compared with the control composites. For example, at 10 wt% of feldspar loading, the flexural strength of the non-compatibilized control composites is approximately 48.4 MPa, whereas the composites with PEAA as compatibilizers were about 49.5 MPa, and the composites with PP-g-MAH as compatibilizers were about 51.5 MPa. Similarly, at a higher feldspar loading level, the flexural strength has improved with the addition of PEAA and PP-g-MAH as the compatibilizers. This increase in flexural strength might be due to the formation of ester bonds in PEAA compatibilizers and adhesive bridging between the feldspar and PP matrix PP-g-MAH, which increases the interfacial bond strength and adhesion.

9.7.5 Effects of Compatibilizers on Flexural Modulus

Figure 9.13 shows the effects of compatibilizers (PEAA and PP-g-MAH) on the flexural modulus of feldspar/PP composites compared with the control composites.

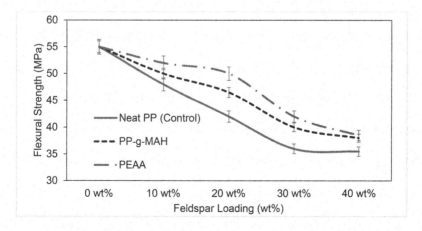

FIGURE 9.12 Flexural strength of feldspar/PP composites. (From Ansari and Ismail 2009a.)

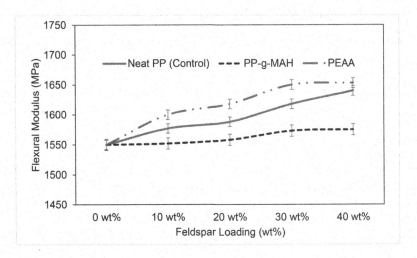

FIGURE 9.13 Flexural modulus of feldspar/PP composites. (From Ansari and Ismail 2009a.)

From the figure it was observed that the flexural modulus charted a similar trend to that of the tensile modulus. The presence of PP-g-MAH improved the flexural modulus more than the control composites due to a better bonding between the feldspar and PP matrix. PEAA-compatibilized feldspar/PP composites show a reduction in the flexural modulus compared with PP-g-MAH-compatibilized and control composites due to the physical interaction of the carboxylic group (–COOH), which reduces the elasticity of the composites (Zaaba, Ismail, and Jaafar 2017; Luthra, Singh, and Kapur 2019; Wang et al. 2019).

Figure 9.13 demonstrates that the addition of PEAA has decreased the flexural modulus of the feldspar/PP composites compared with the control composites; whereas the addition of PP-g-MAH has increased the flexural modulus of the feldspar/PP composites compared with the control composites. For example, at 10 wt% of feldspar loading, the flexural modulus of the non-compatibilized control composites is about 1580 MPa; whereas the flexural modulus of the composites with PEAA as the compatibilizer was about 1556 MPa and the composites with PP-g-MAH as the compatibilizer had a flexural modulus of approximately 1600 MPa. Similarly, at a higher feldspar loading level, the flexural modulus improved with the addition of PP-g-MAH as the compatibilizer and decreased with the addition of PEAA as the compatibilizer. A probable explanation for this is that with the increased concentration of maleic groups in the sample, the breakup tendency of the feldspar agglomerates increases, resulting in a greater dispersion of the filler in the matrix and an increase in the interfacial adhesion because of interactions between them. Therefore, an increase in PP-g-MAH concentration leads to an increase in flexural modulus of the composites.

9.7.6 Effects of Compatibilizers on Impact Strength

Generally, the unnotched impact strength is a measure of crack initiation. The fillers that are not bonded with the polymer can act as a crack initiation source, whereas a good interfacial bonding reduces the effect (George and Ishida 2018; Chavhan and

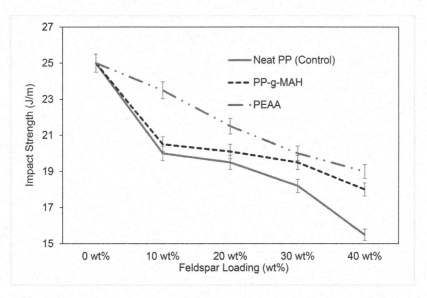

FIGURE 9.14 Effects of compatibilizers on impact strength of feldspar/PP composites. (From Ansari and Ismail 2009a.)

Wankhade 2020). Figure 9.14 shows the effects of compatibilizers (PP-g-MAH, and PEAA) on the impact strength of feldspar/PP composites compared with the control composites. The figure demonstrates that the impact strength increased with the addition of the compatibilizers. For example, at 20 wt% feldspar loading, the impact strength of the control composite was determined to be 18.1 J/m. After the addition of PP-g-MAH and PEAA compatibilizers, the feldspar/PP composites' impact strength increased to 19.6 and 19.2 J/m, respectively. The increase in impact properties after the addition of compatibilizers can be attributed to the immobilization of the macromolecular chains by the effect of the compatibilizers, limiting their ability to deform freely and make the composites less ductile (Pracella et al. 2006; Taniike, Toyonaga, and Terano 2014).

However, at a similar filler loading of PP-g-MAH in feldspar/PP composites improved the impact strength compared with the addition of PEAA and control composites, respectively. This indicates that the presence of PP-g-MAH and PEAA improved the wettability between the feldspar and PP, which consequently increases the impact strength. A similar finding was also observed by Chaiwutthinan et al. (2018). They found that the impact strength was greater for the PP-g-MAH wollastonite-filled composite than the unmodified composites, which indicates a good interfacial bonding between the filler and the polymer compatibility.

9.8 EFFECTS OF SILANE COUPLING AGENT ON MECHANICAL AND MORPHOLOGICAL PROPERTIES

This section discusses the experimental results of feldspar/PP composites with silane coupling agents and the effects on mechanical properties and morphological characteristics.

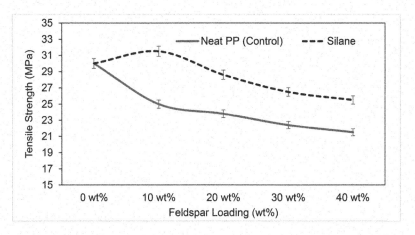

FIGURE 9.15 Effects of silane treatment on tensile strength of feldspar/PP composites. (From Ansari and Ismail 2009b.)

9.8.1 EFFECTS OF SILANE COUPLING AGENT ON TENSILE STRENGTH

The effects of silane treatment on the tensile properties of the treated feldspar/PP composites and untreated feldspar/PP (control composites) were studied. Figure 9.15 shows the effects of silane treatment on the tensile strength of the feldspar/PP composites. The results of the tensile tests are recorded in Table 9.3. The tensile strength of the control composites increased with the addition of silane-treated feldspar. For instance, at 20 wt% of feldspar loading the tensile strength of the control composites was 24.3 MPa. After the addition of silane-treated feldspar with the same filler loading, the tensile strength increased to 28.2 MPa. This indicates that the silane treatment improves the adhesion and the interfacial strength between the feldspar and PP

TABLE 9.3
Tensile Properties of Silane-Treated Feldspar-Filled PP Composites

Felspar Loading (wt%)	Tensile Strength (MPa)	Elongation at Break (%)	Young's Modulus (MPa)
PP	30.6	133	1171
PPF10	25.6	72	1243
PPF20	24.3	27	1389
PPF30	22.9	23	1547
PPF40	21.9	21	1590
PPF10s	30.9	86	1261
PPF20s	28.2	28	1405
PPF30s	26.6	25	1579
PPF40s	25.2	22	1611

Source: Ansari and Ismail (2009b).

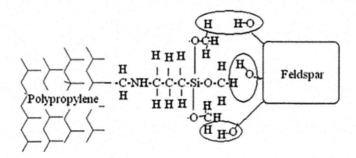

FIGURE 9.16 Schematic illustration of the possible reactions involved in feldspar/PP composites with a 3-aminopropyl trimethoxy silane coupling agent. (From Ansari and Ismail 2009b.)

causing the stresses transferred from PP to feldspar to become more effective and eventually increasing the tensile strength of the composites.

Guo et al. (2019) reported that there was an improvement in the tensile strength with the addition of isocyanate silane coupling agent grafted polypropylene (IS-g-PP) on the wood flour-filled PP composites. Another study by Rane et al. (2017) reported an increase in the tensile strength of the silane coupling agent-treated talc-reinforced polyethylene oxide (PPO) compared with the untreated talc. Sharma et al. (2017) also reported an increase in the silane-treated clay's tensile strength filled with glass/epoxy composites. The incorporation of feldspar into the PP matrix reduced the composites' ability to transfer applied stress, mostly particulate filler with an irregular shape. Similar findings were also observed by Asgari et al. (2017) in their research on silane-based coupling agents of sodium montmorillonite nanoclay on the mechanical properties of clay-filled high-density PE composites.

Figure 9.16 shows the schematic illustration of the proposed reaction involved in feldspar/PP composites with a 3-aminopropyl trimethoxy silane coupling agent. The (–C–H) group of the silane reacts with the (–OH) group of feldspar, and amino group (–NH$_2$) reacts with the (–CH$_3$) group of the PP to form a strong covalent bond (–CH$_2$–NH$_2$–).

Generally, adding a rigid particle into the PP matrix decreases the elongation at break. Figure 9.17 illustrates the effects of silane treatment on the elongation at break of the feldspar/PP composites. From Figure 9.17, it is discovered that the unfilled PP exhibits ductile failure with an elongation at break of 133%. The addition of feldspar into the PP results in immediate transition of deformation characteristic, i.e., from ductile to brittle behavior typically at 10 wt% where the elongation at break of feldspar/PP has been reduced to 72% (Figure 9.17).

However, with the incorporation of silane-treated feldspar in PP, the elongation at break has slightly improved compared with the feldspar/PP without silane treatment (control composite). Particularly 10 wt% of silane-treated feldspar into PP has increased the elongation at break value from 72% to 86% (Figure 9.17). This is due to the good interfacial adhesion between the silane-treated feldspar and PP matrix.

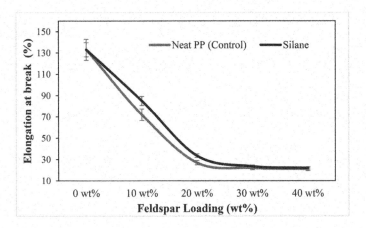

FIGURE 9.17 Effects of silane treatment on elongation at break of feldspar/PP composites. (From Ansari and Ismail 2009b.)

9.8.2 Effects of Silane Coupling Agent on Morphological Properties

The SEM micrograph of silane-treated feldspar/PP composite (20 wt%) is shown in Figure 9.18a. With the addition of silane-treated feldspar, a good interfacial adhesion and less pull-out of feldspar from the PP matrix can be observed and, as a result, it provides a better tensile strength, which implies a decrease in the thickness of the interface between the feldspar particle and the PP matrix. This produces a positive effect on the tensile modulus and tensile strength, which were increased as explained above for these composites. Figure 9.18b shows a portion of feldspar detached from the PP and that voids occurred in the PP. Therefore, the composite without silane-treated feldspar has a lower tensile strength compared with the composite with silane-treated feldspar/PP composites. Figure 9.18c demonstrates silane-treated feldspar/PP composite (40 wt%) with less detachment when compared with the untreated feldspar/PP control composites (40 wt%) (Figure 9.18d).

9.8.3 Effects of Silane Coupling Agent on Tensile Modulus

Figure 9.19 shows the effects of silane treatment on the tensile modulus of feldspar/PP composites. The important factors influencing the tensile modulus were discussed. From the figure it is noticed that at similar filler loading, the silane-treated feldspar/PP composites exhibits a higher tensile modulus than the untreated feldspar/PP (control) composites, particularly at feldspar loading greater than 20 wt%. For example, at 30 wt% feldspar loading, the tensile modulus of the control composite was determined to be 1547 MPa. After the addition of silane-treated feldspar, the tensile modulus increased to 1579 MPa.

When the polymer-filler interfacial adhesion is weak, the composites generally exhibit a low modulus. The interaction of the silane coupling agent on the feldspar and PP interface has improved the bond strength and interfacial adhesions, which corresponds to the tensile modulus improvement. The dependence of the

Effects of Compatibilizers and Silane Coupling Agent

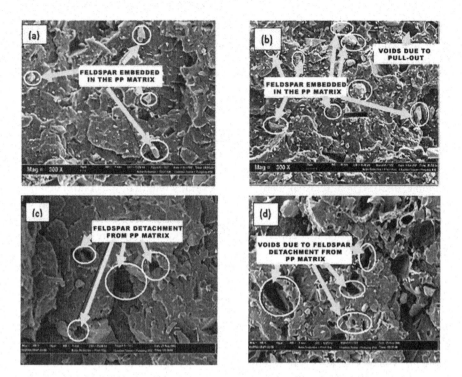

FIGURE 9.18 (a) Tensile fractured surface of 20 wt% feldspar/PP composites with silane treatment (at magnification 300×), (b) untreated feldspar/PP composites (control), (c) tensile fractured surface of 40 wt% feldspar/PP composites with silane treatment (at magnification 300×), and (d) untreated feldspar/PP composites (control). (From Ansari and Ismail 2009b.)

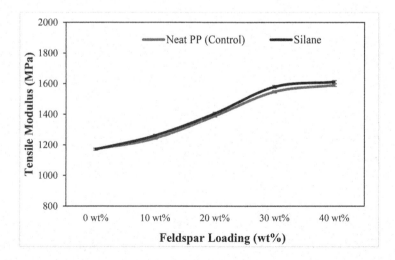

FIGURE 9.19 Effects of silane treatment on tensile modulus of feldspar/PP composites. (From Ansari and Ismail 2009b.)

tensile modulus of the composites on the state of the polymer-filler interface has been studied by many researchers (Parandoush and Lin 2017; Prashanth et al. 2017; Barbon et al. 2018).

9.8.4 Effects of Silane Coupling Agent on Flexural Strength

Figure 9.20 shows the effects of silane treatment on the flexural strength of feldspar/PP composites. The figure demonstrates that at a similar filler loading, the presence of silane-treated feldspar had increased the flexural strength of the composites, which indicated that the composite has become less rigid and more flexible. For example, at 20 wt% of feldspar loading, the flexural strength of the control composite was determined to be 35.5 MPa. After the addition of silane-treated feldspar, the flexural strength was increased to 37.5 MPa.

Based on the results, it is apparent that the addition of silane-treated feldspar to the PP matrix improves the interaction between the PP and feldspar interphase, thus improving the flexural strength and flexural modulus of the composites (Ho, Supri, and Ismail 2015). The effects of silane treatment on the flexural properties has been widely reported by other researchers as well (Atiqah et al. 2018a,b; Mousa et al. 2020).

9.8.5 Effects of Silane Coupling Agent on Flexural Modulus

Figure 9.21 shows the effects of silane treatment on the flexural modulus of feldspar/PP composites. The figure demonstrated that the flexural modulus increased when adding the silane-treated feldspar compared with the untreated feldspar/PP composites. For example, at 20 wt% of feldspar loading, the flexural modulus of the control composite was determined to be 1600 MPa. The addition of silane-treated feldspar increased the flexural modulus to 1612 MPa. This increase in flexural modulus is due

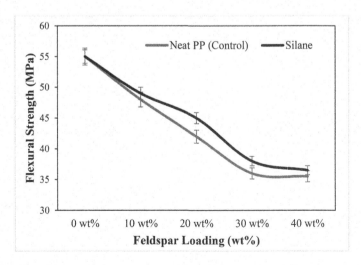

FIGURE 9.20 Effects of silane treatment on flexural strength of feldspar/PP composites. (From Ansari and Ismail 2009b.)

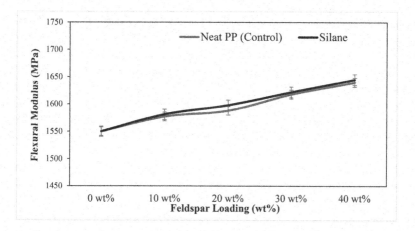

FIGURE 9.21 Effects of silane treatment on flexural modulus of feldspar/PP composites. (From Ansari and Ismail 2009b.)

to the enhancement in the feldspar, and PP matrix adhesion, which has produced a pronounced effect on the tensile modulus explained earlier in Section 9.3. The presence of a silane functional group on the feldspar surface is believed to play a significant role in promoting good interaction and bonding with the PP matrix.

9.8.6 Effects of Silane Coupling Agent on Impact Strength

Figure 9.22 shows the effects of silane treatment on the impact strength of feldspar/PP composites compared with the untreated feldspar/PP control composites. The figure demonstrates that at similar filler loading the presence of a silane coupling agent in feldspar/PP composites improved the impact strength compared with the

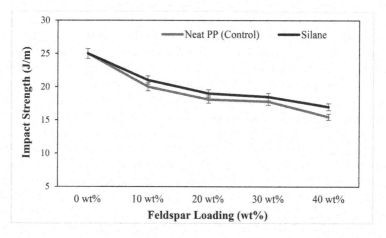

FIGURE 9.22 Effects of silane treatment on impact strength of feldspar/PP composites. (From Ansari and Ismail 2009b.)

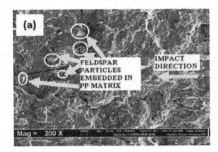 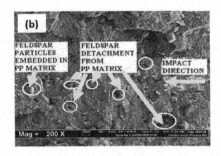

FIGURE 9.23 Impact-fractured surface of 20 wt% feldspar/PP composites at magnification 200×: (a) silane-treated feldspar/PP composite and (b) untreated feldspar/PP composite (control). (From Ansari and Ismail 2009b.)

control composites. For example, at 20 wt% of feldspar loading, the impact strength was found to be 18.1 J/m. After the addition of silane-treated feldspar the impact strength improved to 18.6 J/m. The increase in impact properties can be attributed to the mobilization of the macromolecular chains by the effect of silane treatment on feldspar, limiting their ability to deform freely and making the composite tougher than the control composites. This indicates that the presence of silane with an amino functional group has improved the wettability between feldspar and PP, which consequently increases the impact strength. Chen and Yang (2010) found that the impact strength was greater for the silane-treated wollastonite-reinforced PP composite than the untreated composites, indicating a good interfacial bonding between the silane coupling agent and the filler, and the polymer compatibility with the hydrocarbon of the silane compound.

The SEM micrograph of the impact-fractured surface of silane-treated feldspar/PP (20 wt%) composite is shown in Figure 9.23a. With the silane coupling agent's treatment, a good interfacial adhesion and less pull-out of feldspar from the PP matrix can be observed at the PP-feldspar interface. The feldspar particles were more embedded in the PP matrix, which provides better impact strength. Figure 9.23b shows the impact-fractured surface of the untreated feldspar/PP composite (control), in which the feldspar was detached from the PP and voids occurred in the PP matrix. Therefore, the composite with silane treatment has a better impact than the untreated mineral composite-reinforced PP (Wang, Wang, and Zheng 2014).

9.9 SUMMARY AND CONCLUSIONS

In this chapter, the effects of MWCNT reinforcement on the mechanical and morphological properties of feldspar/PP hybrid nanocomposites and the effects of filler loading and PEAA and PP-g-MAH as compatibilizers were analyzed. Also, the effects of surface treatment by a silane coupling agent on the mechanical and morphological properties of the feldspar/PP composite systems were reported. It was observed from this research that the feldspar/PP reduced the tensile strength and the percentage of elongation at break [E_b]. The tensile strength, flexural strength, and impact strength of the feldspar/PP composites increased with increasing MWCNT loading up to 0.1 wt% and then decreased. The tensile modulus and flexural modulus increased with increasing MWCNT loading. At higher MWCNT loading (>0.1 wt%), the mechanical properties were reduced due to the entanglement and clustering of the CNTs forming bundles. Morphological studies provided by the SEM micrographs revealed that the improvements in tensile strength largely contributed to better dispersion and adhesion among PP, feldspar, and MWCNT, particularly at a low filler loading of 0.1 wt%. The addition of PP-g-MAH improves the interaction between the feldspar and PP, causing the stresses transferred from PP to feldspar to become more effective, thus increasing the composites' tensile strength. However, PEAA shows less effect than PP-g-MAH. The addition of a silane coupling agent improves the interaction between the feldspar and PP, causing the stresses transferred from PP to feldspar to become more effective, thus increasing the tensile strength, tensile modulus, flexural strength, flexural modulus, and impact strength of the silane-treated feldspar/PP composites compared with the untreated feldspar/PP control composites. In general, polymer-filler interaction in the presence of a silane coupling agent is enhanced. Morphological studies provided by the SEM micrographs revealed that the tensile strength and impact strength improvements were largely attributed to the better interfacial adhesion between PP and silane-treated feldspar compared with the untreated feldspar/PP control composites.

The following suggestions have been made to further the research work carried out so far:

1. A study on MWCNT alignment and its effect on the mechanical and electrical properties could be carried out to understand the benefits of MWCNTs.
2. A study on the morphological properties of the fractured surface of the MWCNT/feldspar/PP composites could be performed using transmission electron microscopy.
3. A study on the effects of MWCNTs on the electrical properties, such as electrical conductivity and surface and volume resistivity, of MWCNT-reinforced feldspar/PP composites could be conducted.
4. A study on the effects of MWCNTs on the thermal properties, such as thermal conductivity and flammability, of the composites containing flame retardants, such as aluminum trihydrate (ATH), ammonium phosphates (APP), and pentaerythritol (PER), could be carried out.

ACKNOWLEDGMENTS

Authors would like to thank Universiti Sains Malaysia (USM) for providing research facilities and resources. Also, authors thank Innovative & Research Management Centre (iRMC), Universiti Tenaga National, Malaysia for their support.

REFERENCES

Acierno, S., R. Barretta, R. Luciano, F. Marotti de Sciarra, and P. Russo. 2017. "Experimental Evaluations and Modeling of the Tensile Behavior of Polypropylene/Single-Walled Carbon Nanotubes Fibers." *Composite Structures* 174: 12–18.

Akbari, Hamid Reza, Hassan Sharafi, and Amir Reza Goodarzi. 2020. "Effect of Polypropylene Fiber Inclusion in Kaolin Clay Stabilized with Lime and Nano-Zeolite Considering Temperatures of 20 and 40 C." *Bulletin of Engineering Geology and the Environment* 80: 1–15.

Ansari, M. N. M., and H. Ismail. 2009a. "Effect of Compatibilizers on Mechanical Properties of Feldspar/Polypropylene Composites." *Polymer-Plastics Technology and Engineering* 48(12): 1295–1303.

Ansari, M. N. M., and H. Ismail. 2009b. "The Effect of Silane Coupling Agent on Mechanical Properties of Feldspar Filled Polypropylene Composites." *Journal of Reinforced Plastics and Composites* 28(24): 3049–3060.

Ansari, M. N. M., H. Ismail, and S. H. Sharif Zein. 2009. "Effect of Multi-Walled Carbon Nanotubes on Mechanical Properties of Feldspar Filled Polypropylene Composites." *Journal of Reinforced Plastics and Composites* 28(20): 2473–85.

Asgari, Mohammad, Ahmed Abouelmagd, and Uttandaraman Sundararaj. 2017. "Silane Functionalization of Sodium Montmorillonite Nanoclay and Its Effect on Rheological and Mechanical Properties of HDPE/Clay Nanocomposites." *Applied Clay Science* 146: 439–48.

Asim, Mohammad, Mohammad Jawaid, Naheed Saba, Mohammad Nasir, and Mohamed Thariq HameedSultan. 2017. "Processing of Hybrid Polymer Composites—a Review." In *Hybrid Polymer Composite Materials*, 1–22. Amsterdam, the Netherlands, Elsevier.

Atiqah, A., M. Jawaid, S. M. Sapuan, and M.R. Ishak. 2018a. "Effect of Surface Treatment on the Mechanical Properties of Sugar Palm/Glass Fiber-Reinforced Thermoplastic Polyurethane Hybrid Composites." *BioResources* 13(1). https://doi.org/10.15376/biores.13.1.1174-1188

Atiqah, A., M. Jawaid, S. M. Sapuan, and M. R. Ishak. 2018b. "Mechanical and Thermal Properties of Sugar Palm Fiber Reinforced Thermoplastic Polyurethane Composites: Effect of Silane Treatment and Fiber Loading." *Journal of Renewable Materials* 6(5): 477–92.

Banerjee, Joyita, and Kingshuk Dutta. 2019. "Melt-mixed Carbon Nanotubes/Polymer Nanocomposites." *Polymer Composites* 40(12): 4473–88.

Barbon, Fabíola Jardim, Rafael Ratto Moraes, Noéli Boscato, Rodrigo Alessandretti, and Aloísio Oro Spazzin. 2018. "Feldspar Ceramic Strength and the Reinforcing Effect by Adhesive Cementation under Accelerated Aging." *Brazilian Dental Journal* 29(2): 202–7.

Burmistrov, I, N. Gorshkov, I. Ilinykh, D. Muratov, E. Kolesnikov, E. Yakovlev, I. Mazov, J.-P. Issi, and D. Kuznetsov. 2017. "Mechanical and Electrical Properties of Ethylene-1-Octene and Polypropylene Composites Filled with Carbon Nanotubes." *Composites Science and Technology* 147: 71–77.

Chaiwutthinan, P., S. Suwannachot, and A. Larpkasemsuk. 2018. "Recycled Poly (Ethylene Terephthalate)/Polypropylene/Wollastonite Composites Using PP-g-MA as Compatibilizer: Mechanical, Thermal and Morphological Properties." *Journal of Metals, Materials and Minerals* 28(2): 115–123.

Chan, Jia X., Joon F. Wong, Azman Hassan, Zurina Mohamad, and Norhayani Othman. 2020. "Mechanical Properties of Wollastonite Reinforced Thermoplastic Composites: A Review." *Polymer Composites* 41(2): 395–429.

Chavhan, Ganesh R., and Lalit N. Wankhade. 2020. "Improvement of the Mechanical Properties of Hybrid Composites Prepared by Fibers, Fiber-Metals, and Nano-Filler Particles–a Review." *Materials Today: Proceedings* 27: 72–82.

Chen, Deliang, and Huaming Yang. 2010. "Polypropylene/Combinational Inorganic Filler Micro-/Nanocomposites: Synergistic Effects of Micro-/Nanoscale Combinational Inorganic Fillers on Their Mechanical Properties." *Journal of Applied Polymer Science* 115(1): 624–34.

Chuayjuljit, S., and S. Ketthongmongkol. 2013. "Properties and Morphology of Injection- and Compression-Molded Thermoplastic Polyurethane/Polypropylene-Graft-Maleic Anhydride/Wollastonite Composites." *Journal of Thermoplastic Composite Materials* 26(7): 923–35.

Cisneros-Rosado, David, and Jorge Alonso Uribe-Calderon. 2017. "Effect of Surface Modification of Palygorskite on the Properties of Polypropylene/Polypropylene-g-Maleic Anhydride/Palygorskite Nanocomposites." *International Journal of Polymer Science* 2017: 91435889.

Ding, Qian, Zishou Zhang, Xin Dai, Mei Li, and Kancheng Mai. 2019. "Effect of Hybrid Wollastonite with Different Nucleation and Morphology on the Crystallization and Mechanical Properties of Polypropylene." *Polymer Composites* 40(S1): E638–46.

El-Wazery, M. S. 2017. "Mechanical Characteristics and Novel Applications of Hybrid Polymer Composites-a Review." *Journal of Materials and Environmental Sciences* 8(2): 666–75.

Essabir, Hamid, Mohammed Ouadi Bensalah, Denis Rodrigue, and Rachid Bouhfid. 2017. "A Comparison between Bio-and Mineral Calcium Carbonate on the Properties of Polypropylene Composites." *Construction and Building Materials* 134: 549–55.

Fatt, Wong Joon, Chan Jia Xin, Azman bin Hassan, Zurina binti Mohamad, and Norhayani binti Othman. 2020. "Thermal and Flammability Properties of Wollastonite-Filled Thermoplastic Composites: A Review." *Journal of Materials Science* 56: 8911–50.

Feng, Jianhang, Fan Yang, and Shunzhi Qian. 2020. "Improving the Bond between Polypropylene Fiber and Cement Matrix by Nano Calcium Carbonate Modification." *Construction and Building Materials* 269: 121249.

Amethyst Galleries. 2011. "Amethyst Galleries' Mineral Gallery." Accessed on 25th January 2021. http://www.galleries.com/Feldspar_Group

George, Jeffrey, and Hatsuo Ishida. 2018. "A Review on the Very High Nanofiller-Content Nanocomposites: Their Preparation Methods and Properties with High Aspect Ratio Fillers." *Progress in Polymer Science* 86: 1–39.

Guo, Chuigen, Liping Li, and Huizi Li. 2019. "Evaluation of Interfacial Compatibility in Wood Flour/Polypropylene Composites by Grafting Isocyanate Silane Coupling Agent on Polypropylene." *Journal of Adhesion Science and Technology* 33(5): 468–78.

Hemath, Mohit, Sanjay Mavinkere Rangappa, Vinod Kushvaha, Hom Nath Dhakal, and Suchart Siengchin. 2020. "A Comprehensive Review on Mechanical, Electromagnetic Radiation Shielding, and Thermal Conductivity of Fibers/Inorganic Fillers Reinforced Hybrid Polymer Composites." *Polymer Composites* 41(10): 3940–65.

Ho, S. H., A. G. Supri, and H. Ismail. 2015. "Enhancing Interfacial Adhesion of Potash Feldspar with Silane (Si-69) Coupling Agent on Properties of Ethylene Vinyl Acetate (EVA)/Natural Rubber (NR)/Potash Feldspar Composites." *Journal of Advanced Research in Materials Science* 11: 8–19.

Inácio, André L. N., Renato C. Nonato, and Baltus C. Bonse. 2018. "Mechanical and Thermal Behavior of Aged Composites of Recycled PP/EPDM/Talc Reinforced with Bamboo Fiber." *Polymer Testing* 72: 357–63.

Kaczmarek, Halina, Marta Chylińska, Ewa Klimiec, Bogusław Królikowski, Grzegorz Sionkowski, and Monika Machnik. 2019. "Piezo-Electrets from Polypropylene Composites Doped with Mineral Fillers." *Pure and Applied Chemistry* 91(6): 967–82.

Kahramanov, N. T., N. B. Arzumanova, V. S. Osipchik, Y. N. Kahramanly, F. M. Aliyeva, U. M. Mammadli, G. D. Heydarova, and S. S. Aliyeva. 2017. "The Role of Structurants in the Process of Formation of Structure and Properties of Polymer Composites Based on Random Polypropylene and Mineral Fillers." *Azerbaijan Chemical Journal*, 1(1): 44–49.

Kajiyama, T., T. Yasuda, T. Yamanaka, K. Shimizu, T. Shimizu, E. Takahashi, A. Ujiie, K. Yamamoto, T. Koike, and Y. Nishitani. 2018. "Effect of Addition of Styrene-Ethylene/Butylene-Styrene and the Type of Mica on the Mechanical Properties of Mica-Filled Polyethylene/Polypropylene Blends." *International Polymer Processing* 33(4): 564–73.

Kučera, František, Josef Petruš, Petr Poláček, and Josef Jančář. 2019. "Controlled Reactive Modification of Polypropylene with Maleic Anhydride via Solvent-Free Technique." *Polymer Degradation and Stability* 168: 108934.

Kumar, P. Sarath, Karingamanna Jayanarayanan, and Meera Balachandran. 2020. "Thermal and Mechanical Behavior of Functionalized MWCNT Reinforced Epoxy Carbon Fabric Composites." *Materials Today: Proceedings* 24: 1157–66.

Luthra, Priyanka, Ram Singh, and G. S. Kapur. 2019. "Preparation and Studies of Pigeon Pea Stalk/Polypropylene Composites with and without Compatibilizer." *Polymers and Polymer Composites* 27(6): 337–46.

Mergen, Ömer Bahadır, Ertan Arda, and Gülşen Akın Evingür. 2020. "Electrical, Mechanical, and Optical Changes in MWCNT-Doped PMMA Composite Films." *Journal of Composite Materials* 54(18): 2449–59.

Mittal, Prakhar, Shiva Naresh, Priyanka Luthra, Amardeep Singh, Jatinder Singh Dhaliwal, and Gurpreet Singh Kapur. 2019. "Polypropylene Composites Reinforced with Hybrid Inorganic Fillers: Morphological, Mechanical, and Rheological Properties." *Journal of Thermoplastic Composite Materials* 32(6): 848–64.

Mohammadi, H., and M. R. Moghbeli. 2018. "Organically Modified-Grafted Mica (OMGM) Nanoparticles for Reinforcement of Polypropylene." *Iranian Polymer Journal* 27(2): 125–35.

Mohammadi, Hamed, and Mohammad Reza Moghbeli. 2019. "Polypropylene/Organically Modified-grafted Mica/Organoclay Hybrid Nanocomposites: Preparation, Characterization, and Mechanical Properties." *Polymer Composites* 40(5): 1718–30.

Mousa, Ahmad, Michaela Gedan-Smolka, Udo Wagenknecht, and Sami Massadeh. 2020. "The Effect of Silane-Coated Slag Mineral on the Mechanical and Dynamic Mechanical Properties of Unsaturated Polyester Composite Materials." *Journal of Adhesion Science and Technology* 34(15): 1609–27.

Nguyen-Tran, Huu-Duc, Van-Tho Hoang, Van-Ta Do, Doo-Man Chun, and Young-Jin Yum. 2018. "Effect of Multiwalled Carbon Nanotubes on the Mechanical Properties of Carbon Fiber-Reinforced Polyamide-6/Polypropylene Composites for Lightweight Automotive Parts." *Materials* 11(3): 429.

Parandoush, Pedram, and Dong Lin. 2017. "A Review on Additive Manufacturing of Polymer-Fiber Composites." *Composite Structures* 182: 36–53.

Park, Hyeon Jeong, Arash Badakhsh, Ik Tae Im, Min-Soo Kim, and Chan Woo Park. 2016. "Experimental Study on the Thermal and Mechanical Properties of MWCNT/Polymer and Cu/Polymer Composites." *Applied Thermal Engineering* 107: 907–17.

Pavlidou, Eleni, Dimitrios Bikiaris, A. Vassiliou, Maria Chiotelli, and G. Karayannidis. 2005. "Mechanical Properties and Morphological Examination of Isotactic Polypropylene/SiO$_2$ Nanocomposites Containing PP-g-MA as Compatibilizer." *Journal of Physics: Conference Series* 10:190.

Pracella, Mariano, Donatella Chionna, Irene Anguillesi, Zbigniew Kulinski, and Ewa Piorkowska. 2006. "Functionalization, Compatibilization and Properties of Polypropylene Composites with Hemp Fibres." *Composites Science and Technology* 66(13): 2218–30.

Prashanth, S., K. M. Subbaya, K. Nithin, and S. Sachhidananda. 2017. "Fiber Reinforced Composites-a Review." *Journal of Materials Science and Engineering* 6(341): 22–2169.

Rane, A. V., Kanny, K., Vayyaprontavida Kaliyathan, A., Joshi, S., & Thomas, S. 2017. Mechanical properties of polyphenylene oxide/talc composites with and without coupling agent. *Materials Research Innovations*, 21(5), 325–330.

Rasana, N., K. Jayanarayanan, B. D. S. Deeraj, and K. Joseph. 2019. "The Thermal Degradation and Dynamic Mechanical Properties Modeling of MWCNT/Glass Fiber Multiscale Filler Reinforced Polypropylene Composites." *Composites Science and Technology* 169: 249–59.

Ribbe, Paul H. 2018. *Feldspar Mineralogy*, Vol. 2. Berlin, Walter de Gruyter.
Rothon, Roger, and Christopher DeArmitt. 2017. "Fillers (Including Fiber Reinforcements)." In *Brydson's Plastics Materials*, 169–204. Singapore, Butterworth-Heinemann.
Sápi, Zsombor, Richard Butler, and Andrew Rhead. 2019. "Filler Materials in Composite Out-of-Plane Joints–A Review." *Composite Structures* 207: 787–800.
Sharma, Bikramjit, Rahul Chhibber, and Rajeev Mehta. 2017. "Curing Studies and Mechanical Properties of Glass Fiber Reinforced Composites Based on Silanized Clay Minerals." *Applied Clay Science* 138: 89–99.
Smith, Joseph V. 2012. *Feldspar Minerals: 2 Chemical and Textural Properties*. Berlin, Springer Science & Business Media.
Srivabut, Chainarong, Thanate Ratanawilai, and Salim Hiziroglu. 2018. "Effect of Nanoclay, Talcum, and Calcium Carbonate as Filler on Properties of Composites Manufactured from Recycled Polypropylene and Rubberwood Fiber." *Construction and Building Materials* 162: 450–58.
Świetlicki, Michał, Dariusz Chocyk, Tomasz Klepka, Adam Prószyński, Anita Kwaśniewska, Jarosław Borc, and Grzegorz Gładyszewski. 2020. "The Structure and Mechanical Properties of the Surface Layer of Polypropylene Polymers with Talc Additions." *Materials* 13(3): 698.
Taniike, Toshiaki, Masahito Toyonaga, and Minoru Terano. 2014. "Polypropylene-Grafted Nanoparticles as a Promising Strategy for Boosting Physical Properties of Polypropylene-Based Nanocomposites." *Polymer* 55(4): 1012–19.
Wang, Caili, Dong Wang, and Shuilin Zheng. 2014. "Characterization, Organic Modification of Wollastonite Coated with Nano-Mg (OH) 2 and Its Application in Filling PA6." *Materials Research Bulletin* 50: 273–78.
Wang, Di, Lian-Fang Feng, Xue-Ping Gu, Jia-Jun Wang, Cai-Liang Zhang, and Ai-Hua He. 2019. "Synergetic Effect of a Reactive Compatibilizer and Organo-Montmorillonite on the Dispersion of Polyamide 6/Polydimethylsilicone Blend with a High Viscosity Ratio." *Industrial & Engineering Chemistry Research* 58(9): 3714–20.
Wang, Fangxin, Kai Zhang, Wenyan Liang, Zhenqing Wang, Tong Earn Tay, Shengzhuo Lu, and BinYang. 2020. "Epoxy/CNT@ X Nanocomposite: Improved Quasi-Static, Dynamic Fracture Toughness, and Conductive Functionalities by Non-Ionic Surfactant Treatment." *Polymer Testing* 81: 106256.
Yang, Ming Shan. 2010. "The Reinforcement of Acicular Wollastonite on Polypropylene." *Advanced Materials Research* 92:283–88.
Yang, Ni, Zuo-Cai Zhang, Ning Ma, Huan-Li Liu, Xue-Qing Zhan, Bing Li, Wei Gao, Fang-Chang Tsai, Tao Jiang, and Chang-Jung Chang. 2017. "Effect of Surface Modified Kaolin on Properties of Polypropylene Grafted Maleic Anhydride." *Results in Physics* 7: 969–74.
Yao, J. L., H. X. Zhu, Y. B. Qi, M. J. Guo, Q. Hu, and L. Gao. 2018. "Tough and Reinforced Polypropylene/Kaolin Composites Using Modified Kaolin." *MS&E* 359(1): 12034.
Yetgin, Salih Hakan. 2019. "Effect of Multi Walled Carbon Nanotube on Mechanical, Thermal and Rheological Properties of Polypropylene." *Journal of Materials Research and Technology* 8(5): 4725–35.
Zaaba, Nor Fasihah, Hanafi Ismail, and Mariatti Jaafar. 2017. "A Study of the Degradation of Compatibilized and Uncompatibilized Peanut Shell Powder/Recycled Polypropylene Composites Due to Natural Weathering." *Journal of Vinyl and Additive Technology* 23(4): 290–97.
Zhao, Jinchuan, Qingliang Zhao, Guilong Wang, Chongda Wang, and Chul B. Park. 2020. "Injection Molded Strong Polypropylene Composite Foam Reinforced with Rubber and Talc." *Macromolecular Materials and Engineering* 305(1): 1900630.

10 Ultrasonicated Dolomite as Potential Reinforcing Mineral Filler in Polymer and Copolymer-Based Composites

*Asfa Amalia Ahmad Fauzi,
Azlin Fazlina Osman, and
Khairul Anwar Abdul Halim*
Universiti Malaysia Perlis (UniMAP)
Arau, Malaysia

Hanafi Ismail
Universiti Sains Malaysia
Nibong Tebal, Malaysia

CONTENTS

10.1 Introduction 199
10.2 Polymer Composite with Dolomite Filler 200
10.3 Ultrasonication as the Method to Reduce Particle Size and Improve Dispersion of Dolomite 202
10.4 The Use of Ultrasonication Process in the Production of Polyethylene Vinyl Acetate (PEVA)/Dolomite Composite 203
     10.4.1 Improvement in Mechanical Properties of Polyethylene Vinyl Acetate (PEVA) through Addition of Ultrasonicated Dolomite 204
10.5 Conclusions 207
Acknowledgment 207
References 207

10.1 INTRODUCTION

Many of our modern technologies require materials with combination properties that cannot be met by conventional metals, ceramics and polymeric materials. Composites have been created to improve combinations of mechanical characteristics such as stiffness, toughness and ambient and high-temperature strength (Osman and Mariatti 2006). This is especially true for materials that are needed for aerospace, underwater and transportation applications. A composite material can be defined as a macroscopic combination of two or more distinct materials, with a recognizable interface between them that exhibits a significant proportion of the properties of both materials such that a better combination of properties is realized (Osman and Mariatti 2006). Composites are comprised of a matrix and filler/reinforcement phase. Fibers are probably the most important class of reinforcement/filler material due to their ability to transfer strength to matrix materials and greatly influence their properties. Filler is considered to be a "particle" if all of its dimensions are roughly equal. Thus, particulate-reinforced composites include those reinforced by spheres, rods, flakes and many other shapes of roughly equal axes. Generally, the common fillers used are the ones categorized as inorganic and mineral based, for example, montmorillonite (MMT), bentonite, silica and calcium carbonate (Pegoretti and Dorigato 2020). The addition of a small amount of mineral-based nanofiller (MMT) was proved to provide great enhancement in tensile strength, biostability and thermal stability to the polyethylene-co-vinyl acetate matrix without reducing its flexibility (Osman et al. 2015, 2017; Alakrach et al. 2016; Abdul Hamid et al. 2020a) This is because the high surface area and well-dispersed nanofiller resulted in enhanced interactions between the nanofiller and the host polymer. Another type of inorganic mineral-based filler, such as dolomite, is also being used in the development of polymer composites and nanocomposites due to its abundancy, low cost and reinforcing capability.

10.2 POLYMER COMPOSITE WITH DOLOMITE FILLER

Filler and nanofiller, derived or obtained from natural minerals such as dolomite, is among the best reinforcement material for polymeric materials as it is abundant, low cost, has a high aspect ratio and tailorable surface chemistry (Nik Nur Azza et al. 2014; Nik Adik et al. 2016; Mohd Din et al. 2018). Compared with other types of mineral-based fillers such as clays and silica, dolomite is not frequently used and studied for the purpose of polymer reinforcement. So far, only a few published studies have been found on polymer/dolomite-based composites. These works are summarized below.

According to the work by Mohd Din et al. (2018), the mechanical properties of polypropylene were not successfully improved with the addition of dolomite. It was found that the polypropylene-dolomite composite has lower tensile, impact and flexural strength compared with virgin polypropylene. This was due to poor interactions between dolomite filler and polypropylene matrix as a result of dissimilar polarity between both constituents. Like other polyolefins, polypropylene is hydrophobic, whereas dolomite is hydrophilic, resulting in phase-separated polymer composite (microcomposite). Many researchers also found that dolomite loading affects the polymer composite's characteristics, especially mechanical properties. The mechanical properties of polymer composites usually decrease with a higher percentage of dolomite loading. For instance, Ankabi et al. (2015) observed a decrement in mechanical properties when dolomite was added as filler in polypropylene. On addition of a higher percentage of dolomite, the mechanical properties of the polypropylene-dolomite composite were further decreased, especially its elongation at break value. This might be due to the poor dolomite distribution and dispersion in the matrix caused by agglomeration of dolomite filler; hence, it is hard for the polymer chains to penetrate into the filler as the spaces between the dolomite particles are decreasing. Thermal properties of a polymer composite are also affected by the addition of different dolomite loading. For example, Mohd Din et al. (2018) proved that the thermal stability of polypropylene decreases with increasing of dolomite loading in its structure. Higher dolomite filler content creates a phase-separated polymer composite due to the presence of bulky size dolomite particles at certain areas of the matrix structure. Due to this inhomogeneous morphology, it is hard to improve the thermal stability of the host polymer.

Ankabi et al. (2015) employed a grafting method to improve the mechanical properties of the polypropylene-dolomite composite. The research involved the use of polypropylene-grafted maleic anhydrate (PP-g-MA) with a small amount of compatibilizer. Results showed that there was an improvement in mechanical properties when 20% of dolomite was used as filler. Tensile strength of the polypropylene was increased by 37%. This research revealed that the use of compatibilizer can enhance the interfacial adhesion between the polymer and dolomite filler. Ghada et al. (2010) performed an investigation on the effect of dolomite filler addition on the properties of polyvinyl chloride (PVC) composite. They found that the impact strength and elongation at break of the PVC were significantly improved with the addition of dolomite. Another study indicates the possibility of using dolomite as filler in enhancing the mechanical properties of the phenolic composite. The micro-hardness number of the phenolic composite can be increased with the addition of 28 wt% dolomite (Md Saleh et al. 2014). In research where polyester and dolomite were employed as matrix and filler, respectively, the resultant composite possessed greater mechanical properties as opposed to the neat polyester. In addition, modulus and hardness values were successfully increased when the dolomite was added in higher loading (Adesakin et al. 2013). Another work by Liu et al. (2009) proved that the mechanical properties of polypropylene can be significantly improved when the dolomite filler is modified with stearic acid. They found that the tensile strength and elongation at break values of polypropylene containing the modified filler were superior to polypropylene containing the unmodified filler. Ali et al. (2006) also noticed that higher tensile strength can be obtained when a low amount of dolomite filler is added into the polyurethane host polymer. However, when more filler is added, the tensile strength decreases. The compression strength data also follow the trend of the tensile strength data, in which the value decreased when high loading of filler was added. The overcrowding of the dolomite causes the spaces between the filler to decrease; hence, it is difficult for polymer chains to penetrate in between the filler particles. Ahmad Saidi et al. (2019) discovered that the incorporation of dolomite into polybutylene terephthalate matrix resulted in the improvement of the mechanical properties of the host polymer. The flexural properties, Young's modulus and tensile strength increased significantly with the addition of dolomite filler in the amount of less than 10% of the total composite composition. The dolomite particles were uniformly distributed at loading less than 10%; therefore, the interaction between filler and polymer was enhanced.

Nik Adik et al. (2016) reported that thermal stability of polypropylene was enhanced when reinforced with 25 wt% dolomite filler that has been treated with stearic acid. This proved that when the filler is chemically modified, well-blended filler and polymer matrix can be achieved and homogeneous polymer composite is formed. Thus, the polymer composite with the treated dolomite may exhibit greater thermal stability than the composite with the untreated dolomite. The flammability of the polybutylene terephthalate composite is also improved with the addition of dolomite (Ahmad Saidi et al. 2019). Also, other research discovered that the addition of dolomite into PVC could better improve the thermal stability of the matrix than marble powder. It is reported that the dispersion of dolomite in PVC is better than the dispersion of marble powder in PVC (Ghada et al. 2010). Lastly, in the most recent publication, dolomite filler has been proven to significantly improve the tensile and tear strength of the thermoplastic starch film, showing that this mineral filler is also capable to enhance the mechanical properties of the natural or bio-based polymers (Osman et al. 2021).

10.3 ULTRASONICATION AS THE METHOD TO REDUCE PARTICLE SIZE AND IMPROVE DISPERSION OF DOLOMITE

In recent years, ultrasonication has become one of the methods to disperse, homogenize and de-agglomerate fillers such as multiwalled carbon nanotube (MWCNT), MMT, graphene and silica. Ultrasonication helps to reduce the particle size and de-agglomerate the filler to improve its dispersion state in polymer matrix (Ahmad Fauzi et al. 2018; Abdul Hamid et al. 2020b). Generally, there are two ways to perform the ultrasonication process; via probe method and via bath method. However, both methods apply ultrasound to the sample. During the ultrasonication process, waves are propagating into the particles through liquid medium; thus, the alternating high- and low-pressure cycles are formed. During the low-pressure cycles, high-intensity sonic waves create a large number of microbubbles that later collapse during the high-pressure cycles in a very short time: this is called ultrasonic cavitation. These microbubbles cause high local temperature, high-speed impinging liquid jets and strong hydrodynamic shear forces. De-agglomeration of particles can be achieved through this effect (Kaboorani et al. 2013; Afzal et al. 2018). Thus, the size of large filler that originated from highly agglomerated particles can be reduced. The probe type sonicator is known to be more efficient due to the high intensity of sonication applied directly to the sample, imparting more concentrated energy to the sample. On the other hand, the bath type sonicator isolates the sample from the energy source and requires greater energy input than the probe sonicator because the entire water bath is energized (Afzal et al. 2018). Several studies also proved that the probe type sonicator provides greater impact to the particles causing the particles to disintegrate and de-agglomerate. The use of an ultrasonic probe to pre-swell the MMT in the water medium resulted in an increase of its basal spacing and reduction in its tactoid size. Consequently, an improvement in the MMT dispersion and distribution in the ethylene vinyl acetate (EVA) copolymer matrix was obtained on the melt mixing process between the MMT filler and the copolymer matrix (Ahmad Fauzi et al. 2019; Abdul Hamid et al. 2020a). However, not all materials are suitable for the probe type because excessive energy can bring adverse effect to the particles (Yamamoto et al. 2008; Durge et al. 2014). The inherent properties of single multiwalled nanotubes (SWNTs) can deteriorate if a high-power probe type sonicator is applied (Yamamoto et al. 2008). Therefore, some materials like SWNTs are more suitable for bath type sonication.

The homogenized, well-dispersed, emulsified and disintegrated particles are the outcomes after using the ultrasonication method and these particular characteristics are influenced by amplitude, frequency and time (Kojima et al. 2010; Nguyen et al. 2011. A study by Kaboorani et al. (2013) showed that the ultrasonication process with high amplitude is capable in dispersing nanoclay in the polyvinyl alcohol (PVA) matrix and allows improvement in the shear strength of the PVA composite. Well-dispersed nanoclay can more efficiently reinforce the PVA matrix. Increasing amplitude also decreases the size of particles. According to Kojima et al. (2010), the size of vaterite became smaller when a higher amplitude ultrasonic probe was applied. Nguyen et al. (2011) also suggested that the size of particles reduced with higher frequency and amplitude of the ultrasonic probe. The duration of the ultrasonication process also may influence the size and morphology of the particles. It had been proved that the size of particle became smaller as the time of ultrasonication use was increased (Yasmin et al. 2006). However, it was also discovered that the size of particle becomes bigger with longer exposure to the ultrasonication process as re-agglomeration of particles can occur. This suggests that an optimum ultrasonication time needs to be determined for different types of filler as they possess different characteristics and properties.

10.4 THE USE OF ULTRASONICATION PROCESS IN THE PRODUCTION OF POLYETHYLENE VINYL ACETATE (PEVA)/DOLOMITE COMPOSITE

We have performed an investigation on the effect of the ultrasonication process of dolomite on the mechanical properties of the resultant polyethylene vinyl acetate (PEVA)-dolomite composite. In this research, Branson Digital Ultrasonic Disrupter/Homogenizer (Model 450 D) was employed to sonicate the dolomite. The filler was sonicated for 2, 3 and 5 hours with 30% amplitude, while the pulse-on and pulse-off times were set at 20 and 10 seconds, respectively. Morphology analysis was done on these samples by using a scanning electron microscope (SEM), model SEM-JEOL JSM-6460LA with magnification of 500× and voltage of 10 kV. Figure 10.1 shows the SEM images of dolomite before and after ultrasonication for 2, 3 and 5 hours. There is reduction in size of dolomite particles after ultrasonication for 2 hours (Figure 10.1b) when benchmarked with the pristine dolomite (Figure 10.1a). This result is similar to the work of Mahbubul et al. (2015) in which the average particle size of alumina decreased during the ultrasonication process. As mentioned earlier, ultrasonic cavitation reduces the size of dolomite particles. Unexpectedly, the size of the dolomite particles increased when the filler was further ultrasonicated for 3 and 5 hours. As seen in Figure 10.1c and d, dolomite particles are larger compared with those ultrasonicated for 2 hours (Figure 10.1b).

FIGURE 10.1 SEM images of (a) pristine dolomite, (b) dolomite ultrasonicated for 2 hours (dol_2hr), (c) dolomite ultrasonicated for 3 hours (dol_3hr) and (d) dolomite ultrasonicated for 5 hours (dol_5hr).

This finding is in agreement with the research of Ali et al. (2014) in which they have observed an increase in the vermiculite particles as the ultrasonicated time increased due to recurrence of the particle aggregation. Nguyen et al. (2011) also stated that after a certain time of ultrasonication, the particle size could become larger as the particles might regroup back and yet have low driven energy to de-agglomerate. According to Afzal et al. (2018), a stable particle in solution may be achieved if the ultrasonication time used is sufficient, thus less agglomerated particles can be obtained. However, re-agglomeration of particles may occur if the processing time exceeds the optimum limit. In our case, the optimum ultrasonication time to best reduce the dolomite particle size is 2 hours, meaning that if this duration is exceed then a reverse effect could be observed.

10.4.1 Improvement in Mechanical Properties of Polyethylene Vinyl Acetate (PEVA) through Addition of Ultrasonicated Dolomite

Based on the SEM analysis, 2 hours was chosen as an optimum ultrasonication time for dolomite. This parameter was employed to produce the PEVA/dolomite composites. PEVA functioned as matrix material while dolomite that has been ultrasonicated for 2 hours in distilled water (dol_2hr) was employed as filler. PEVA is a type of copolymer that consists of two types of monomers: semi-crystalline polyethylene (PE) and amorphous vinyl acetate (VA). Each monomer has different properties due to dissimilar polarity of both. Ethylene is a non-polar (hydrophobic) monomer, whereas vinyl acetate is a polar (hydrophilic) monomer. The commercial PEVAs vary the VA percentage, thus their properties depend on the VA percentage. PEVA becomes more rubber-like as the VA percentage increases. This type of PEVA is used as wax, hot melt adhesive and in medical applications (Barrueso-Martinez et al. 2003; Osman et al. 2017). PEVA properties are likely to have PE properties as the VA percentage is low; it is used in wrapping food and paper industries as it has glossy, soft and flexible properties (Vasilev et al. 2020).

In this study, we have used PEVA with 26% VA content that was manufactured by Hanwha Total Petrochemical Co., Ltd. (Chungcheongnam-do, South Korea). The mechanical properties of the PEVA/dol_2hr composites were analyzed in relation to dolomite loading (1%, 3% and 5%). The pristine dolomite was supplied by Perlis Dolomite Industries Sdn Bhd (PDI) (Padang Besar, Perlis) in powder form with a 150-μ particle size. The PEVA/dol_2hr composite was prepared using a twin-screw extruder (Lab Tech) LTE 16-40, which has a 16-mm screw diameter at 160°C and 50 rpm speed. Then, the sample was compressed into a 1-mm-thick sheet using a compression molding machine (GOTECH CO model GT-7014-H30C). The samples were then punched with an ASTM D638 M-5 cutter for mechanical testing purposes. The tensile test was done by using an Instron machine model 5569 with a crosshead speed of 50 mm/min. Tensile properties were evaluated based on tensile strength, break of elongation, modulus of elasticity and tensile toughness. Figure 10.2a–d summarizes the tensile strength, break of elongation, modulus of elasticity and tensile toughness of the PEVA/dolomite (dol_2hr) with different filler loading. Generally, the tensile strength, modulus of elasticity and tensile toughness of the PEVA increased as the amount of filler increased. Conversely, break of elongation shows a decreasing trend as filler loading increased. The tensile properties of the PEVA composite containing 1 wt% dolomite show statistically no significant difference with that of the virgin PEVA. Further increase of dolomite loading to 3 and 5 wt% resulted in a significant increase in those properties. This shows that the ultrasonicated dolomite filler has the capability to improve the strength, stiffness and toughness of the PEVA copolymer when added in the amount of 2–5 wt%. Among all the materials, the PEVA composite with 5 wt% dolomite shows the highest tensile strength, modulus of elasticity and tensile toughness.

In terms of tensile strength, the PEVA/dol_2hr composite containing 5 wt% dolomite shows the highest value with an increment of 29% when benchmarked with the virgin PEVA. This improvement was due to good interaction between the matrix and filler, which led to an efficient stress transferring mechanism between filler and matrix. As mentioned previously, ultrasonication caused de-agglomeration of dolomite and subsequent reduction in its particle size; hence, this could facilitate its dispersion in the copolymer matrix and improve its interface bonding with the copolymer chains. This finding is similar to that observed by Osman et al. (2021) and Ridhwan et al. (2013), in which the tensile strength of polymer matrix increased when smaller-sized dolomite filler was added (Osman et al. 2021; Ridhwan et al. 2013). Several published papers reported that 5 wt% of dolomite loading results in an improvement in tensile strength, but further addition of dolomite causes reduction in this property. The improvement is due to the dolomite particle, which can be well

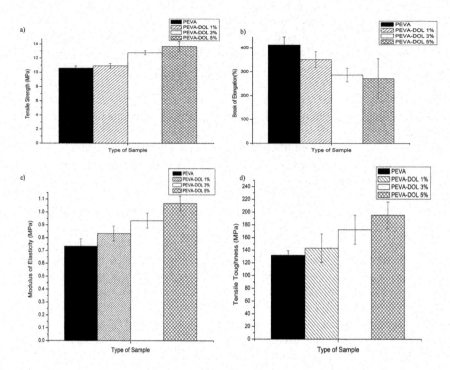

FIGURE 10.2 (a) Tensile strength, (b) break of elongation, (c) modulus of elasticity, and (d) tensile toughness of PEVA composite with different loadings of ultrasonicated dolomite (dol_2hr).

distributed at 5 wt%, whereas at higher wt% (more than 5 wt%), overcrowding of particles happens and they tend to agglomerate in the matrices (Ankabi et al. 2015; Nik Adik et al. 2016; Ahmad Saidi et al. 2019).

The elongation at break value shows a decreasing trend as dolomite loading increased from 0 to 5 wt% (Figure 10.2b). At 1 wt% dolomite filler, the elongation at break of the PEVA composite decreased 14.9% as opposed to the virgin PEVA, whereas at 5 wt% dolomite loading it is further decreased by 34.2%. Adding a stiff filler like dolomite into an elastic polymer can increase the stiffness of the matrix. Thus, the ductility of the resultant polymer composite is decreased. This explains the reason for the decreasing trend observed in the elongation at break of the PEVA/dol_2hr composite as more filler was added into the copolymer structure. Our result is in good agreement with the findings of other researchers in which they have stated that increasing dolomite loading causes a decrease in the elongation at break value of the matrix (Ahmad Saidi et al. 2019). This phenomenon might also be due to the reduction in deformation of the rigid interface between the filler and the polymer matrix (Ankabi et al. 2015).

Figure 10.2c shows the modulus of elasticity of the PEVA/dol_2hr composite with different dolomite loadings. Clearly the value of the modulus of elasticity increased as the dolomite loading increased. PEVA composite with 5 wt% dolomite possesses the highest modulus of elasticity with an increment of 46% when benchmarked with the virgin PEVA. Increasing modulus of elasticity is also reported by Nik Adik et al. (2016) and Adesakin et al. (2013). According to Ahmad Saidi et al. (2019), the stiffness of dolomite filler restricts the chain mobility of the PEVA matrix. Figure 10.2d shows that the tensile toughness of the PEVA/dol_2hr composite also increased as dolomite loading increased from 0 to 5 wt%. The best tensile toughness was achieved by the composite with 5 wt% dolomite with the increment of 48.5% from the value of the virgin PEVA. On ultrasonication, the dolomite particles become smaller, more mobile and easily dispersed throughout the PEVA matrix. More PEVA-dolomite interactions can be developed, thus enhancement in the energy absorption mechanism during tensile deformation would enhance the toughness of the matrix and resist its sudden fracture.

10.5 CONCLUSIONS

This chapter highlights the promising properties of the polymer composites incorporating natural, inorganic and mineral-based filler, such as dolomite. Here, we have reported our findings based on the investigation of the PEVA/dolomite composite system. In addition, the effect of using different ultrasonication durations/times on the morphology of the dolomite was also studied. From the SEM analysis, we found that the dolomite's particle size became smaller after ultrasonicated for 2 hours, but then it increased after being ultrasonicated for 3 and 5 hours. As the purpose of this study was to obtain dolomite particles with reduced size and agglomeration, the dolomite subjected to 2 hours of ultrasonication process (dol_2hr) was selected as filler for the production of the PEVA/dolomite composite. The tensile test was performed to evaluate the mechanical properties of the resultant composites. It was found that the tensile strength, modulus of elasticity and tensile toughness of the composite were enhanced when the dolomite filler loading increased from 0 to 5 wt%. This improvement was due to good interaction between the matrix and filler, which led to an efficient stress-transferring mechanism between filler and matrix. The applied ultrasonication process caused de-agglomeration of dolomite and subsequent reduction in its particle size; hence, this could facilitate its dispersion in the copolymer matrix and improve its interface bonding with the copolymer chains. The findings proved the potential of ultrasonication method in producing dolomite filler capable of reinforcing the copolymer matrix.

ACKNOWLEDGMENT

The authors would like to acknowledge the support from the Fundamental Research Grant Scheme (FRGS) Grant FRGS/1/2019/TK05/UNIMAP/02/6 from the Ministry of Education Malaysia.

REFERENCES

Abdul Hamid, A.R., A. F. Osman, Z. Mustafa, and R. Ananthakrishnan. 2020a. "Pre-swelling Process of The Surface Modified Montmorillonite (O-MMT) as a Strategy to Enhance Exfoliation and Dispersion." *Journal of Advanced Manufacturing Technology (JAMT)* 14(2): 29–42. https://jamt.utem.edu.my/jamt/article/view/5937

Abdul Hamid, Asna Rasyidah, Azlin Fazlina Osman, Zaleha Mustafa, Subrata Mandal, and Rajakumar Ananthakrishnan. 2020b. "Tensile, Fatigue and Thermomechanical Properties of Poly(Ethylene-Co-Vinyl Acetate) Nanocomposites Incorporating Low and High Loadings of Pre-Swelled Organically Modified Montmorillonite." *Polymer Testing* 85: 106426. https://doi.org/10.1016/j.polymertesting.2020.106426

Adesakin, A. O., O. O. Ajayi, P. E. Imosili, B. E. Attahdaniel, and S. O. O. Olusunle. 2013. "Characterization and Evaluation of Mechanical Properties of Dolomite as Filler in Polyester." *Chemistry and Materials Research* 3(8): 36–40.

Afzal, Asif, Ibrahim Nawfal, I. M. Mahbubul, and Sunil Siddalingapa Kumbar. 2018. "An Overview on the Effect of Ultrasonication Duration on Different Properties of Nanofluids." *Journal of Thermal Analysis and Calorimetry* 135(1): 393–418. https://doi.org/10.1007/s10973-018-7144-8

Ahmad Fauzi, Asfa Amalia, Azlin Fazlina Osman, Mohd Aidil Adhha Abdullah, Subrata Mandal, and Rajakumar Ananthakrishan. 2019. "Ethylene Vinyl Acetate Nanocomposites with Hybrid Silicate Nanofillers of Destabilized Natural and Commercial Bentonites and Organomontmorillonites." *Journal of Vinyl and Additive Technology* 25(4): 396–411. https://doi.org/10.1002/vnl.21708

Ahmad Fauzi, A.A, Osman, A.F., Abdullah, M.A.A. and Mandal, S. 2018. "Destabilization of Natural and Commercial Bentonite Interlayers by Ultrasonication, pH control and Salt Addition." *Solid State Phenomena*, 280:115–120. https://doi.org/10.4028/www.scientific.net/SSP.280.115

Ahmad Saidi, Muhammad Akmal, Farah Syazwani Mazlan, Azman Hassan, Rashita Abd Rashid, and Abdul Razak Rahmad. 2019. "Flammability, Thermal and Mechanical Properties of Polybutylene Terephthalate/Dolomite Composite." *Journal of physical Science* 30(3): 175–189. https://doi.org/10.21315/jps2019.30.3.11

Alakrach A. M., Azlin F. Osman, N. Z. Noriman, B. O. Betar, and Omar S. Dahham. 2016. "Thermal Properties of Ethyl Vinyl Acetate (EVA) Nanocomposites for Biomedical Applications." *MATEC Web of Conferences* 78: 7–11. https://doi.org/10.1051/matecconf/20167801074

Ali, Faman, Laurence Reinert, Jean-Marc Leveque, Laurent Duclaux, Fabrice Muller, Shaukat Saeed, and Syed Sakhawat Shah. 2014. "Effect of Sonication Conditions: Solvent, Time, Temperature and Reactor Type on the Preparation of Micron Sized Vermiculite Particles." *Ultrasonics Sonochemistry* 21:1002–1009. http://dx.doi.org/10.1016/j.ultsonch.2013.10.010

Ali, Vazid, Neelkamal, Fozia Z. Haque, M. Zulfequar, and M. Husain. 2006. "Preparation and Characterization of Polyether-Based Polyurethane Dolomite Composite." *Journal Applied Polymer Science* 103: 2337–2342.

Ankabi, M. N., O. Ogbobe, M. U. Obidiegwu, P. C. Uzoma, G. C. Onuegbu, and P. I. Anynwu. 2015. "Effects of Dolomite Filler and Compatibilizer on the Mechanical Properties of Polypropylene." *IREJEST* 13(1):11–16.

Barrueso-Martinez, Maria Luisa, Teresa del Pilar Ferrandiz-Gomez, Maria Dolores Romero-Sanchez, and Jose Miguel Martin-Martinez. 2003. "Characterization of EVA-based Adhesives Containing Different Amounts of Rosin Ester or Polyterpene Tackifier." *The Journal of Adhesion* 79(8): 805–824. http://dx.doi.org/10.1080/00218460309547

Durge, Rakhee, R. V. Kshirsagar, and Pankaj Tambe. 2014. "Effect of Sonication Energy on the Yield of Graphene Nanosheets by Liquid-Phase Exfoliation of Graphite." *Procedia Engineering* 97(2014): 1457–1465. https://doi.org/10.1016/j.proeng.2014.12.429

Ghada, Bounamous, Zaghdoudi Rachida, Meghezzi Ahmed, and Dazi Faycal. 2010. "Effect of Marble Powder and Dolomite on Mechanical Properties and the Thermal Stability of Poly(vinyl chloride)." *Asian Journal of Chemistry* 22(9): 6687–6692.

Kaboorani, Alireza, Bernard Riedl, and Pierre Blanchet. 2013. "Ultrasonication Technique: A Method for Dispersing Nanoclay in Wood Adhesives." *Journals of Nanomaterials* 2013: 1–9. http://dx.doi.org/10.1155/2013/341897

Kojima, Yoshiyuki, Kohei Yamaguchi, and Nobuyuki Nishimiya. 2010. "Effect of Amplitude and Frequency of Ultrasonic Irradiation on Morphological Characteristics control of Calcium Carbonate." *Ultrasonics Sonochemistry* 17(3): 617–620. https://doi.org/10.1016/j.ultsonch.2009.10.020

Liu, Xin, Weilin Xu, and Peng Xuqiang. 2009. "Effect of Stearic Acid on Interface and Performance of Polypropylen/superfine Down Powder Composites." *Polymer Composites* 679: 1855–1863. https://doi.org/10.1002/pc.20759

Mahbubul, I. M., I. M. Shahrul, S. S. Khaleduzzaman, R. Saidur, M. A. Amalina, and A. Turgut. 2015. "Experimental Investigation on Effect of Ultrasonication Duration on Colloidal Dispersion and Thermophysical of Alumina-Water Nanofluid." *International Journal of Heat and Mass Transfer* 88: 73–81. https://doi.org/10.1016/j.ijheatmasstransfer.2015.04.048

Md Saleh, Siti Shuhada, Hazizan Md Akil, Muhammad Helmi Abdul Kudus, and Muhammad Razlan Zakaria. 2014. "A Comparative Study of Dolomite and MWCNTS-Dolomite As Filler in Phenolic Composites." *Malaysian Polymer Journal* 9(2): 67–69.

Mohd Din, Suria Fatin, Rashitah Abd. Rashid, Muhammad Akmal Ahmad Saidi, and Norhayani Othman. 2018. "Mechanical, Thermal and Flammability Properties of Dolomite Filled Polypropylene Composites." *PERINTIS eJournal* 8(2): 58–73.

Nik Adik, N. N. A., Ong Hui Lin, Hazizan Md Akil, Andrei Victor Sandu, Al Rey Villagracia, and Gil Nonanto Santos. 2016. "Effects of Stearic Acid on Tensile, Morphological and Thermal Analysis of Polypropylene (PP)/Dolomite (Dol) Composites." *Materiale Plastice* 53(1): 61–64.

Nik Nur Azza, N. A., Ong Hui Lin, Hidayu Jamil Noorina, Hazizan Md. Akil, and S. T. Sam. 2014. "Analysis of Ground Dolomite: Effect of Grinding on the Production of Submicron Particles." *Applied Mechanics and Material* 679: 145–148. https://doi.org/10.4028/www.scientific.net/AMM.679.145

Nguyen, Van Son, Didier Rouxel, Rachid Hadji, Brice Vincent, and Yves Fort. 2011. "Effect of Ultrasonication and Dispersion Stability on Cluster Size of Alumina Nanoscale Particles in Aqueous Solutions." *Ultrasonic Sonochemistry* 18 (1): 382–388. https://doi.org/10.1016/j.ultsonch.2010.07.003

Osman, A. F., and M. Mariatti. 2006. "Properties of Aluminum Filled Polypropylene Composites." *Polymers & Polymer Composites* 14(6): 623–633.

Osman, Azlin F., Tuty Fareyhynn M. Fitri, Md. Rakibuddin, Fatimah Hashim, Syed Ahmad Tajudin Tuan Johari, Rajakumar Ananthakrishnan, and Rafiza Ramli. 2017. "Pre-Dispersed Organo-Montmorillonite (Organo-MMT) Nanofiller: Morphology, Cytocompatibility and Impact on Flexibility, Toughness and Biostability of Biomedical Ethyl Vinyl Acetate (EVA) Copolymer." *Materials Science & Engineering C* 74: 194–206. https://doi.org/10.1016/j.msec.2016.11.137

Osman, Azlin Fazlina, Hussein Kalo, Mohd Saifullah Hassan, Tew Wei Hong, and Farehah Azmi. 2015. "Pre-dispersing of Montmorillonite Nanofiller: Impact on Morphology and Performance of Melt Compounded Ethyl Vinyl Acetate Nanocomposites." *Journal of Applied Polymer Science* 133(1): 43204. https://doi.org/10.1002/app.43204

Osman, A.F., Siah, L., Alrashdi, A.A., Ul-Hamid, A., Ibrahim, I. 2021 "Improving the Tensile and Tear Properties of Thermoplastic Starch/Dolomite Biocomposite Film through Sonication Process." *Polymers* 13(2): 274. https://doi.org/10.3390/polym13020274

Pegoretti, Alessandro, and Andrea Dorigato. 2020. "Polymer Composites: Reinforcing Fillers." *Encyclopedia of Polymer Science and Technology* May, 1–72. https://doi.org/10.1002/0471440264.pst130.pub2

Ridhwan, J. N. M., N. Z. Noriman, M. A. A. Mohd Salleh, S. T. Sam, L. Musa, and N. Z. Nik Yahya. 2013. "The Effect of Different Size "Batu Reput" (Dolomite) as a Filler in SMR L and ENR-50." *Advance Materials Research* 795(2013): 383–387.

Vasilev, S., Vodyashkin, A., Vasileva, D., Zelenovskiy, P., Chezganov, D., Yuzhakov, V., Shur, V., O'Reilly, E., & Vinogradov, A. 2020. "An Investigative Study on the Effect of Pre-Coating Polymer Solutions on the Fabrication of Low Cost Anti-Adhesive Release Paper." *Nanomaterials* 10(8):1436. https://doi.org/10.3390/nano10081436

Yamamoto, Tatsuhiro, Yuhei Miyauchi, Jin Motoyanagi, Takamori Fukushima, Takuzo Aida, Masaru Kato, and Shigeo Maruyama. 2008. "Improved Bath Sonication Method for Dispersion of Individual Single Walled Carbon Nanotubes Using New Triphenylene-Base Surfactant." *Japanese Journal Applied Physics* 47(4): 2000–2004.

Yasmin, Asma, Jyi-Jiin Luo, and Isaac M. Daniel. 2006. "Processing of Expanded Graphite Reinforced Polymer Nanocomposites." *Composites Science and Technology* 66(9): 1182–1189. https://doi.org/10.1016/j.compscitech.2005.10.014

11 Modified Carboxymethyl Cellulose/Halloysite Nanotube (CMC/HNT) Using Sodium Dodecyl Sulfate (SDS)

Kathiravan Suppiah
Universiti Malaysia Perlis, Arau, Malaysia
and
Universitas Sumatera Utara
Medan, Indonesia

Rozyanty Abdul Rahman, Pei Leng Teh, and Cheow Keat Yeoh
Universiti Malaysia Perlis
Arau, Malaysia

CONTENTS

11.1 Introduction	212
11.2 Preparation and Characterization of CMC/HNT Bio-Nanocomposite Films	213
11.2.1 Materials	213
11.2.2 Chemical Modification of HNT	213
11.2.3 Preparation of CMC/HNT Bio-Nanocomposite Films	213
11.3 Fourier Transform Infrared Spectroscopic Analysis	214
11.3.1 Tensile Properties	215
11.3.2 Morphological Analysis	219
11.3.3 Moisture Content	222
11.3.4 Thermal Stability Properties	223
11.3.5 X-Ray Diffraction Analysis	225
11.4 Conclusion	227
Acknowledgment	227
References	227

DOI: 10.1201/9781003221012-11

11.1 INTRODUCTION

In recent years, the attention of researchers toward the search for alternatives to replace non-renewable resources is significant due to increasing concern about ecosystem preservations. Synthetic polymers are mostly produced from petrochemicals that generate enormous environmental issues due to their non-degradable and non-renewable nature. Thus, the development of bio-based materials or bio-composites obtained from renewable resources is highlighted (Nishio, 2006; Singha et al. 2009; Battegazzore et al. 2020; Shamsuyeva et al. 2020). Besides that, bio-composite materials are also considered as sustainable products. The sustainable bio-composites are also known as a bio-based product derived from renewable resources with recycling capability and triggered biodegradability (i.e., stable in their intended lifetime but would biodegrade after disposal in composting conditions) with commercial viability and environmental acceptability (Mohanty et al. 2000). The effective bio-composite formulations of such bio-based products from natural fiber reinforcements also result in new commercial applications that would promote the sustainability of the products.

Extensive effort has been made to develop and use bio-composite materials in various applications due to its renewability, biodegradability, low cost, non-petroleum-based source and low carbon dioxide release (Moon et al. 2011). Cellulose and its derivatives have become popular bio-based materials. They have been extensively employed in composites due to their biodegradability, cost-effectiveness and inexhaustibility (Sharma et al. 2020; Taheri et al. 2020). Cellulose, the structural component of plant walls, is considered the most abundant natural polymer and renewable resource on the earth. However, the extended intramolecular and intermolecular network of hydrogen bonds within cellulose provides chain stiffness, which results in insolubility of the biopolymer in almost all organic and inorganic solvents, limiting its application in composite fields (Martins et al. 2012). In contrast, the derivative modification of cellulose can overcome these limitations. Carboxymethyl cellulose (CMC), a common derivative of cellulose, is water soluble; anionic polysaccharides with carboxymethyl groups ($-CH_2-COONa$) bonded to some of the hydroxyl groups in cellulose backbone (Rubilar et al. 2013). Also, CMC's desirable characteristics, such as good film forming properties, hydrophilicity, high viscosity, biocompatibility and no adverse effects of human health (both non-toxic and non-allergenic), make it ideal to be used in drug delivery, detergents, cosmetics, pharmaceutical and composite fields (De Salvi et al. 2012). The unique material properties of CMC promote its utilization in diverse fields; however, in general, it is very susceptible to moisture and leads to poor mechanical properties (Perotti et al. 2014).

A common approach to overcome this drawback is by adding filler, particularly nanofiller to biopolymers to improve mechanical properties and form bio-nanocomposites. Among various nanofillers, halloysite nanotubes (HNTs) with a large aspect ratio have proven to be more effective in polymer matrices (Huang et al. 2003). The HNTs offer an inexpensive, low-tech alternative that is morphologically similar to multiwalled carbon nanotubes (MWCNTs) and not limited to its economic viability. Also, HNTs possess one-dimensional tubular porous structures, enabling its usage in versatile sustainable materials applications (Huang et al. 2003). These characteristics generate increased mechanical properties, improve thermal resistance and reduce gas permeability for HNT-polymer nanocomposites (Bigucci et al. 2015).

Although HNTs have numerous advantages benefiting bio-nanocomposites formation, the HNT's very stable structure and hard surface interaction becomes a major problem in the interaction between matrix and filler when it is incorporated with polymer matrices. Another difficulty is their strong tendency to form agglomerates due to the small size and high surface area, which makes the HNT strongly bound together by van der Waals attractive forces, forming bundles and large agglomerates of HNT (Spitalsky et al. 2010; Yu et al. 2014). This results in reduction of properties of the bio-nanocomposites involving HNT as nanofiller. Hence, to optimize the properties of the desired composites, the nanotube dispersion and stress transfer must be optimized (Liu et al. 2014). Therefore, in many cases, functionalizing HNTs by modifying them chemically (also known as surface modification) is vital to enhance the properties of HNT-based bio-nanocomposites. In this work, the chemical modification of HNTs using sodium dodecyl sulfate (SDS) was performed to produce treated CMC/HNT bio-nanocomposite films using the solvent casting method.

11.2 PREPARATION AND CHARACTERIZATION OF CMC/HNT BIO-NANOCOMPOSITE FILMS

11.2.1 MATERIALS

CMC powder used in this work (with a molecular weight of 90,000 and degree of substitution of 0.7) was purchased from Acros Organics (Geel, Belgium). The ultrafine-grade HNT clay was supplied by Imerys Tableware Asia Limited (Auckland, New Zealand). Ethanol was used as a solvent for chemical modification. SDS was used as a chemical modifier. Both ethanol and SDS were obtained from Sigma Aldrich (Penang, Malaysia).

11.2.2 CHEMICAL MODIFICATION OF HNT

Three percent SDS was dissolved into 100 mL of ethanol (v/v). The HNT powder was added slowly into the solution and stirred using a magnetic stirrer for 2 hours and continued for another 24 hours. The treated HNT nanofiller was then filtered and dried in an oven at 80°C for 3 hours.

11.2.3 PREPARATION OF CMC/HNT BIO-NANOCOMPOSITE FILMS

The CMC and CMC/HNT bio-nanocomposite films with 0, 5, 10, 15 and 20 wt% of HNT content were prepared using the solution casting method, respectively. The 2 g of CMC and desired amount of HNT nanofiller containing 0.10–0.40 g were added. Different ratios of CMC were dispersed in 80 mL of distilled water under mechanical stirring at 250 rpm for 30 minutes using a water bath at 90°C. Different contents of HNT were dispersed in 20 mL of distilled water under magnetic stirring for 30 minutes. The HNT was then poured into CMC, and both were mixed at 250 rpm for 1 hour at 90°C in the water bath. Finally, 100-mL of samples were

TABLE 11.1
The Compositions of the CMC/HNT Bio-Nanocomposite Films

Materials	CMC (wt%)	HNT (wt%)	SDS Treatment (%)
Untreated CMC/HNT bio-nanocomposite films	100	0	-
	95	5	-
	90	10	-
	85	15	-
	80	20	-
SDS-treated CMC/HNT bio-nanocomposite films	100	0	-
	95	5	3[a]
	90	10	3[a]
	85	15	3[a]
	80	20	3[a]

Source: From Salmah et al. 2012.
[a] Based on the wt% of HNT filler.

poured into a glass mold and dried at 50°C for 20 hours in an oven for casting the bio-nanocomposite film. The procedures were repeated for the treated CMC/HNT bio-nanocomposite films. The formulation of untreated and treated CMC/HNT bio-nanocomposite films with different HNT content is listed in Table 11.1.

11.3 FOURIER TRANSFORM INFRARED SPECTROSCOPIC ANALYSIS

The Fourier transform infrared (FTIR) spectrum of untreated and SDS-treated CMC/HNT bio-nanocomposite films are illustrated in Figure 11.1. The FTIR spectrums of both untreated and SDS-treated bio-composite films exhibited the broadband centered at 3422 and 3392 cm^{-1}, attributed to the stretching of hydroxyl group (–OH) and intermolecular and intramolecular hydrogen bonds of CMC and HNT, respectively. The absorption band at 2910 cm^{-1} for the untreated CMC/HNT bio-nanocomposite films indicates the aliphatic (–CH) stretching vibrations from CMC. Meanwhile, peaks at 1604 and 1430 cm^{-1} were related to the asymmetric and symmetric stretching of carboxylate groups (–COO) from CMC. The signal at 1329 cm^{-1} represents (–CH) bending and the broad peak at 1057 cm^{-1} attributed to stretching on polysaccharide skeleton (–COC) groups of CMC.

In addition, the (Al) O–H stretching vibration at 3620 cm^{-1}, the bending of–OH groups at 1647 cm^{-1} and the absorption bands between 1000 and 1200 cm^{-1} due to stretching vibration of Si-O and Si-O-Si of HNT disappeared in the spectrum of both untreated and SDS-treated CMC/HNT bio-nanocomposite films. This indicates that the respective groups of HNT overlapped with CMC groups of the same bandwidth and showed almost no significant changes in the spectrum. However, a small peak was observed in untreated and SDS-treated bio-nanocomposites at 919 and 912 cm^{-1} due to Si-O-Si groups of HNT.

Modified CMC/HNT Using SDS

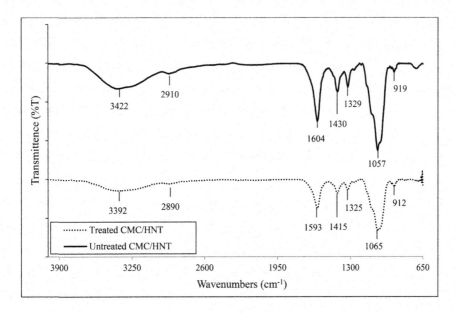

FIGURE 11.1 FTIR spectra of untreated and SDS-treated CMC/HNT bio-nanocomposite films.

For the SDS-treated CMC/HNT bio-nanocomposite, introduction of SDS onto the surface of HNT shifted a few peaks to lower wavelengths and reduced peak intensity due to the presence of the intermolecular reaction between HNT and SDS. The absorption band for SDS-treated bio-nanocomposite films at 2890 cm^{-1} shifted to lower wavelengths due to the presence of long alkyl chains from SDS attached to the HNT surface via covalent bonding. The peaks at 1593, 1415, 1325 and 1065 cm^{-1} that appeared in the spectrum of SDS-treated bio-nanocomposites also showed weakened intensity.

Also, the peak at 1065 cm^{-1} for the treated bio-nanocomposites shifted to a higher wavelength with low intensity due to the presence of the sulfate group (S=O) of SDS. The spectrum of SDS-treated CMC/HNT bio-nanocomposites exhibits reduction in peak intensity of the hydroxyl group from 3422 to 3392 cm^{-1}. This is mainly due to the reaction between the polar head group of SDS and the hydroxyl group of HNT through covalent bonding. The schematic reaction of HNT and SDS is presented in Figure 11.2. Meanwhile, Figure 11.3 represents the schematic illustration of possible interaction mechanisms for SDS-treated HNT nanofiller with the CMC matrix chains.

11.3.1 Tensile Properties

Figure 11.4 presents the effect of HNT content on tensile strength of untreated and SDS-treated CMC/HNT bio-nanocomposites. The figure shows that the tensile strength of both untreated and treated CMC/HNT bio-nanocomposite films shows optimum values at 10 wt% of HNT content. Both bio-nanocomposites possessed higher tensile strength compared with neat CMC films. However, the SDS-treated CMC/HNT bio-nanocomposite films exhibited higher tensile strength compared with untreated bio-nanocomposite films.

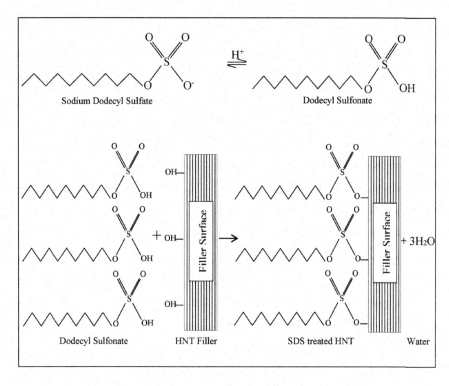

FIGURE 11.2 The proposed schematic reaction of HNT nanofiller SDS.

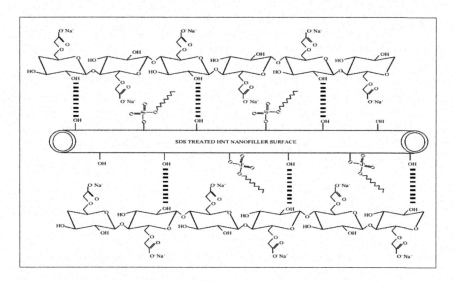

FIGURE 11.3 Schematic illustration of the possible interaction mechanism of SDS-treated HNT nanofiller with CMC chains.

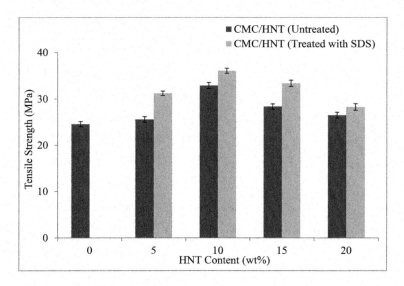

FIGURE 11.4 Effect of HNT on tensile strength of untreated and SDS-treated CMC/HNT bio-nanocomposite films.

The tensile strength of SDS-treated CMC/HNT bio-nanocomposites films showed an improvement with an average tensile strength of 14.1% compared with untreated bio-nanocomposite films. The tensile strength of treated bio-nanocomposites with SDS at 10 wt% of HNT content also increased about 9.67% compared with the untreated bio-nanocomposites. These results show that SDS, which is an anionic surfactant, acts as a medium to enhance the interaction between HNT nanofiller and CMC matrix. These strong interfacial interactions also lead to the improved load transfer from the CMC matrix to the treated HNT nanofiller and resulted in higher tensile strength.

Also, the enhancement of tensile strength on treated CMC/HNT bio-nanocomposites is due to structural rearrangement of HNT into a more ordered form with the aid of SDS chemical functionalization. The higher tensile strength obtained at 10 wt% of HNT content of treated CMC/HNT bio-nanocomposites attributed to the better dispersion of the treated HNT filler in the CMC matrix and improved filler-matrix interaction. SDS as a chemical modifier also improves the solubility of HNT and permits the covalent interaction with CMC matrix. This improved interaction leads to better adhesion at the HNT/CMC interface and enhanced mechanical strength of the SDS-treated CMC/HNT bio-nanocomposite films.

According to Goh et al.(2010), the tensile strength of the polyetherimide (PEI)/MWCNT nanocomposite membrane was improved with the aid of SDS as a surfactant. The nanotubes were treated with SDS to achieve fine dispersion of nanotubes and facilitate strong interfacial adhesion with the polymer matrix. Apart from that, the agglomeration and entanglement of the nanotubes were also greatly reduced and led to better dispersion of treated nanotubes with the polymer matrix.

Figure 11.5 illustrates the effect of HNT content on elongation at break of untreated and SDS-treated CMC/HNT bio-nanocomposite films. It can be seen that the elongation at break of untreated and treated CMC/HNT bio-nanocomposites with SDS

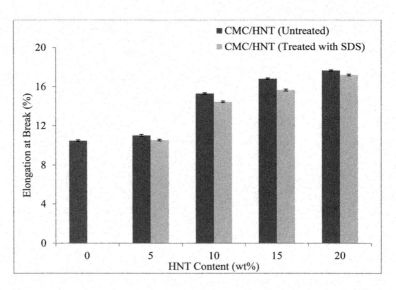

FIGURE 11.5 Effect of HNT on elongation at break of untreated and SDS-treated CMC/HNT bio-nanocomposite films.

increased with increasing HNT content. The inclusion of SDS-treated HNT nanofiller has increased the elongation at break of treated CMC/HNT bio-nanocomposite films up to 20 wt% of HNT content about 64.28% compared with the neat CMC film.

However, the elongation at break of treated CMC/HNT bio-nanocomposite films is lower than the untreated bio-nanocomposite films at similar HNT content. The decrement in elongation at break of treated CMC/HNT bio-nanocomposites compared with untreated bio-nanocomposites at similar HNT loading is mainly due to the enhancement of adhesion of the interface between modified HNT nanofiller with SDS and the CMC matrix. The SDS-treated HNT nanofiller was able to restrict the chain mobility in treated CMC/HNT bio-nanocomposites, but the ductility of bio-nanocomposites increased as the treated HNT nanofiller loading increased up to 20 wt%. This is mainly attributed to the increase in HNT nanofiller content in treated CMC/HNT bio-nanocomposites, which results in more filler-filler interactions compared with filler-matrix interactions.

The modulus of elasticity of untreated and SDS-treated CMC/HNT bio-nanocomposite films at different amounts of HNT nanofiller is shown in Figure 11.6. Both untreated and SDS-treated CMC//HNT bio-nanocomposite films increased with increasing of HNT filler loading. Nevertheless, the SDS-treated CMC/HNT bio-nanocomposite films possessed a higher modulus of elasticity than the untreated CMC/HNT bio-nanocomposites. At similar HNT filler loading, the SDS-treated CMC/HNT bio-nanocomposite films improved the modulus of elasticity at an average of 12.1% compared with untreated CMC/HNT bio-nanocomposites.

Moreover, the modulus of elasticity of treated CMC/HNT with SDS increased by 11.0% with HNT content from 5 to 20 wt% compared with untreated bio-nanocomposite films. This observation reveals that the presence of SDS in CMC/HNT

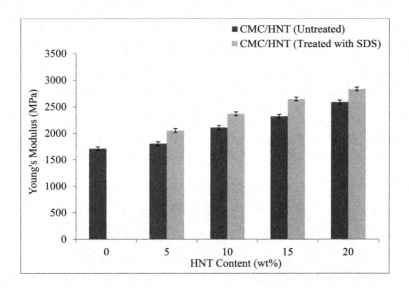

FIGURE 11.6 Effect of HNT on modulus of elasticity of untreated and SDS-treated CMC/HNT bio-nanocomposite films.

bio-nanocomposite films enhanced the interfacial adhesion between filler-matrix and improved filler dispersion, which leads to an increase in modulus of elasticity. Also, the SDS treatment enhanced the surface adhesion between CMC matrix and HNT nanofiller by decreasing the hydroxyl group of the HNT nanofiller in treated CMC/HNT bio-nanocomposites.

A similar trend was also found by Hartline (2012). The results show that the modulus of elasticity for the polylactic acid (PLA)/HNT nanocomposites with SDS is increased with increasing HNT content up to 5 wt%. Also, the modulus of elasticity of PLA/HNT with SDS exhibits higher modulus of elasticity compared with PLA/HNT without SDS. At 5 wt% of HNT content, the modulus of elasticity of PLA/HNT/SDS increased about 21.2% compared with PLA/HNT nanocomposites.

11.3.2 Morphological Analysis

Figure 11.7a–d shows the field emission scanning electron microscopic analysis (FESEM) micrographs of the tensile fractured surface of untreated and SDS-treated CMC/HNT bio-nanocomposite films containing 10 and 20 wt% of HNT loading, respectively. For untreated bio-nanocomposites, when the HNT's loading is low, which is at 10 wt% of HNT (Figure 11.7a), it was well dispersed with homogeneity and smooth surface in the CMC matrix even with some fillers detached but still showed the highest value of tensile strength. However, obtaining homogenous dispersion at 20 wt% of HNT content is difficult (Figure 11.7b). The distributions of HNT particles in CMC matrix also lead to the agglomeration of the HNT particles in bio-nanocomposites containing the higher filler loading.

Also, the presence of cavities mainly due to the weak surface link between the CMC matrix and HNT nanofiller and high filler-filler interactions that caused HNTs cannot transfer an effective stress from the matrix. The large amounts of HNTs are also easily agglomerated and the presence of agglomerated causes cavities between the HNT nanofiller and CMC matrix. The micrographs for untreated bio-nanocomposites showed poor interfacial adhesion and dispersion of HNT particles at high HNT content (20 wt%), which has given the lowest value of tensile strength, as shown in Figure 11.7b. The aggregated HNTs usually act as stress concentration points when fracturing the materials, deteriorating the mechanical properties (Liu et al. 2014).

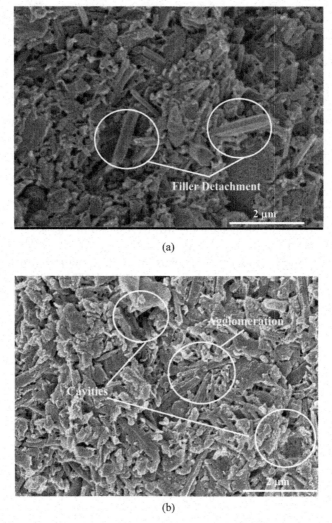

FIGURE 11.7 FESEM micrographs of the tensile fractured surface of untreated CMC/HNT bio-nanocomposite films at (a) 10 wt% and (b) 20 wt% of HNT content and SDS-treated CMC/HNT bio-nanocomposite films at (c) 10 wt% and (d) 20 wt% of HNT content.

(Continued)

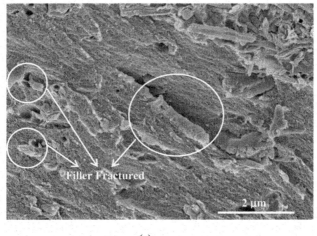

(c)

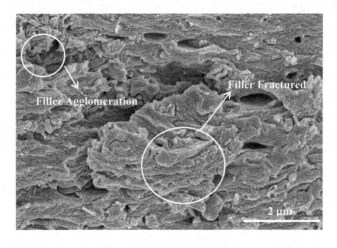

(d)

FIGURE 11.7 *(Continued)*

After the chemical modification with SDS, both FESEM micrographs exhibit good dispersion and filler-matrix interaction, which leads to reduction in detachment of HNT nanofiller from the CMC matrix. However, the filler agglomeration was still observed at 20 wt% of HNT content, as shown in Figure 11.7d. The size of agglomerated particles that appeared in the morphology of untreated bio-nanocomposite films was found to be much smaller in SDS-treated bio-nanocomposite films due to the good interfacial bonding between the CMC matrix and SDS-treated HNT nanofiller.

It corresponded with the presence of SDS that hydrophobically modified the HNT filler and enhanced the interfacial adhesion with the CMC matrix, which showed the fracture happened not only on the matrix but also on the filler itself. This has contributed to the higher strength, which was needed for the sample failure. The tensile properties of the treated CMC/HNT bio-nanocomposite films are also well justified by the FESEM micrographs as the SDS-treated bio-nanocomposites possessed higher tensile strength compared with untreated CMC/HNT bio-nanocomposite films.

11.3.3 Moisture Content

The moisture content of both untreated and SDS-treated CMC/HNT bio-nanocomposite films as a function of filler loading are illustrated in Figure 11.8. From the figure, it can be deduced that the moisture content of untreated and treated CMC/HNT bio-nanocomposite films showed a decreasing trend with increasing content of HNT nanofiller from 5 to 20 wt%. The SDS-treated CMC/HNT bio-nanocomposite films exhibit much lower moisture content compared with untreated bio-nanocomposite films. The moisture content of SDS-treated CMC/HNT bio-nanocomposite film at 10 wt% of HNT loading decreased by 3.4% compared with the same HNT loading of untreated bio-nanocomposite film. The treated CMC/HNT bio-nanocomposites also recorded the lowest moisture content at 20 wt% of HNT content, which is about 7.3% and reduced by 2.6% compared with untreated CMC/HNT bio-nanocomposite film at the same HNT content.

The decrease in moisture content for the treated bio-nanocomposites was mainly due to the presence of SDS on the surface of HNT nanofiller, which leads to the reduction of hydrophilicity of the HNT. The attribution of SDS as an anionic surfactant in treated CMC/HNT bio-nanocomposites also aids to reduce the –OH groups in HNT nanofiller and increase the hydrophobic surface of HNT. These

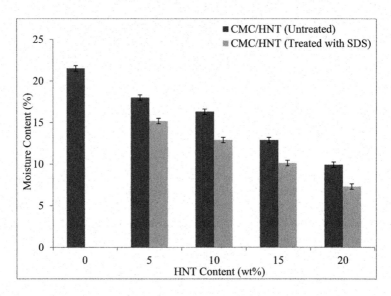

FIGURE 11.8 Effect of HNT content on moisture content of SDS-treated CMC/HNT bio-nanocomposite films.

reduced –OH repeating side groups interact with the CMC chains and led to the lower moisture absorption capacity by decreasing the intermolecular distance between the CMC chains, hence preventing the moisture into the CMC matrix. This is because the SDS could serve as a link between HNT nanofiller and CMC matrix, providing hydrophobic interaction that can improve the contact at the interface. Also, increased hydrophobic surface of HNT nanofiller acts as a moisture barrier in treated CMC/HNT bio-nanocomposite films.

11.3.4 THERMAL STABILITY PROPERTIES

Figures 11.9 and 11.10 represent the thermogravimetric analysis (TGA) and derivative thermogravimetry (DTG) curves of untreated and SDS-treated CMC/HNT bio-nanocomposite films at different HNT content, respectively. Table 11.2 summarizes the TGA data of untreated and SDS-treated CMC/HNT bio-nanocomposite films. The TGA curves of SDS-treated CMC/HNT bio-nanocomposite films with shows three degradation stages. The first stage starts at around 50°C with weight loss around 16.2% due to the elimination of water. The second stage begins at about 250°C and reaches maximum at around 310°C with weight loss of 20% due to pyrolysis of polysaccharide followed by thermal decomposition, which ended at around 520°C.

Table 11.2 shows that the SDS-treated CMC/HNT bio-nanocomposite films exhibit much lower weight loss at 100°C compared with untreated CMC/HNT bio-nanocomposite films. The results clearly show that the moisture content of the treated CMC/HNT bio-nanocomposite films decreased after the chemical treatment with SDS and it is proven by the decrease in moisture content of SDS-treated CMC/HNT bio-nanocomposite films compared with untreated CMC/HNT bio-nanocomposites in Section 11.3.3. This is due to the reduction in interlayer spaces

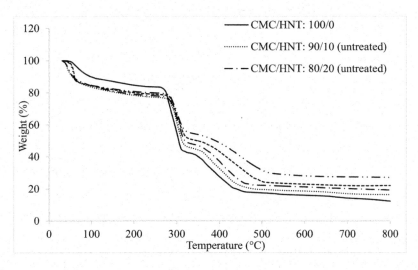

FIGURE 11.9 TGA curves of untreated and SDS-treated CMC/HNT bio-nanocomposite films.

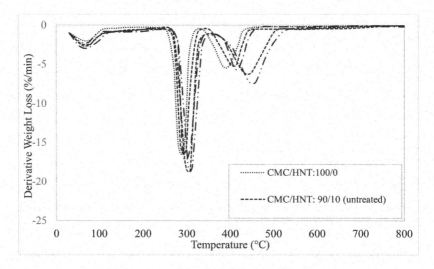

FIGURE 11.10 DTG curves of untreated and SDS-treated CMC/HNT bio-nanocomposite films SDS.

between HNT nanofiller and the CMC matrix with the presence of SDS, which improves the barrier properties by decreasing the hydrophilicity of the treated CMC/HNT bio-nanocomposites. Also, the decreased interlayer spaces enable a decrease in the rate of heat transfer, which leads to suppression of the weight loss, and enhancing thermal stability of the SDS-treated bio-nanocomposite films.

The table also indicates that the thermal degradation temperatures (T_{d1} and T_{d2}) of SDS-treated CMC/HNT bio-nanocomposite films have shifted to a higher temperature compared with the neat CMC film. Moreover, the thermal degradation temperature of treated CMC/HNT bio-nanocomposites was also higher than the untreated CMC/HNT bio-nanocomposite films and increased with increasing HNT content. This confirms that the presence of SDS in treated CMC/HNT bio-nanocomposite

TABLE 11.2

The TGA and DTG Data of Untreated and SDS-Treated CMC/HNT Bio-Nanocomposite Films at Different Temperatures

CMC/HNT	Weight Loss at 100°C (%)	T_{d1}	T_{d2}	T_{50}	Residue Remaining at 800°C (%)
100/0	10.02	291	390	305	12.3
90/10 untreated	16.52	295	410	312	16.3
80/20 untreated	18.76	299	418	320	19.2
90/10 treated	15.67	305	440	349	22.0
80/20 treated	15.45	308	450	390	27.0

films enhanced the interfacial compatibility where the filler-matrix interaction facilitated mass and heat transport and leads to higher thermal stability.

The decomposition temperature at 50% of weight loss (T_{50}) for the treated CMC/HNT bio-nanocomposite films at 10 and 20 wt% was also shifted to a higher temperature (T_{50} = 349°C and 390°C), which is 37°C and 70°C higher than the untreated CMC/HNT bio-nanocomposites. The SDS-treated CMC/HNT bio-nanocomposite films also exhibit higher char residue remaining at 800°C compared with untreated CMC/HNT bio-nanocomposite films. It is believed that the SDS attributes to the formation of char with a better insulator by creating char layer, which acts as a protective layer to the chains of CMC/HNT bio-nanocomposite films to keep them from thermal attack.

11.3.5 X-Ray Diffraction Analysis

Figure 11.11 displays the X-ray diffraction (XRD) curves of both untreated and SDS-treated CMC/HNT bio-nanocomposite films at various HNT loadings. Table 11.3 provides the XRD angle of the peaks, 2θ (°), and basal spacing, (d), data of untreated and SDS-treated CMC/HNT bio-nanocomposite films at various HNT contents. The figure shows that the diffraction peak intensity of both untreated and treated CMC/HNT bio-nanocomposite films are higher than that of neat CMC film.

In addition, the diffraction peak intensity of treated CMC/HNT bio-nanocomposites also exhibits higher intensity peak compared with the untreated bio-nanocomposite films with the same HNT loading. This is mainly attributed to the presence of SDS, which aids the dispersion of HNT nanofiller in the CMC matrix and enhances the filler-matrix interaction to form more compact structure compared with untreated

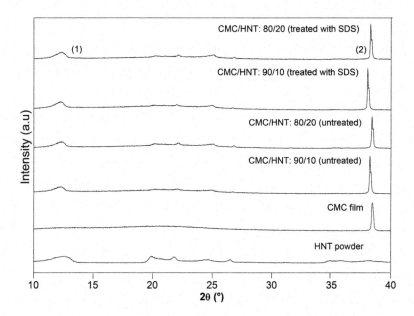

FIGURE 11.11 The XRD curves of SDS-treated CMC/HNT bio-nanocomposite films.

CMC/HNT bio-nanocomposite film at the same HNT loading. Also, the XRD curves represent shifting of the diffraction peaks to lower 2θ and increased the d-spacing values for both untreated and SDS-treated CMC/HNT bio-nanocomposite films compared with neat CMC film.

The SDS-treated CMC/HNT bio-nanocomposite films, however, shifted the diffraction peaks to much lower 2θ and higher d-spacing values compared with the untreated bio-nanocomposite films of the same HNT content. The SDS-treated CMC/HNT bio-nanocomposite film at 10 wt% of HNT content exhibited the lowest 2θ and highest d-spacing values compared with other bio-nanocomposite films with different HNT content and the untreated CMC/HNT bio-nanocomposite films. Thus, the modifications involving SDS in CMC/HNT bio-nanocomposite films were successful where the increase in d-spacing values indicates the improvement in intercalation of more CMC matrix into the interlayer galleries of HNT particles. Increased filler-matrix interaction with the presence of SDS in treated CMC/HNT bio-nanocomposite films also attributes to the lower 2θ, higher d-spacing values and higher intensity, which correlated to higher crystallinity (Bee et al. 2014). The results are in agreement with the tensile strength of treated CMC/HNT bio-nanocomposite films, in which the treated bio-nanocomposite films exhibit higher tensile strength compared with untreated bio-nanocomposites.

The SDS-treated CMC/HNT bio-nanocomposite films at 20 wt% of HNT also reveal lower 2θ and higher d-spacing values than the untreated bio-nanocomposite at the same HNT content, even though the 2θ and lower d-spacing values are higher than 10 wt% of HNT. This indicates that the SDS also reduced the agglomeration of HNT nanofiller by improving dispersion and enhancing the interfacial interaction between CMC matrix and HNT filler. Table 11.3 shows that the diffraction peaks for the CMC

TABLE 11.3
The Diffraction Angle of the Peaks, 2θ (°) and Basal Spacing (d), of SDS-Treated CMC/HNT Bio-Nanocomposite Films

CMC/HNT Bio-Nanocomposite Films (wt%)	2θ (°)	d-Spacing (Å)
100/0	1. –	1. –
	2. 38.41	2. 2.344
HNT powder	1. 12.57	1. 7.042
	2. –	2. –
90/10 untreated	1. 12.23	1. 7.237
	2. 38.20	2. 2.356
80/20 untreated	1. 12.47	1. 7.098
	2. 38.37	2. 2.346
90/10 treated	1. 12.02	1. 7.363
	2. 38.01	2. 2.367
80/20 treated	1. 12.26	1. 7.219
	2. 38.27	2. 2.352

have been shifted to the lower 2θ, which is 38.01° and 38.27° at 10 and 20 wt% of SDS-treated CMC/HNT bio-nanocomposite films, respectively. These peaks appeared at lower 2θ compared with neat CMC film and untreated CMC/HNT bio-nanocomposite films, indicating the CMC matrix was effectively intercalated with the HNT and there was good dispersion of HNT filler in the CMC matrix, which caused the structural rearrangement of CMC chains to form highly ordered crystallite structures.

11.4 CONCLUSION

The FTIR spectra showed that the reaction had taken place between SDS and HNT, which led to the formation of hydrogen bonds and reduction in hydrophilicity of the bio-nanocomposites. Also, the addition of HNT had shifted the diffraction peaks to a lower diffraction angle, increased peak intensity and increased basal spacing values of the bio-nanocomposites. The SDS-treated bio-nanocomposites exhibited much higher peak intensity and increased basal spacing compared with untreated bio-nanocomposites. The FESEM images also revealed that SDS-treated CMC/HNT bio-nanocomposite films improved the interfacial interaction between treated HNT and CMC. The incorporation of HNT into CMC/HNT bio-nanocomposites increased the tensile strength up to 10 wt% of HNT filler content followed by a decrement at 15 and 20 wt%. However, the tensile strengths of filled CMCs are higher than the unfilled CMCs. Also, the modulus of elasticity and elongation at break of the CMC/HNT bio-nanocomposites increased with increasing HNT content. The SDS-treated CMC/HNT bio-nanocomposites significantly enhanced the tensile properties compared with untreated bio-nanocomposites. The improvement in hydrophobicity on the addition of treated HNT also can be explained by the decrement of moisture content for SDS-treated CMC/HNT bio-nanocomposites compared with untreated bio-nanocomposites. The thermal stability of SDS-treated CMC/HNT bio-nanocomposite films was also enhanced with increasing HNT content where the weight loss at 100°C reduced higher thermal degradation temperatures (T_{d1} and T_{d2}) and the decomposition temperature at 50% of weight loss (T_{50}) and higher char residue remaining at 800°C compared with untreated bio-nanocomposites.

ACKNOWLEDGMENT

The financial support of Fundamental Research Grant Scheme (FRGS) Grant FRGS/1/2018/TK05/UNIMAP/02/14 is gratefully acknowledged.

REFERENCES

Battegazzore, D., Frache, A., and Carosio, F. 2020. "Layer-by-Layer Nanostructured Interphase Produces Mechanically Strong and Flame Retardant Bio-Composites." *Composites Part B: Engineering*, 200, 108310. https://doi.org/10.1016/j.compositesb.2020.108310

Bee, S., Ratnam, C., Sin, L., Tee, T., Hui, D., Kadhum, A. A. H., Rahmat, A. R., and Lau, J. 2014. "Effects of Electron Beam Irradiation on Mechanical Properties and Nanostructural–Morphology of Montmorillonite Added Polyvinyl Alcohol Composite." *Composites Part B: Engineering*, 63, 141–153. https://doi.org/10.1016/j.compositesb.2014.03.021

Bigucci, F., Abruzzo, A., Vitali, B., Saladini, B., Cerchiara, T., Gallucci, M.C., and Luppi, B. 2015. "Vaginal Inserts Based on Chitosan And Carboxymethylcellulose Complexes For Local Delivery of ChlorhexIdine: Preparation, Characterization and Antimicrobial Activity." *International Journal of Pharmaceutics*, 478(2), 456–463. https://doi.org/10.1016/j.ijpharm.2014.12.008

De Salvi, D.T., Barud, H.S., Caiut, J.M., Messaddeq, Y., and Ribeiro, S.J. 2012. "Self-Supported Bacterial Cellulose/Boehmite Organic–Inorganic Hybrid Films." *Journal of Sol-Gel Science and Technology*, 63, 211–218. https://doi.org/10.1007/s10971-012-2678-x

Goh, P.S., Ng, B.C., Ismail, A.F., Aziz, M., and Sanip, S.M. 2010. "Surfactant Dispersed Multi-Walled Carbon Nanotube/Polyetherimide Nanocomposite Membrane." *Solid State Sciences*, 12(12), 2155–2162. https://doi.org/10.1016/j.solidstatesciences.2010.09.017

Hartline, M. C. 2012. *"Biodegradable Polymer/Halloysite Nanocomposites."* Electronic Theses and Dissertations." https://digital.library.txstate.edu/handle/10877/4412.

Huang, H., He, P., Hu, N., and Zeng, Y. 2003. "Electrochemical and Electrocatalytic Properties of Myoglobin and Hemoglobin Incorporated In Carboxymethyl Cellulose Films." *Bioelectrochemistry*, 61, 29–38. https://doi.org/10.1016/S1567-5394(03)00057-4

Liu, M., Jia, Z., Jia, D., and Zhou, C. 2014. "Recent Advance in Research on Halloysite Nanotubes Polymer Nanocomposite." *Progress in Polymer Science*, 39(8), 1498–1525. https://doi.org/10.1016/j.progpolymsci.2014.04.004

Martins, J.T., Cerqueira, M.A., and Vicente, A.A. 2012. "Influence of α-tocopherol on Physicochemical Properties of Chitosan-Based Films." *Food Hydrocolloids*, 27(1), 220–227. https://doi.org/10.1016/j.foodhyd.2011.06.011

Mohanty, A.K., Misra, M., and Hinrichsen, G. 2000. "Biofibres, Biodegradable Polymers and Biocomposites: An Overview." *Macromolecular Materials and Engineering*, 276(1), 1–24. https://doi.org/10.1002/(SICI)1439-2054(20000301)276:1<1::AID-MAME1>3.0.CO;2-W

Moon, R.J., Martini, A., Nairn, J., Simonsen, J., and Youngblood, J. 2011. "Cellulose Nanomaterials Review: Structure, Properties and Nanocomposites." *Chemical Society Reviews*, 40(7), 3941–3994. https://doi.org/10.1039/C0CS00108B

Nishio, Y. 2006. "Material Functionalization of Cellulose and Related Polysaccharides Via Diverse Microcompositions." *Advances in Polymer Science, Polysaccharides II*, 97–151. https://doi.org/10.1007/12_095

Perotti, G.F., Tronto, J., Bizeto, M.A., Izumi, C., Temperini, M.L., Lugao, A.B., Parra, D.F., and Constantino, V.R. 2014. "Biopolymer–Clay Nanocomposites: Cassava Starch and Synthetic Clay Cast Films." *Journal of the Brazilian Chemical Society*, 25(2), 320–330. https://doi.org/10.5935/0103-5053.20130300

Rubilar, J.F., Cruz, R.M., Silva, H.D., Vicente, A.A., Khmelinskii, I., and Vieira, M.C. 2013. "Physico-Mechanical Properties of Chitosan Films with Carvacrol and Grape Seed Extract." *Journal of Food Engineering*, 115(4), 466–474. https://doi.org/10.1016/j.jfoodeng.2012.07.009

Salmah, H., Amri, F., and Kamarudin, H., 2012. "Properties of Chitosan-Filled Polypropylene (PP) Composites: The Effect of Acetic Acid." *Polymer-Plastics Technology and Engineering*, 51(1), 86–91. https://doi.org/10.1080/03602559.2011.618156

Shamsuyeva, M., Chang, B.P., Vellguth, N., Misra, M., Mohanty, A., and Endres, H.J. 2020. "Surface Modification of Flax Fibers for Manufacture of Engineering Thermoplastic Biocomposites." *Journal of Composites Science*, 4(2), 64. https://doi.org/10.3390/jcs4020064

Sharma, C., Bhardwaj, N.K., and Pathak, P. 2020. "Ternary Nano-Biocomposite Films Using Synergistic Combination of Bacterial Cellulose with Chitosan and Gelatin for Tissue Engineering Applications." *Journal of Biomaterials Science, Polymer Edition*, 32(2), 166–188. https://doi.org/10.1080/09205063.2020.1822122

Singha, A.S., Thakur, V.K., Mehta, I.K., Shama, A., Khanna, A.J., Rana, R.K., and Rana, A.K. 2009. "Surface-Modified Hibiscus Sabdariffa Fibers: Physicochemical, Thermal, and Morphological Properties Evaluation." *International Journal of Polymer Analysis and Characterization*, 14(8), 695–711.

Spitalsky, Z., Tasis, D., Papagelis, K., and Galiotis, C. 2010. "Carbon Nanotube-Polymer Composites: Chemistry, Processing, Mechanical and Electrical Properties." *Progress in Polymer Science*, 35(3), 357–401. https://doi.org/10.1016/j.progpolymsci.2009.09.003

Taheri, H., Hietala M., and Oksman, K. 2020. "One-Step Twin-Screw Extrusion Process of Cellulose Fibers and Hydroxyethyl Cellulose to Produce Fibrillated Cellulose Biocomposite." *Cellulose*, 27, 8105–8119. https://doi.org/10.1007/s10570-020-03287-3

Yu, H., Qin, Z., Sun, B., Yang, X., and Yao, J. 2014. "Reinforcement of Transparent Poly (3-Hydroxybutyrate-Co-3-Hydroxyvalerate) By Incorporation of Functionalized Carbon Nanotubes as A Novel Bionanocomposite For Food Packaging." *Composites Science and Technology*, 94, 96–104. https://doi.org/10.1016/j.compscitech.2014.01.018

Index

Note: Locators in *italics* represent figures and **bold** indicate tables in the text.

A

Acetobacter, 72
Achromobacter, 72
Acid hydrolysis, 71–72, 75, 81
Acrylonitrile-butadiene-styrene (ABS) copolymer, 5, 29
Aerobacter, 72
AHP, *see* Analytical hierarchy process
Alkali hydrolysis, 71, 72
Amber silica, 4
American Concrete Institute (ACI) guidelines, 48
American Society for Testing and Material (ASTM), 18–19, 104, 105, 140, 141, 155–157, 205
(3-Aminopropyl)triethoxysilane (APTES), 52, *52*
Aminopropyltrietoxysilane (APES), 127
Analytical hierarchy process (AHP), 26, 27, 30, 32, 34, 35, 37
Analytical network process (ANP), 30, 32, 35, 37
ANP, *see* Analytical network process
APES, *see* Aminopropyltrietoxysilane
APTES, *see* (3-aminopropyl)triethoxysilane
Aramid (Kevlar®), 46
AR-glass (ARG) TRM; *see also* Epoxy-coated TRM
  aromatic-cured epoxy coating, 58, *58*
  characteristic elongation, 56, *57*
  composite materials, strength curves of, 55–56, *56*
  Cost/Performance Index, 61, **62**
  effects of silanization, 52, *52*
  E-SEM magnifications, 53, *53*, *54*
  experimental research, 50–55
  fabric pre-impregnation, technology of, 50–51
  formulation design, 51–54
  mean tensile strength values, 58–59, *59*
  original ARG fabric, 53, *53*
  pre-impregnated *(pre-preg),* 51
  properties, 50, **50**
  uniaxial tensile testing, approaches in, 54–55
Artificial intelligent methods, 30
Automotive applications, 16–18, 27, 32
Azotobacter, 72

B

Bacillus subtilis (gram-positive), 84
Bentonite, 10, 30, 36, 37, 200
Biological process of hydrolysis, 71, 72

C

CaCO$_3$, *see* Calcium carbonate
Calcium carbonate (CaCO$_3$), 6–8, 27, 29, 138, 171, 200
  and dolomite, 7
  mineral additives, 6–7, 27
  polymer matrix, 7
  PPS nanocomposites, 7
  properties of PP, 2, 18, **18**
  stearate treatment, 7
  toughening mechanism with rigid particles, 7–8, *8*
Calcium hydroxide (Ca(OH)$_2$), 37
Carbon, 7, 30, 35, 46, 48, 56, 57, 61, 68, 69, 104, 125, 127, 172, 202, 212
Carbon FRP (C-FRP), 61, 63
Carbon nanotubes (CNTs), 48, 68, 82, 172, 173, 193, 212
Carboxymethyl cellulose/halloysite nanotube (CMC/HNT) using SDS bio-nanocomposite films
  chemical modification of HNT, 213
  materials, 213
  preparation of, 213–214, **214**
  FTIR, *215*, *216*
  moisture content, *222*, 222–223
  morphological analysis, 219–222, *220–221*
  tensile properties, 215–219, *217*, *218*, *219*
  thermal stability properties, *223*, 223–225, **224**, *224*
  X-ray diffraction analysis, *225*, 225–227, **226**
Case-based reasoning, 30
Cellulose nanocrystals (CNCs), 69
  delivery of drugs, 83–84
  drug carrier in pharmaceutical applications, 83
  functionalized, 82, *82*
  hydrolysis process, 71–72
  influence of, **74**, **79–80**
  "percolation network," 71
  physical and chemical properties, 72
  polydopamine-coated CNCs (PD-CNCs), 84
  polymer nanocomposite-reinforced, 69, **76–77**, 78, 82, *82*
  synthetic functionalized, approaches of, 82, *82*
  ZnO NPs, 81

231

Cement-based composite, 29, 30
Cementitious-based composite, 29
Cetyltrimethylammonium bromide (CTAB), 84
Clay
   antimicrobial properties, 30
   fibers, 68
   fillers, 28
   fire, 10
   inorganic, 78
   layers of clay silicate, 11
   in medical applications, 85
   minerals, 69–70, 85, 138
   nano-clay, 27, 28
   nanotubes, 68
   PP-clay nanocomposites, 17
   sepiolite, 155
CMC/HNT, *see* Carboxymethyl cellulose/halloysite nanotube
CNCs, *see* Cellulose nanocrystals
CNTs, *see* Carbon nanotubes
Coefficient of thermal expansion (CTE), 3, 4, 6
Complex proportional assessment (COPRAS), 34
Computer-aided systems, 30
Cristobalite, 5

D

Data envelopment analysis (DEA), 30, 34
DEA, *see* Data envelopment analysis
Derivative thermogravimetry (DTG), 146, 163, 223, 224
DETA, *see* Diethylenetriamine
Dibenzothiazyl disulfide (MBTS), 123
Diethylenetriamine (DETA), 51, 53–55, 58–61
Differential scanning calorimetry (DSC) analysis, 59
Doxorubicin (DOX), 83, 84, 85, 86
DSC, *see* Differential scanning calorimetry analysis

E

EBRs, *see* Externally bonded reinforcements
ELECTRE, *see* Elimination and Choice Expressing the Reality
ELECTRE III, 33
ELECTRE IV, 33
Electrical applications, 18
Electron beam (EB) irradiation, 154
Electron beam radiation, 139
Elimination and Choice Expressing the Reality (ELECTRE), 30, 32, 33, 35
Energy dispersion X-ray spectrometers (EDX), 106, 107, 108, 141
Environmental scanning electron microscope (E-SEM), 53, *53*, *54*
Enzymatic hydrolysis, 72

EPDM, *see* Ethylene propylene diene monomer
Epoxy-coated TRM
   AR-glass TRM
      experimental research, 50–55
      fabric pre-impregnation, technology of, 50–51
      formulation design, 51–54
      uniaxial tensile testing, approaches in, 54–55
   coating techniques for multifilament fabrics, 48, **49**
   external fibers (sleeve), 48
   influence of coating formulation, 55–57
   influence of coating viscosity, 60, 60–61, *61*
   monolithic system, EBR composite, 46, *46*
   organic binder, adoption of, 46
   thermal response, 57–59
   yarns (core or bundle), 48
Equivalent spherical diameter (ESD), 13
Escherichia coli (gram-negative), 84
E-SEM, *see* Environmental scanning electron microscope
Ethylene propylene diene monomer (EPDM), 139
   effect of GP, 123
   and sepiolite-filled composites, *see* Sepiolite-filled EPDM composites
Ethylene propylene diene monomer (EPDM) rubber, 139
Ethylene vinyl acetate (EVA) copolymer matrix, 202
Exploitation index (EI), 56, *57*
Externally bonded reinforcements (EBRs), 45

F

Fabric pre-impregnation, technology of, 50–51
FESEM, *see* Field emission scanning electron microscopy analysis
Fiber-reinforced cementitious materials (FRCMs), 47
Fiber-reinforced polymers (FRPs), 45
   adoption of, 46
   carbon FRP, 61, 63
   EB composites, 50, 57
   epoxy resins, 46
   impregnation mechanisms of, 47, *47*
   reinforced concrete (RC) elements, 45
Field emission scanning electron microscopy analysis (FESEM)
   non-irradiated and irradiated EPDM/sepiolite composites, 141, 147–149, *148*
   of untreated and SDS-treated CMC/HNT bio-nanocomposite films, 219–222, *220*, 227
Filler characteristics, **12**
   and effects on composite properties, 11–16
   particle-matrix compatibility, 15–16, *16*

Index

particle shape, 12–13, *14, 15*
particle size and distribution, 13–15
particle surface area and surface energy, 15
Filler-reinforced polymer nanocomposites, 72–86
   barrier properties, 75–79, **76–77**
   biomedical applications, 83–86
   flame retardancy, 81–83
   mechanical properties, 73–75, **74**
   thermal stability, **79–80**, 79–81
Flory Rehner equilibrium, 124
Formic acid, 72
Fourier Transform Infrared Spectroscopy (FTIR), 131–133
   glut palmitate coupling agent, 131–133, *132, 133*
   Perkin Elmer System 2000, 125
   using SDS
     moisture content, *222*, 222–223
     morphological analysis, 219–222, *220–221*
     tensile properties, 215–219, *217, 218, 219*
     thermal stability properties, *223*, 223–225, **224**, *224*
     X-ray diffraction analysis, *225*, 225–227, **226**
FRCMs, *see* Fiber-reinforced cementitious materials
FRPs, *see* Fiber-reinforced polymers
FTIR, *see* Fourier Transform Infrared Spectroscopy

G

Glass, 7, 13, 17, 29, 46, 48, 52, 63, 84, 187, 214
Gluconacetobacter xylinus, 72
Glut palmitate (GP) coupling agent, 122
   methodology, 123–125
     characterization, 123–125
     materials, 123
     preparation of rubber composite, 123
   results, 125–133
     cure characteristic, *125*, 125–126, *126*
     FTIR, 131–133, *132, 133*
     mechanical properties, *126*, 126–129, *127, 128*
     rubber filler interaction study, *129*, 129
     SEM study, 129–131, *130, 131*

H

Halloysite nanotubes (HNTs), 85, 212, 213, 220
High-density polyethylene (HDPE), 36, 78, 81, 123, 154, 164
Horizontal burning mode (HB), 156
Housing material, 19
HPMCs, *see* Hybrid polymer matrix composites

Hybrid polymer matrix composites (HPMCs), 170–172
Hydrated magnesium silicate, 138

I

Industrial applications
   applications, 16–19
     automotive applications, 16–18
     electrical applications, 18
     housing material, 19
   demand for materials, 1–2
   exports, 2
   filler characteristics
     and effects on composite properties, 11–16
     particle-matrix comp atibility, 15–16
     particle shape, 12–13
     particle size and distribution, 13–15
     particle surface area and surface energy, 15
   fillers, 2
   hybridization of mineral fillers in polymer composites, 3
   mineral fillers, 3–11
     $CaCO_3$, 6–8
     kaolin, 10–11
     mica, 4–5
     silica, 5–6
     talc, 8–10
Inorganic fillers, 2, 11, 27, 81, 171
Irradiated LDPE/sepiolite nanocomposites
   determination and preparation, **155**, 155–157
   materials and method, 155–157
   properties and characterization, 157–166
     flammability properties, 164–166, *165*
     gel content, 157–159, *158*
     morphology analysis, 164, *165*
     tensile properties, 159–161, *160*
     thermal properties, **161**, 161–164, *162*, **163**
     X-ray diffraction analysis, 157, *158*
N-isopropyl-N'-phenyl-p-phenylenediamine (IPPD), 123

K

Kaolin, 10–11; *see also* Clay
   chemical formula, 10
   molecular structure of, 10, *10*
   use of, 11
Knowledge-based systems, 30

L

LDPE, *see* Low-density polyethylene nanocomposites
Limestone, *see* Calcium carbonate

Index

Limiting oxygen index (LOI), 82, 83, 156, 164
Linear low-density polyethylene (LLDPE), 153–166
Low-density polyethylene (LDPE), *see* Irradiated LDPE/sepiolite nanocomposites

M

Maleic acid, 72
Material selection
   characteristics of materials, 26, 35–37
   methods of, 30–35
      AHP, 32
      ANP, 32
      TOPSIS, 32
   ranking methods, 30, *31*
   screening methods, 30, *31*
   tools, 33–35
      advantages and disadvantages, 35, **36**
      DEA, 34
      ELECTRE, 33
      MAUT, 33
      PROMETHEE, 34–35
      PSI, 33
      regression analysis, 35
      SAW, 33
      VIKOR, 34
MAUT, *see* Multi-attribute utility theory
Melt flow rate (MFR), 155
Methyl ethyl ketone peroxide (MEKPO), 103
Mica, 4–5, 8, 13, 171
   anisotropic properties, 17
   mechanical properties of PBT, 5
   molecular structure, 4, *5*
   muscovite (white or ruby mica), 4
   phlogopite (amber silica), 4
   thermal insulating properties, 3
   vibrational properties, 19
Micro-calcium carbonate particles, 29
Mineral-filled polymer composites
   applications of, 29–30
   in material selection, *see* Material selection
   minerals, type of, 27–28
   properties of, 28–29
Mineral fillers, **4**; *see also Individual entries*
   calcium carbonate, 6–8
   kaolin, 10–11
   mica, 4–5
   silica, 5–6
   talc, 8–10
Mineral silica, 6, 13
Minerals, type of, 27–28
Minimum inhibitory concentration (MIC), 84
MMT, *see* Montmorillonite
Montmorillonite (MMT), 11, 17, 68, 69–70, 139, 187, 200
Multi-attribute decision making (MADM), 30

Multi-attribute utility theory (MAUT), 30, 33
Multi-criteria decision making (MCDM), 30, 32–35
Multi-objective decision making (MODM), 30
Multiwalled carbon nanotubes (MWCNTs) and feldspar PP hybrid composites, *see* MWCNT/feldspar PP hybrid composites
Muscovite mica, 4
MWCNT/feldspar PP hybrid composites
   effect of compatibilizers, 177–185
      on flexural modulus, 183–184, *184*
      on flexural strength, 183, *183*
      on impact strength, 184–185, *185*
      on morphological properties, *181*, 181–182
      on tensile modulus, 182
      on tensile strength, *178*, 178–181, **179**, *180*
   effects of silane coupling agent, 185–192
      on flexural modulus, 190–191, *191*
      on flexural strength, 190, *190*
      on impact strength, *191*, 191–192, *192*
      on morphological properties, 188, *189*
      on tensile modulus, 188–190, *189*
      on tensile strength, *186*, **186**, 186–188, *187*, 188
   effects on flexural properties, 175–177, *176*, *177*
   effects on impact strength, 177, *178*
   effects on morphological properties, *174*, 174–175, *175*
   effects on tensile properties, *172*, 172–173, **173**
   HPMCs, 170–172
MWCNTs, *see* Multiwalled carbon nanotubes

N

Nanocrystals, 69, 71–72, 73, 81
Nanofillers
   advantages of, 69
   1D nanofillers, 68
   2D nanofillers, 68
   3D nanofillers, 68, 69
   filler-reinforced polymer nanocomposites, 72–86
      barrier properties, 75–79, *78*
      biomedical applications, 83–86, *86*
      flame retardancy, 81–83
      mechanical properties, 73–75
      thermal stability, 79–81
   matrix-nanofiller network, 73
   preparation of, 69–72
      CNCs, 71–72
      MMT, 69–70
      SiO_2 NPs, 70–71

Index

Nanogranules, 69
Nanoparticles (NPs), 69, 70–71, *86*, 179
Nano-silica (nSIL) coating, 56
Natural hydraulic lime (NHL), 50
Natural resources
   classifications of, 27, *27*
   non-renewable resources, 27
   renewable resources, 27
Natural rubber (NR)
   Hevea brasiliensis tree, 122
   vulcanized silica-filled, *see* Vulcanized silica-filled natural rubber
Natural zeolite filler
   crystallinity with XRD, 109–110
   with SEM-EDX, 106–109
      component characterization, 107–108, *108*
      morphological properties, *106*, 106–107
   and unsaturated polyester resin
      characterization, 104–105
      density, 113–114, *114*
      fabrication of composites, 104, *104*
      flexural strength, *111*, 111–112
      impact strength, 112–113, *113*
      materials, 103
      morphological properties, 116–117, *117*
      sample preparation, 103
      tensile strength, *110*, 110–111
      water absorption, 114–116, *115*, *116*
Neural network, 30
Nitrile butadiene rubber (NBR), 139

O

Oxalic acid, 72
Oxidation degradation, 71

P

PBO (Zylon®), *see* Poly(p-phenylene-2,6-benzobisoxazole)
PE co-acrylic acid (PEAA), 177–179, 181–185, *181*, 192, 193
"Percolation network," 71
PEVA, *see* Polyethylene vinyl acetate
PEVA/dolomite composite
   mechanical properties, 204–207, *206*
   production of, 203–204, *204*
Poly(butylene succinate) (PBS), 78
Poly(lactic acid) (PLA), 78, 81
Poly(p-phenylene-2,6-benzobisoxazole), 46
Polybutylene terephthalate (PBT) composites, 5, 202
Polydopamine-coated CNCs (PD-CNCs), 84
Polyethylene (PE), 19, 54, 78, 81, 123, 139, 153, 154, 172, 187, 200, 203, 205

Polyethylene oxide (PPO), 187
Polyethylene vinyl acetate (PEVA), 203–207
Poly(methyl methacrylate) (PMMA) matrix, 173
Polymer matrix composites (PMC), 102, 171
Polypropylene (PP)-based composite material, 171
Polypropylene (PE)-ethylene copolymer composite, 28
Polypropylene-grafted maleic anhydride (PP-g-MA), 178–180, 201
Polystyrene (PS), 81
Polyvinyl alcohol (PVA), 203
Polyvinyl chloride (PVC) composite, 18, 201
Preference ranking organization method for enrichment evaluations (PROMETHEE), 26, 30, 32, 34–35
Preference Selection Index (PSI), 30, 33
Principal component analysis (PCA), 33
PROMETHEE, *see* Preference ranking organization method for enrichment evaluations
PSI, *see* Preference Selection Index

Q

Quality functional deployment (QFD), 26, 30
Quality function deployment for the environment (QFDE), 30
Quartz, 5–6

R

RC, *see* Reinforced concrete elements
Regression analysis, 35
Reinforced concrete (RC) elements, 45
Renewable Energy Plan, 34
RILEM, 55
Rubber filler interaction study, 129
Ruby mica, *see* Muscovite mica

S

SAW, *see* Simple additive weighting
Scanning electron microscope-energy dispersive X-ray (SEM-EDX), 106–109
Scanning electron microscopy (SEM) study, 129–131
   of feldspar, 174
   of impact-fractured surface of silane-treated feldspar/PP, 192
   of natural zeolite, 104
   of silica particles, 13, *14*, *15*
SDS, *see* Sodium dodecyl sulfate
SEM, *see* Scanning electron microscopy study
SEM-EDX, *see* Scanning electron microscope-energy dispersive X-ray

Sepiolite-filled EPDM composites
  effect of gamma irradiation, 138–139
  non-irradiated and irradiated EPDM/sepiolite composites
    cross-link density, 144–145, *145*
    FESEM of tensile fractured surface, 147–149
    tensile properties of, 141–144, *142*, *143*, **144**
    thermal and morphological properties, 145–149
  preparation of, 140–141
    characterization, 141
    materials, 140
    preparation of sample, 140, **140**
  TGA analysis, 145–147, **147**
Silanol (Si-OH) groups, 121
Silica, 2, 5–6, 200; *see also* Silica nanoparticles; Silicon dioxide
  angular silica, 13, *15*
  crystalline forms or polymorphs, 5–6
  elongated silica, 13, *15*
  mineral silica, 5, 6
  organic silicones or silanes, 6
  shapes of fillers, 13, *14*
Silica nanoparticles (SiO$_2$ NPs), 70–71
Silicon dioxide (SiO$_2$), 69, **74**, **80**, 121
Siloxane (Si-O-Si) groups, 121, 132, 214
Silver NPs (AgNPs), 84
Simple additive weighting (SAW), 30, 33
Single multiwalled nanotubes (SWNTs), 203
SiO$_2$ NPs, *see* Silica nanoparticles
Sodium dodecyl sulfate (SDS)
  chemical modification of HNTs, 213
    FTIR, *see* Fourier Transform Infrared Spectroscopy
Specific surface area (SSA), 15, 48, 71
SSA, *see* specific surface area
Statistical analysis (stepwise regression), 30
Stearic acid, 11, 123, 125, 201–202
Sulfur, 75, 81, 123, 125, 138
Surface modification, 9–10, 16, 56, 69, 79, 83, 213
Sustainable bio-composites, 212

T

Talc, 8–10
  in automotive industry, 2
  filler in PP composites, 2
  in Malaysia, 2
  mechanical parameters, 9–10
  molecular structure of, 8, *8*
  neutral layers, 8
  physical properties, 9
  in PP, drawbacks of, 9
  properties of PP, 18, **18**

Technique of ranking preferences by similarity of the ideal solutions (TOPSIS), 30, 32, 34, 35, 37
Tensile modulus
  effects of compatibilizers, 182
  effects of silane coupling agent, 188–190
Tensiometer, 104, *105*
Tetraethyl orthosilicate (TEOS), 71
Tetramethoxysilane (TMOS), 71
Textile-reinforced concrete (TRC), 57
Textile-reinforced mortar (TRM), 45–63, 47
TGA, *see* Thermogravimetric analysis
Thermogravimetric (TGA) analysis, *145*, 145–147, *146*, **147**, 155
Three-dimensional (3D)-printed polymermineral composite, 29
TOPSIS, *see* Technique of ranking preferences by similarity of the ideal solutions
Transmission electron microscopy (TEM), 156, 164, 193
TRC, *see* Textile-reinforced concrete
Trichoderma viride G, 72
Tridymite, 5

U

Ultimate tensile elongation (UTE) capability, 59
Ultimate tensile strength (UTS) data, 58–59
Ultrasonication process
  improves dispersion of dolomite, 202–203
  as method to reduce particle size, 202–203
  polymer composite with dolomite filler, 200–202
  in production of PEVA/dolomite composite, 203–204, *204*
Ultrasonic cavitation, 202, 203
Uniaxial tensile testing, approaches in, 54–55, *55*
Universal testing machine (UTM), 55, 104, 166
Unsaturated polyester, 102–118
UTE, *see* Ultimate tensile elongation capability
UTM, *see* Universal testing machine
UTS, *see* Ultimate tensile strength data

V

VIKOR, *see* Vlse Kriterijumska Optimizacija Kompromisno Resenje
Vinyl acetate (VA), 205
Vlse Kriterijumska Optimizacija Kompromisno Resenje (VIKOR), 26, 30, 34–35
Vulcanization, 122, 125, 138–140, 142, 154

Index

Vulcanized silica-filled natural rubber
    effect of GP coupling agent, *see* Glut palmitate coupling agent
    methodology, 123–125
        characterization, 123–125
        materials, 123
        preparation of rubber composite, 123
    results, 125–133
        cure characteristic, *125*, 125–126, *126*
        FTIR, 131–133, *132*, *133*
        mechanical properties, *126*, 126–129, *127*, *128*
        rubber filler interaction study, *129*, 129
        SEM study, 129–131, *130*, *131*

W

Water vapor transmission rate (WVTR), 78
White mica, *see* Muscovite mica
Wollastonite, 2, 28, 171, 179, 185, 192

X

X-ray diffraction (XRD) analysis
    CMC/HNT using SDS, *225*, 225–227
    crystallinity of natural zeolite filler with, 109–110
    D500 X-ray diffractometer, 157
    irradiated LDPE/sepiolite nanocomposites, 157, *158*
    non-activated and activated natural zeolite, 109, *109*
XRD, *see* X-ray diffraction analysis

Y

Young's modulus, *see* Tensile modulus

Z

Zeolites, *see* Natural zeolite filler
Zinc oxide (ZnO), 68, 81, 123